with additional contributions by

Nicky Agate and Sean Harvey

ROUGH
GUIDES

NEW YORK • LONDON • DELHI

www.roughguides.com

Contents

◀◀ Union Square and the Empire State Building ◀ Chrysler Building

Introduction to

New York City

New York City is like no other place on earth, and its adrenaline-charged buzz tends to live up to even the most inflated expectations. Simply put, this is a metropolis that never sleeps, rarely apologizes, and works longer and harder than anywhere else. It's a town of icons, too, and it's hard to go anywhere without encountering a view of something world-famous, whether it's the mammoth Brooklyn Bridge, the cathedral-like Grand Central Terminal, or the lovely green sward of Central Park. Confronted by so much beauty, history, and energy, you would really have to be made of stone not to be moved by it.

It is testament to New York's resilience and strength that you would have a hard time believing that the events of **September 11, 2001**, took place just five years ago. There is some physical evidence of what happened that day at Ground Zero – not to mention a greater alertness to possible terrorism all over the city – but New York's maverick spirit shines brighter than ever, and it's certain you'll want to return here over and over again.

You could spend weeks in New York and still barely scratch the surface, but there are some key attractions and pleasures you won't want to miss. There are the different **ethnic neighborhoods**, like lower Manhattan's Chinatown and the traditionally Jewish Lower East Side (not so much anymore), and the artier concentrations of SoHo, TriBeCa, and the East and West Villages. Of course, there is the celebrated **architecture** of corporate Manhattan, with the skyscrapers in Downtown and Midtown forming the most indelible images. There are the **museums**, not just the Metropolitan and MoMA, but countless other smaller collections that afford weeks of happy wandering. In between sights, you can **eat** just about anything, at any time, cooked in any style; you can **drink** in any kind of company; and sit through any number of

On the menu

Don't come to New York on a diet or you'll miss out on one of its greatest pleasures: **food**, and lots of it. There are some types of cuisine in which New York particularly excels. The Lower East Side is great for Jewish-American deli fare, such as overstuffed pastrami sandwiches and bagels with cream cheese and lox, while all over town (Midtown especially) are traditional steakhouses serving massive aged porterhouse or tender sirloin. The city is also covered with **pizza places** serving the classic New York slice: thin, crunchy crust covered with red sauce and cheese, typically eaten folded in half and on the go.

Take the A train

Manhattan can seem a wearingly complicated place to **get around**. The city's grid-pattern arrangement appears straightforward on the map, but in fact can be very confusing on foot – not to mention the many subway lines that just don't meet up where you would expect them to. Don't be daunted by **subways** and buses, though, since with a little know-how you'll find them efficient and fast. And if you're at all unsure, just ask – New Yorkers are accurate direction-givers and take a surprising interest in initiating visitors into the great mysteries of their city.

obscure **films**. The more established arts – **dance**, **theater**, and **music** – are superbly catered for, while New York's **clubs** are as varied and exciting as you might expect. For the avid consumer, the choice of **shops** is vast, almost numbingly exhaustive in this heartland of the great capitalist dream.

What to see

New York City comprises the central island of **Manhattan** along with four outer boroughs – **Brooklyn**, **Queens**, **the Bronx**, and **Staten Island**. Manhattan, to many, *is* New York: whatever your interests, it's here that you'll spend the most time and are likely to stay. New York is very much a city of **neighborhoods** and is best explored on foot – a fact reflected in the chapters of this guide, which are divided to reflect the best walking tours.

The guide starts at the southern tip of the island and moves north: offshore, **the Statue of**

▲ Times Square

Liberty and **Ellis Island** make up the first part of New York (and America) that most nineteenth-century immigrants would have seen. The **Financial District** takes in the skyscrapers and historic buildings of Manhattan's southern reaches and was hardest hit by the destruction of perhaps its most famous landmark, the twin towers of the World Trade Center. Just northeast is the area around **City Hall**, New York's well-appointed municipal center, which adjoins **TriBeCa**, known for its swanky restaurants, galleries and nightlife. Moving east, **Chinatown** is Manhattan's most populous ethnic neighborhood, a vibrant locale that's great for food and shopping. Nearby, **Little Italy** bears few traces of its once-strong immigrant presence, while the **Lower East Side**, the city's traditional gateway neighborhood for new immigrants, is nowadays increasingly taken over by trendy bars and clubs. To the west, **SoHo** is one of the premiere districts for galleries and the commercial art scene, not to mention designer shopping. Continuing north, the **West** and **East Villages** form a focus of bars, restaurants, and shops catering to students and would-be bohemians – and of course tourists. Best known for its art galleries and active gay scene, **Chelsea** is a largely residential neighborhood that borders on Manhattan's old **Garment District**. **Murray Hill** contains the city's largest skyscraper and most enduring symbol, the **Empire State Building**.

Beyond **42nd Street**, the main east–west artery of Midtown, the character of the city changes quite radically, and the skyline becomes more high-rise and home to some of New York's most awe-inspiring, neck-cricking architecture. There are also some

7

superb museums and the city's best shopping as you work your way north up **Fifth Avenue** as far as 59th Street. Here, the classic Manhattan vistas are broken by the broad expanse of **Central Park**, a supreme piece of nineteenth-century landscaping, without which life in Manhattan would be unthinkable. Flanking the park, the mostly residential and fairly affluent **Upper West Side** boasts Lincoln Center, Manhattan's temple to the performing arts, the American Museum of Natural History, and Riverside Park along the Hudson River. On the other side of the park, the **Upper East Side** is wealthier and more grandiose, with its nineteenth-century millionaires' mansions now transformed into a string of magnificent museums known as the "Museum Mile," the most prominent being the vast **Metropolitan Museum of Art**. Alongside is a patrician residential neighborhood that boasts some of the swankiest addresses in Manhattan, and a nest of designer shopping along Madison Avenue in the seventies. Immediately above Central Park, **Harlem**, the historic black city-within-a-city, has a healthy sense of an improving go-ahead community; a jaunt further north is most likely required only to see the unusual Cloisters, a nineteenth-century mock-up of a medieval monastery, packed with great European Romanesque and Gothic art and (transplanted) architecture.

▲ Central Park

▶ Ground Zero

When to go

New York's **climate** ranges from the stickily hot and humid in mid-summer to well below freezing in January and February: deep midwinter and high summer (many people find the city unbearable in July and August) are much the worst time you could come. Spring is gentle, if unpredictable, and usually wet, while fall is perhaps the best season: come at either time and you'll find it easier to get things done and the people more welcoming. Whatever time of year you come, dress in layers: buildings tend to be overheated during winter months and air-conditioned to the point of iciness in summer. Also be sure to bring comfortable and sturdy shoes – you're going to be doing a lot of walking.

Average New York monthly temperatures and rainfall

	Jan	Feb	Mar	Apr	May	June	July	Aug	Sept	Oct	Nov	Dec
Max. temp. (°F)	38	40	50	61	72	80	85	84	76	65	54	43
Min. temp. (°F)	26	27	35	44	54	63	69	67	60	50	41	31
Max. temp. (°C)	3	4	10	16	22	27	29	29	24	18	12	6
Min. temp. (°C)	-3	-3	2	7	12	17	21	19	16	10	5	-1
Rainfall (inches)	3.5	3.1	4.0	3.8	4.4	3.6	4.4	4.1	4.0	3.4	4.4	3.8
Rainfall (mm)	89	79	102	97	112	91	112	104	102	86	112	97

13

things not to miss

It's not possible to see everything that New York City has to offer in one trip – and we don't suggest you try. What follows is a selective taste of the city's highlights: its best landmark tours, most engaging museums, and liveliest neighborhoods. They're arranged in five color-coded categories, which you can browse through to find the very best things to see and experience. All highlights have a page reference to take you straight into the Guide, where you can find out more.

01 Radio City Music Hall Page **133** • The tour of this Art Deco masterpiece is one of the city's best – and the sunset view from the stage is particularly impressive.

02 Ice-skating at Rockefeller Center
Page **92** • Taking a turn on the ice in the midst of this fine piece of urban planning is an experience you'll not soon forget.

03 Macy's Page **284** • It's a feat not to get lost inside the world's largest department store.

04 The American Museum of Natural History Page **148** • This fine museum and its Hayden Planetarium are educational, entertaining draws.

05 Coney Island Page **167** • Eat hot dogs at *Nathan's Famous* and take a ride on the Cyclone; this is what amusement parks were like before Disney.

06 Grand Central Terminal Page **89** • This Beaux Arts masterpiece is impressive enough, though taking a tour will let you in on some of its many secrets.

07 Central Park Page **114** • The "lungs of the city" has something for everyone, whether lounging on Sheep Meadow or taking in a summer concert.

08 Katz's Deli Page **212** • Savor the incredible pastrami and corned beef at this Lower East Side mainstay, serving massive sandwiches and pickles since 1888.

09 A baseball game at Yankee Stadium

Page 175 • There's no better way to feel like a real New Yorker than to cheer on the Bronx Bombers at home.

10 Empire State Building

Page 86 • After 9/11, the Empire State Building is once again the city's tallest skyscraper; the view from its top has to been seen to be believed.

11 The Halloween Parade

Page 305 • Greenwich Village's Halloween Parade is a cacophonous cavalcade of freaks, frights, and bizarre floats.

12 The Brooklyn Bridge

Page 45 • A walk across this stately marvel, during the day or at night, is the best way to see Manhattan's downtown skyline.

13 The Metropolitan Museum of Art

Page 122 • You could spend weeks inside this, the country's largest – and many say best – art museum.

Basics

Basics

Arrival

New York's major airports are all within an hour from the city center by taxi or bus, depending on traffic conditions. The city's train and bus terminals are centrally located and connected to major subway stations.

By air

Three major airports serve New York. International and domestic flights are handled at John F. Kennedy (JFK) (☎718/244-4444), in the borough of Queens, and Newark (☎973/961-6000), in northern New Jersey; LaGuardia (☎718/533-3400), also in Queens, handles domestic flights only.

Taxis are the easiest option if you are in a group or are arriving at an antisocial hour. Expect to pay $25–35 from LaGuardia, a flat rate of $45 from JFK, and $40–55 from Newark; you'll be responsible for the turnpike and tunnel tolls – an extra $5 or so. And don't forget a tip of fifteen to twenty percent.

Another good way into Manhattan is by bus; the two Manhattan terminals, used by all airport buses, are Grand Central Station and the Port Authority Bus Terminal. For further general information (driving directions, etc) on getting to and from the airports, call ☎1-800/AIR-RIDE or check out the airline sites at ⓦwww.panynj.gov.

JFK

New York Airport Service **buses** leave JFK for Grand Central Station, Port Authority Bus Terminal, Penn Station, and Midtown hotels every fifteen to twenty minutes between 6.15am and 11.10pm. In the other direction, they run from the same locations every fifteen to thirty minutes between 5am and 10pm. Journeys take 45–60 minutes, depending on the time of day; the fare is $13 one-way, $23 round-trip. For further details call ☎212/875-8200 or check ⓦwww .nyairportservice.com.

AirTrain JFK – a train service that connects the airport and various subway lines – runs every few minutes, 24 hours daily, from JFK to Jamaica Station on the #E and

#J/#Z subway lines, as well on the Long Island Rail Road (LIRR); AirTrain also runs to the Howard Beach stop on the #A line. The cost is $5 on a MetroCard (see overleaf). From the Jamaica and Howard Beach stations, one subway fare ($2 on a MetroCard) takes you anywhere in the city. This isn't your best option late at night, though, as trains run infrequently and can be rather deserted.

LaGuardia

New York Airport Service **buses** run between LaGuardia and Manhattan (Grand Central Station, Port Authority Bus Terminal, and Penn Station) every fifteen to thirty minutes. From LaGuardia, the service operates 7.20am to 11pm. From Grand Central the service runs from 5am to 8pm; from Port Authority 5.50am to 7.40pm; and from Penn Station 7.40am to 7.10pm. Journey time is 45–60 minutes, depending on traffic, and the fare is $10 one-way, $17 round-trip. For more details call ☎212/875-8200 or see Ⓦwww.nyairportservice.com.

The best (and least-known) bargain in New York airport transit is the #M60 bus, which for $2 (MetroCard or exact change only) takes you into Manhattan, across 125th Street and down Broadway to 106th Street. Ask for a transfer when you get on the bus and you can get almost anywhere. Journey time ranges from twenty minutes late at night to an hour in rush-hour traffic.

Newark

Newark Airport Express **buses** leave for Manhattan every twenty to thirty minutes (4am to 12.45pm), stopping at Port Authority, Grand Central, and Penn Station; going the other way, they run just as frequently (5am to 1.30am); service to and from the Port Authority runs 24 hours a day. In either direction, the journey takes 45–60 minutes depending on traffic, and the fare is $12 one-way, $19 round-trip. For details call ☎1-877/863 9275 or see Ⓦwww.coachusa.com.

AirTrain Newark takes you from the airport to Newark Liberty International Airport train station, where you can connect with New Jersey Transit trains, which terminate at New York Penn Station. The fare is $14 one-way and includes the cost of your AirTrain ticket. From the airport train station you can also take an Amtrak train to New York, though this is significantly more expensive. For details call ☎1-888/397-4636 or visit Ⓦwww.panynj.gov.

By bus or train

If you come by Greyhound, Trailways, Bonanza, or any other long-distance **bus** line, you'll arrive at the Port Authority Bus Terminal at 42nd Street and Eighth Avenue. If you come by Amtrak **train**, you'll arrive at Penn Station, on 32nd Street between Seventh and Eighth avenues. Both the bus terminal and train station are well-positioned for all manner of subway service.

City transportation

Public transit in New York is on the whole quite good, cheap, and comprehensive, covering most conceivable corners of the city, whether by **bus** or **subway**. Don't be afraid to ask someone for help if you're confused – it will likely take you a while to become familiar with the system. You'll no doubt find the need for a **taxi** from time to time, especially if you feel uncomfortable in an area at night; you shouldn't ever have trouble tracking one down – the ubiquitous yellow cabs are always on the prowl for passengers. Don't eschew **walking**, either: it's a great way to get around and maybe the best way to get to know the city.

The subway

Initially intimidating and incomprehensible, the New York **subway** is also the fastest and most efficient way to get from point A to point B in Manhattan and the outer boroughs, and it is safer and more user-friendly than it once was. Put aside your qualms: seven million people ride the subway every day, quite a few for the first time.

Any subway journey costs $2, payable by **MetroCard**, which allows you to transfer (for free) from subway to bus, bus to subway, or bus to bus within a period of two hours. The card is available from station vending machines or station agent-manned booths in one of two forms: as a simple amount from $2 to $100, or an "unlimited ride" version, which allows for unlimited travel over a certain period of time. A one-day "Fun Pass" costs $7, a seven-day pass $24, and a monthly pass $76. Subway maps can be obtained from all subway stations, as well as the main concourse of Grand Central and the Convention and Visitors Bureau, at Seventh Avenue and 53rd Street. A subway map can also be found at the back of this book; for general subway and bus information, including service changes, call ☎718/330-1234 (24hr daily) or visit ⓦwww.mta.nyc.ny.us.

Buses

The **bus system** is simpler than the subway, and you can see where you're going and hop off at anything interesting. It also features many more crosstown routes. The major disadvantage is that the buses can be extremely slow – in peak hours almost down to walking pace, and extremely full to boot. In response to cries of overcrowding along several routes, the MTA introduced "accordion buses" – two buses attached by a flexible rubber accordion, which helps the big vehicle turn corners. However, because these run slightly less frequently than the ones they replaced, they still get crowded.

Anywhere in the city the bus **fare** is $2, payable by MetroCard (the most convenient way) or with exact change (no pennies and no bills). Bus **maps**, like subway maps, can be obtained at the main concourse of Grand Central or the Convention and Visitors Bureau; you can also often (though not always) pick up bus maps from subway stations.

Taxis

Taxis are always worth considering, especially if you're in a hurry, in a group, or it's late at night. Always use medallion cabs, immediately recognizable by their yellow paintwork and medallion on the hood; gypsy cabs, unlicensed, uninsured operators who tout for business wherever tourists arrive, should be avoided – especially at the airports, where sketchy characters hustle for business.

Up to four people can travel in an ordinary medallion cab. **Fares** are $2.50 for the first fifth of a mile and 40¢ for each fifth of a mile thereafter (or for each two minutes in stopped or slow traffic). Between the hours of 8pm and 6am there is a 50¢ surcharge, and from Monday to Friday between the hours of 4pm and 8pm there's a "peak hour" surcharge of $1. Trips outside Manhattan can incur toll fees; not all of the crossings cost money, however, and the driver should ask you which route you wish to take. Don't forget to **tip**, either: this should be fifteen to twenty percent of the fare; you'll get a dirty look if you offer less. Note that cab drivers don't like splitting anything bigger than a $10 bill, and are in their rights to refuse a bill over $20.

Walking

Few cities equal New York for street-level stimulation. As such, getting around **on foot** is often the most exciting – and tiring – method of exploring. Figure fifteen minutes to walk ten north–south blocks – rather more at rush hour. However you plan your wanderings you're still going to spend much of your time walking. Footwear is important (sneakers are good for spring/summer; winter needs something waterproof). So is safety: a lot more people are injured in New York carelessly crossing the street than are mugged. Pedestrian crossings don't give you automatic right of way unless the WALK sign is on – and, even then, cars may be turning, so be alert.

Information and websites

The best place for information is the New York Convention and Visitors Bureau, 810 Seventh Ave, at 53rd (Mon–Fri 8.30am–6pm, weekends and holidays 9am–5pm; ☏212/484-1222, ⊚www.nycvisit.com). They have up-to-date leaflets on what's going on in the arts and elsewhere plus bus and subway maps and information on hotels and accommodation – though they can't actually book anything for you. Their free quarterly Official NYC Guide is a useful resource, giving cursory rundowns on what's what with restaurants, hotels, shopping, sights, and mainstream arts events.

Visitors bureaus

Bloomingdale's NY Visitors Center
Lexington Ave, at 59th ☏212/705-2098.

Macy's Visitor Center 151 W 34th
St, at 6th ☏212/494-3827.

NYU Information Center Shimkin
Hall, room 123, 50 W 4th St, at Greene
Street/Washington Square ☏212/998-4636.

**Saks Fifth Avenue Ambassador
Concierge Desk** 611 5th Ave, at 49th
☏212/940-4141.

Times Square Visitor Center 1560
Broadway, between 46th and 47th
☏212/768-1560, ⊛www
.timessquarenyc.org.

Websites

CitySearch NY ⊛newyork.citysearch
.com. A solid site with listings, customer
reviews, and "best of" picks for every
category you can imagine.

NYC Transit Authority ⊛www.mta
.nyc.ny.us. Official subway, bus, Metro-
North, and LIRR website, with schedules,
fare info, service advisories, history,
and trivia.

NYC Visitors Bureau ⊛www
.nycvisit.com. Official website of the New
York Convention and Visitors Bureau.

PaperMag ⊛www.papermag.com.
Updated daily and covering the cultural
gamut, this hip guide has been on the
cutting edge of every trend.

Parks Department ⊛www.nycparks
.org. The official word on all of the
events in the city's parks.

Time Out New York ⊛www
.timeoutny.com. What's on this week
in music, clubs, book readings,
museums, and movies, plus other
features.

The Village Voice ⊛www
.villagevoice.com. The best thing about
this older (some say out-of-touch)
alternative weekly is the witty listings
section, "Choices."

City tours

There are many different ways to take in the city: exploring streets and neighborhoods on your own; heading up to the tops of buildings like the Empire State, to get a good perspective on the lay of the land, or going on any number of city **tours**, which might let you experience New York from angles you'd never considered. If you're nervous about exploring New York, or overwhelmed by the possibilities the city offers, look into **Big Apple Greeter**, 1 Centre St, 19th floor (☏212/669-8159, ⓦwww.bigapplegreeter.org), a nonprofit organization that matches visitors with their corps of 500 trained volunteer "greeters."

Bus tours

Apart from equipping yourself with a decent map, perhaps the most obvious way to orient yourself to the city is to take a bus tour. These are extremely popular, though frankly you're swept around so quickly as to scarcely see anything. Still, the tops of double deckers are a great place to figure out what's where for later explorations. In general, an all-city tour over two days will cost $37–75, although half-day or limited-area tours can be had for around $30. Buses run seven days a week, from (approximately) 9am to 6pm,

with special rates and times for evening tours. The most professional and best-established tour company is **Gray Line**, based out of Port Authority at 42nd St and 8th Ave (☏212/397-2600, ⓦ www.graylinenewyork.com), whose red double-decker buses can be seen making the rounds all over the city, from Harlem to Midtown to Brooklyn.

Helicopter tours

A more exciting option is to look at the city from the air, by **helicopter**. This is expensive, but you won't easily forget the experience. Liberty Helicopter Tours, with locations including the Downtown Manhattan Heliport, Pier 6 and the East River, and the VIP Heliport, 30th St and 12th Ave (☎212/967-6464, reserve online at ⓦwww.libertyhelicopters.com), offers flights ranging from $30 for two-and-a-half minutes to $169 for about a quarter hour. If you leave from 30th Street, the best seat for photos is on the right in the back. Helicopters take off regularly between 9am and 9pm daily unless winds and visibility are bad. You don't need a reservation for tours from 30th Street, but you do for other locations – at any rate, in high season (and nice weather) you may have quite a wait if you just show up.

Boat tours

A great way to see the island of Manhattan from the water is a voyage on the **Circle Line ferry** (☎212/563-3200, ⓦwww.circleline42.com). Departing from Pier 83 at W 42nd St and 12th Ave, the ferry circumnavigates Manhattan, taking in everything from Downtown's skyscrapers to the more subdued stretches of Harlem and the Bronx – complete with a live wisecracking commentary; the three-hour tour is $28 for adults, $15 for children under 12,

and $23 for seniors. Circle Line also runs super-fast 30-minute cruises on its **Beast** speedboat (May–Oct; $17, $11 for kids under 12), as well as summertime live-music cruises – check the website for the latest details on who's playing.

One of the city's true bargains is the free **Staten Island ferry** (see p.30), which leaves regularly from South Ferry on the lower tip of Manhattan. The ferry offers great views of New York Harbor and the Statue of Liberty as it makes its way to the underappreciated borough of Staten Island.

Walking tours

Options for **walking tours** of Manhattan or the outer boroughs are many and varied. Usually led by experts, they offer fact-filled wanders through neighborhoods or focus on particular subjects. You'll find fliers for some of them at the various visitor centers; for what's happening in the current week, check the **New York Times** (Friday or Sunday), the weekly **Village Voice** or **Time Out New York** (both out on Wednesday), or any of the free weekly papers around town. Detailed opposite are some of the more interesting tours – they don't all operate year-round, though, so phone ahead or check their websites for complete schedules.

Walking tour organizations

The 92nd Street Y 1395 Lexington Ave, between 91st and 92nd ☎212/415-5500, ☮www.92ndsty.org. None better, offering an assortment of walking tours ranging from straight explorations of specific New York neighborhoods to art tours and walking tours of political New York. Average costs are $20–55 per person; specific tours can be organized to accommodate groups with special interests.

Big Onion Walking Tours ☎212/439-1090, ☮www.bigonion.com. Big Onion specializes in tours with an ethnic and historical focus: pick one particular group, or take the "Immigrant New York" tour and learn about everyone. Cost for the two-hour tour is $15 (or $10 for students and $12 for seniors); the "Multi-Ethnic Eating Tour," including food, costs $19 (students $14, seniors $16).

Greenwich Village Literary Pub Crawl ☎212/613-5796. A two-and-a-half-hour tour guided by actors from the New Ensemble Theater Company, who lead you to several of the most prominent pubs in literary history and read from associated works. Tours meet at the *White Horse Tavern*, 567 Hudson St, at 2pm every Saturday. Reservations

are highly recommended: $12, students and seniors $9.

Harlem Heritage Tours 230 W 116th St, suite #5C ☎212/280-7888, ☮www.harlemheritage.com. Cultural tours of Harlem, general and specific (such as "Harlem Jazz Clubs"), are led midday and in the evening by very helpful tour guides. Walking tours are $20–30; the "Harlem Jazz Nights" tour is $99. Reservations are recommended. Call for details.

Harlem Spirituals Gospel and Jazz Tours 690 8th Ave, 2nd floor ☎212/391-0900, ☮www.harlemspirituals.com. Various tours of Harlem, the Bronx, and Brooklyn, ranging from Sunday-morning church visits to nighttime soul-food and jazz affairs, which take in dinner and a club. Professionally run and excellent value, with prices in the range of $45–115 per person (discounts for children). Reservations necessary.

Lower East Side Tenement Museum 108 Orchard St ☎212/431-0233, ☮www.tenement.org. This museum (see p.61) organizes weekend walking tours (April–Dec) of the Lower East Side, focusing on the heritage of the various ethnic groups who live there, community rebuilding, and relations among different groups. $12, students and seniors $10; combined tickets for museum admission and a tour are available at a reduced price.

Municipal Art Society 457 Madison Ave, between 50th and 51st

☏212/439-1049 or 935-3960, ✆www
.mas.org/events/tours.cfm. Opinionated
tours look at neighborhoods from an
architectural, cultural, historical, and
often political perspective. Wednesday
lunchtime tours ($10 donation) of
Grand Central Station start at 12.30pm
from the information booth. Most other
tours also start at 12.30pm, last for 90
minutes, and cost $12, with discounts
for students and seniors. Weekend and

day-long tours cost more.
Noshwalks 2265 Broadway #225
☏212/222-2243, ✆www.noshwalks
.com. Weekend "noshing tours" of
New York's ethnic neighborhoods, from
Italian food in the Bronx's real Little Italy
to *pierogis* in Polish Greenpoint and
cuchifritos in Spanish Harlem. The two-
and-a-half to three-hour-long tours also
take in local sites and secrets and cost
$20, not including food.

Media

**The days are long gone when New York could support twenty
daily newspapers.** Today, only three remain: the **New York
Times** and tabloids the **Daily News** and the **New York Post**.

The *New York Times*, an American institution, prides itself on
being the "paper of record"
– the closest thing America has
to a quality national paper. It has
solid, sometimes stolid, international coverage, and places much
emphasis on its news analysis.
The Sunday edition is a thumping
bundle of newsprint divided into
a number of supplements that
take days to read. The legendary
crossword puzzle in Sunday's
New York Times Magazine should

keep you occupied all day.

The *Times'* archrivals concentrate on local news, usually
screamed out in often-humorous
banner headlines. The *Daily News*
is renowned as a picture newspaper but with intelligent features
and many racy headlines. The
New York Post, the city's oldest
newspaper, started in 1801 by
Alexander Hamilton, has been
in decline for many years. It is
known for its sensationalism and
conservative slant.

Of the weekly papers, the *Village Voice* is the most widely read, mainly for its comprehensive arts coverage and investigative features. The *Voice*'s main competitor, the *New York Press*, is an edgier alternative, angrier and not afraid to offend just about everyone. Its listings are thorough and informative, though.

Guide

Guide

1

The Statue of Liberty and Ellis Island

The southern tip of Manhattan and the enclosing shores of New Jersey, Staten Island, and Brooklyn form the broad expanse of New York Harbor, one of the finest natural harbors in the world and one of the things that persuaded the first Dutch settlers to make their home here several centuries ago. Take to the water via ferry to get the best views of the classic downtown skyline, or to get out to the **Statue of Liberty** on Liberty Island and **Ellis Island**, two high-priority targets for a trip to the city.

The best way to reach the ferries is to take the #1 to South Ferry or the #4 or #5 to Bowling Green.

The Statue of Liberty

Daily except Dec 25th 9am–6pm (closes earlier outside high season); free; ☎212/363-3200, ⊛www.nps.gov/stli.

1 Getting to the islands

Circle Line **ferries** go to both Liberty and Ellis islands and leave from Battery Park in lower Manhattan year-round daily from 9am–4pm every 20–30min (round-trip $11.50, seniors $9.50, children ages 3–12 $4.50; purchase tickets from Castle Clinton in the park, in advance at ⓦ www.statuereservations.com, or by phone on ☎ 1-888/782-8834); the ferry goes first to Liberty Island and then continues to Ellis. It's best to leave as early in the day as possible, both to avoid long lines (especially in the summer) and to insure you get to see both islands; if you take the last ferry of the day, you won't be able to visit Ellis Island. Liberty Island needs a good hour at least, especially if the weather's nice; Ellis Island demands a minimum of two hours for its Museum of Immigration. If you'd like to go inside the Statue of Liberty, you have to take a tour, which, though free, must be booked online in advance (same details as above).

Alternatively, the **Staten Island Ferry** (free; ☎ 212/639-9675, ⓦ www.siferry.com; take the #R or #W to Whitehall Street) departs every half-hour from the new Whitehall Ferry Terminal and shuttles some 20 million passengers annually. While it provides a beautiful panorama of the harbor and downtown skyline, the Staten Island Ferry doesn't actually make stops on the islands.

The **Statue of Liberty** has for a century been a monument to the American Dream, a potent reminder that the USA is, at its heart, a land of immigrants. It was New York Harbor where the first big waves of European immigrants arrived, their ships entering through the Verrazano Narrows to round the bend of the bay and catch a first glimpse of "Liberty Enlightening the World."

The statue, which depicts Liberty throwing off her shackles and holding a beacon to light the world, was built by Frédéric Auguste Bartholdi in Paris between 1874 and 1884. Bartholdi started with a terracotta model and enlarged it through four successive versions to its present size, a construction of thin copper sheets bolted together and supported by an iron framework designed by Gustave Eiffel. The arm carrying the torch was exhibited in Madison Square Park for seven years, but the whole statue wasn't officially accepted on behalf of the American people until 1884, after which it was taken apart, crated up, and shipped to New York. The statue was unveiled by President Grover Cleveland in 1886 in a flag-waving shindig that has never really stopped.

You can take one of two **tours**: the **Promenade**, which takes in the statue's entrance hall and an upstairs exhibition, and the **Observatory**, which takes in all this plus the 192 steps to the top of the pedestal (the crown has been closed since 9/11, and it's unlikely to reopen). The downstairs lobby shows the original torch and flame, which was completed first and used to raise funds for the rest of the statue. Upstairs a small exhibition tells the statue's story with prints, photographs, posters, cuttings, and replicas of bits of the statue and the plastercasts made to build it. There are images of the statue from all kinds of sources – indicative of just how iconic an image it is. At the top of the pedestal you can look up into the center of the statue's skirts, with its rivetted, bolted interior and spiral staircase, as well as taking a turn around the balcony outside, where the views are predictably superb.

Ellis Island

Daily 9am–5pm; free; ☎212/363-3200, ✪www.ellisisland.org.

Just across the water from Liberty Island sits **Ellis Island**, the first stop for over twelve million immigrants hoping to settle in the USA. The island became an immigration station in 1892, a processing point for the massive influx of mostly Southern and Eastern European immigrants. The station closed in 1954, and in 1990 reopened as the **Ellis Island Museum of Immigration**, in what is an ambitious attempt to recapture the spirit of the place, with films, exhibits, and tapes documenting the celebration of America as an immigrant nation.

1

Some 100 million Americans can trace their roots back through Ellis Island and, for them especially, the museum is an engaging display. On the first floor, in the old railroad ticket office, is the excellent "Peopling of America" exhibit, which chronicles four centuries of American immigration, offering a statistical portrait of who the arrivals were and where they came from. The huge, vaulted **Registry Room** on the second floor, scene of so much trepidation, elation, and despair, has been left bare, with just a couple of inspectors' desks and American flags. In the side-hall interview rooms, recordings of those who passed through Ellis Island recall the experience, along with photographs and thoughtful, informative explanatory text, while upstairs small domestic artifacts – train timetables and familiar items brought from home – make up the evocative "Treasure from Home" exhibit.

The museum's **American Family Immigration History Center** (⊛www.ellisislandrecords.org) is of great use to genealogical researchers, offering an interactive research database (free) that contains information from ship manifests and passenger lists concerning over 22 million immigrants who passed through the Port of New York between 1892 and 1924. On the fortified spurs of the island, names of immigrant families who passed through the building over the years are engraved in copper, paid for by a minimum donation of $100 from their descendants. This "American Immigrant Wall of Honor," launched in 1990, helped fund the island's restoration and features the names of over 600,000 individuals and families.

The Financial District

While most visitors to the southern end of Manhattan make the pilgrimage to Ground Zero, former site of the World Trade Center, the area is also home to some of the city's most historic sights. New York began here, and its development is reflected in the dense, twisted streets of what is now known as the **Financial District**, heart of the nation's business trade. Many of the early colonial buildings that once lined these streets either burned down during the American Revolution or the Great Fire of 1835, or were later demolished by big businesses eager to boost their corporate images with headquarters near **Wall Street**. The explosive commercial development of nearby **South Street Seaport** and the conversion of old office space to residential units have helped the Financial District shed its nine-to-five aura.

Along Wall Street

The Dutch arrived here first, building a wooden wall at the edge of New Amsterdam in 1635 to protect themselves from

British settlers to the north and giving the narrow canyon of today's **Wall Street** its name. Still today, from behind the Neoclassical facade of the **New York Stock Exchange** at 8 Wall St (Map 4, E7), the purse strings of the capitalist world are pulled. Unfortunately, since 9/11 the Stock Exchange has been closed to the public, and the surrounding heavy police presence gives the place the feel of a military fortress.

Federal Hall National Memorial

Map 4, E6. 26 Wall St. Mon–Fri 9am–5pm; free; ☎212/825-6888, ⓦwww.nps.gov/feha. #1, #2, #4, or #5 to Wall Street.

At the street's canyon-like head, the **Federal Hall National Memorial** can't help but look like an Ionic temple that woke up one morning and found itself surrounded by skyscrapers. The building was built by Town and Davis as the Customs House in the 1830s and served briefly as the first capitol of the United States. There is an exhibition inside that tells of how democracy got its start some sixty years earlier when printer John Peter Zenger was acquitted of libel in 1735.

Trinity Church and around

At Wall Street's western end is **Trinity Church** (Map 4, E6; Mon–Sat free guided tours daily at 2pm), first built in 1698, though the current version went up in 1846. For fifty years, this was the city's tallest building, a reminder of just how relatively recent high-rise Manhattan sprung up. Trinity's cemetery is the final resting place for such luminaries as the first secretary of the Treasury (and man on the $10 bill) Alexander Hamilton, steamboat king Robert Fulton, signer of the Declaration of Independence Francis Lewis, and many others.

Trinity Church is an oddity amid its office-building neighbors, several of which are worth nosing into. Immediately opposite the church, **One Wall Street** is among the best, with an Art Deco lobby done up in red and gold. Further east down Wall Street, the **Morgan Guaranty Trust Building** at no. 23 bears the scars of a weird happening on

September 16, 1920, when a horse-drawn cart exploded in front. The explosion remains unexplained to this day and the pockmark scars on the building's wall have never been repaired.

The World Trade Center 1972–2001

On **September 11th, 2001**, a hijacked airline slammed into the north tower of the **World Trade Center** at 8.46am; seventeen minutes later another hijacked plane struck the south tower. As thousands looked on in horror – in addition to millions more viewing on TV – the south tower collapsed at 9.59am, its twin at 10.28am. All seven buildings of the World Trade Center complex eventually collapsed, and the Center was reduced to a monument of steel, concrete, and glass rubble. As black clouds billowed above, the whole area was covered in a blanket of concrete dust several inches thick; mountains of other debris reached up several hundred feet in the air.

The devastation was staggering. While most of the 50,000 working in the towers had been evacuated before the towers fell, many never made it out; hundreds of firemen, policemen, and rescue workers who arrived on the scene when the planes struck were crushed when the buildings fell. In all, **2986 people died** at the WTC and in the simultaneous attack on the Pentagon in Washington, DC.

In the days after the attack, Downtown was basically shut down, and the seven-square-block vicinity immediately around the WTC – soon to be known as **Ground Zero** – was the obvious focus of the rescue effort. New Yorkers lined up to give blood and volunteer to help the rescue workers; vigils were held throughout the city, most notably in Union Square, which became peppered with all manner of candles and makeshift shrines.

The **future** of the WTC site is still in flux today, as successive Freedom Tower designs for the site have been scrapped and redesigned, most recently because of security concerns raised by the NYD. That said, construction has begun on a new WTC subway hub and the cornerstone laid for whatever building will eventually arise.

Ground Zero and around

The former site of the World Trade Center, **Ground Zero** remains a gaping hole on Manhattan's lower West Side. Seven buildings in total were destroyed as a result of the terrorist attacks on 9/11, while eleven other structures surrounding the complex suffered serious damage, including the Federal Building and the New York Police Command Center.

Today, many visitors make the pilgrimage to Ground Zero to see what's left of the WTC for themselves. The viewing platform which stood here immediately after 9/11 has been dismantled, but you can still get a good look at Ground Zero by circling the fenced-in site. There is also an elevated **walkway** at the south end of the space that gives you the best view into the vacant pit where construction is ongoing. At the time of writing, building has yet to begin on the new Freedom Tower, though ground has been broken on a new subway station here, which is scheduled to be completed in 2009.

The Federal Reserve Plaza

Take Nassau Street north of Wall to Maiden Lane, where you'll find Philip Johnson's and John Burgee's **Federal Reserve Plaza**, which complements the original 1924 Federal Reserve Bank (Map 4, E6). Eighty feet below the somber neo-Gothic interior of the bank are most of the free world's gold reserves. It is possible – but tricky – to tour; contact the Public Information Department, Federal Reserve Bank, 33 Liberty St (☎212/720-6130, ⊛www.ny.frb.org), several weeks in advance – tickets have to be mailed.

St Paul's Chapel and south on Broadway

The oldest church in Manhattan, **St Paul's Chapel** (Map 4, E5; Mon–Fri 10am–6pm, Sun 9am–4pm; free) dates from 1766 – eighty years earlier than Trinity Church, almost prehistoric by New York standards. George Washington worshipped here, and his pew, zealously treasured, is on show. For the past few decades, St Paul's sat squarely in the shadow of the Twin Towers, but emerged miraculously intact after the attacks of 9/11.

Heading south along Broadway, a most impressive leftover of the confident days before the Wall Street Crash is the old **Cunard Building**, at no. 25 (Map 4, D8). Its marble walls and high dome once housed a steamship's booking office – hence the elaborate, whimsical murals of various ships and nautical mythology splashed around the ceiling. Today, it houses a post office – one that's been fitted with little feeling for the exuberant space it occupies. On the second floor is the **New York City Police Museum** (Tues–Sat 10am–5pm, Sun 11am–5pm; free; ☎212/480-3110, ⓦwww.nycpolicemuseum.org), housing a serviceable collection of 250 years' worth of memorabilia of the New York Police Department, including popular exhibits on notorious New York criminals as well as the fallen heroes of 9/11.

At 26 Broadway, located in the former headquarters of **John D. Rockefeller's Standard Oil Company**, is the **Museum of American Financial History**, 28 Broadway (Tues–Sat 10am–4pm; $2; ☎212/908-4110, ⓦwww.financialhistory.org). This is the largest public archive of financial documents and artifacts in the world, featuring such finance-related objects as the bond signed by Washington bearing the first dollar sign ever used on a federal document. On Fridays, the museum also offers a "World of Finance" walking tour ($15).

Bowling Green

Map 4, E7. #4 or #5 to Bowling Green.

Broadway comes to a gentle end at **Bowling Green Park**, originally the city's meat market, but in 1733 turned into an oval of turf used for the eponymous game by colonial Brits on a lease of "one peppercorn per year." In 1626, the green had been the location of one of Manhattan's more memorable business deals, when Peter Minuit, first director general of the Dutch colony of New Amsterdam, bought the whole island from the Indians for a bucket of trade goods worth sixty guilders (about $24). The other side of the story (and the part you never hear) was that these particular Indians didn't actually own or live on the island.

The green sees plenty of office folk picnicking in the shadow of Cass Gilbert's **US Customs House**, a heroic monument to the Port of New York and home of the **Smithsonian National Museum of the American Indian**, 1 Bowling Green (daily 10am–5pm, Thurs until 8pm; free; ☎212/514-3700, ⊛www.si.edu/nmai). This excellent collection of artifacts from almost every tribe native to the Americas was largely assembled by one man, George Gustav Heye (1874–1957), who traveled throughout the Americas picking up such works for over fifty years. Highlights include totem poles and other wood carvings from the Pacific Northwest, quilled hides and feathered headdresses from the Great Plains, and thousand-year-old pottery from the mysterious vanished civilization that once thrived around the Grand Canyon in the American Southwest. Built in 1907, the Customs House itself was intended to pay homage to the booming maritime market. The four **statues** were sculpted by Daniel Chester French, who also created the Lincoln Memorial in Washington, DC. As if French foresaw the House's current use, the sculptor blatantly comments on the mistreatment of Indians in his statues.

Battery Park and Castle Clinton

Map 4, D8. #4 or #5 to Bowling Green.

Due west, lower Manhattan lets out its breath in **Battery Park**, a bright and breezy space with tall trees, green grass, lots of flowers, and views overlooking the panorama of the Statue of Liberty, Ellis Island, and Governors Island. At the park's main entrance stands the mutilated sculpture *The Sphere*, a representation of Earth created by Fritz Koenig in 1971 as a monument to world peace; this sculpture stood in the World Trade Center plaza until 9/11, when it was heavily damaged – it's an eerie, immediate reminder of that day's destruction. Various other monuments and statues ranging from Jewish immigrants to Celtic settlers to the city's first wireless-telegraph operators adorn the park.

Before a landfill closed the gap, **Castle Clinton**, the 1811 fort on the west side of the park, was on an island, one of several forts defending New York Harbor. Later it acted as a pre–Ellis Island drop-off point for arriving immigrants. Today, the squat castle is the place to buy tickets for, and board ferries to, the Statue of Liberty and Ellis Island (see p.30).

The Skyscraper Museum

Map 4, D8. 39 Battery Place. Wed–Sun noon–6pm; $5, students and seniors $2.50; ☏212/968-1961, ⊛www.skyscraper.org.

At the northwest tip of Battery Park, the **Skyscraper Museum** stands fittingly at the edge of lower Manhattan's great skyscraper canyons. The museum is dedicated to the mammoth towers of America, with coverage of the fierce competitions between those who erected the Chrysler and Empire State buildings in Manhattan in the 1920s and 1930s, and the subsequent duels for size supremacy between New York and Chicago in the 1960s and 1970s. Also on display is the original model for the late World Trade Center. The 5000-square-foot museum space is an architectural marvel in itself, using vertical mini-tower display cases and glass ceilings to convey a sense of soaring height – despite its location in the ground-floor bowels of the *Ritz-Carlton* hotel and condominium tower.

Battery Park City

Map 4, C7. #4 or #5 to Bowling Green.

The hole dug for the foundations of the Twin Towers threw up a million cubic yards of earth and rock; these excavations were dumped into the Hudson River to form the 23-acre base of **Battery Park City**, a self-sufficient island of office blocks, apartments, chain boutiques, and landscaped esplanade that feels a far cry indeed from much of Manhattan.

At its very southern end is the entrance to the peaceful, Zen-like **Robert F. Wagner Jr. Park**. In the park, a hexagonal, pale-granite building designed in 1997 by Kevin Roche will catch your eye. That's the **Museum of Jewish Heritage**, 18 First Place (Map 4, C8; Sun–Tues & Thurs 10am–5.45pm, Wed until 8pm, Fri 10am–5pm, closed Jewish holidays; $10, students $5, children free; ℡646/437-4200, ⊛www.mjhnyc.org), was created as a memorial to the Holocaust. Three floors of exhibits feature historical and cultural artifacts ranging from the practical accoutrements of everyday Eastern European Jewish life to the prison garb survivors wore in Nazi concentration camps, along with photographs, personal belongings, and narratives.

Water and Pearl streets

Retrace your steps through Robert F. Wagner Jr. Park to **Water Street** and turn east down Old Slip. The pocket-size palazzo, which was once the **First Precinct Police Station**, slots easily into the narrow strip, a cheerful throwback to a different era. A little to the south, off Water Street, stands the **Vietnam Veterans' Memorial**, an unappealing rectangular glass-block monument surrounded by a peaceful park that boasts a nice view of the East River.

The eighteenth-century **Fraunces Tavern Museum**, 54 Pearl St, at Broad (Map 4, F8; Tues–Fri noon–5pm, Sat 10am–5pm; $3, children, seniors, students $2; ℡212/425-1778, ⊛www.frauncestavernmuseum.org), has survived extensive modification, several fires, and nineteenth-century use as a hotel. The Tavern's second floor has been renovated to match its appearance when George Washington said his farewell here to his senior officers at the end of the Revolutionary

War, and there are 45 Revolution-era paintings on display from the museum's permanent collection.

At 6 Pearl St, you'll find **New York Unearthed** (Mon–Fri noon–6pm by advance appointment only; free; ☎212/748-8753), the South Street Seaport Museum's tiny hands-on annex devoted to the city's archeology. There are all manner of local artifacts here, from pre-Columbian pottery shards to high-end nineteenth-century china. The best part is that visitors get to interact with the archeologists who work here, providing a once-in-a-lifetime opportunity to see how they document, restore, and place artifacts in context.

South Street Seaport

Map 4, H6. #A, #E, #J, #M, #1, #2, #4, or #5 to Fulton Street–Broadway Nassau.

At the eastern end of Fulton Street, the **South Street Seaport** is unremarkable, if lively – the place is mostly characterized by commercial gentrification designed to woo developers and tourists, which it does in spades. The gritty, workaday Fulton Street Fish Market was located here until it moved to the Bronx in 2005. The Seaport dates back to the 1600s, when this stretch of the waterside was New York's sailship port. When the FDR Drive was constructed in the 1950s, the Seaport's decline was rapid, but private initiative beginning in 1967 rescued the remaining warehouses and saved the historic seaport just in time. Regular guided tours of the Seaport run from the **Visitors' Center**, located at 12–14 Fulton St.

The South Street Seaport Museum

Map 4, G5. 207 Water St. April–Oct daily 10am–6pm, Nov–March Fri–Sun 10am–5pm; $8, includes all tours, films, galleries, and museum-owned ships; ☎212/748-8600, ⊛www.southstseaport.org.

Housed in a series of painstakingly restored 1830s warehouses, the **South Street Seaport Museum** offers a fairly interesting collection of refitted ships and chubby tugboats; it's the largest collection of sailing vessels – by tonnage – in the US. Downtown New York City seems so far removed these days from its origins as a major center of shipping and sailing that the collection frankly seems a bit out of place in the heart of the Financial District. That said, it is one of the best collections of its kind and will appeal to maritime enthusiasts.

Pier 17 and the rest of the seaport
Map 4, H6.

To many, **Pier 17**, just south of the Brooklyn Bridge, has become the focal point of the district, created from the old fish market pier that was demolished and then restored in 1982. A three-story glass-and-steel **pavilion** houses all kinds of restaurants and shops; a bit more interesting is the outdoor promenade, always crowded in the summer, when you can listen to free live music or tour historic moored ships.

Just across South Street, there's an assemblage of upmarket chain shops. Yet keep your eyes peeled for some unusual buildings preserved here, like at **203 Front St**; this giant J. Crew store was an 1880s hotel that catered to unmarried laborers on the dock. Not far away, cleaned-up **Schermer-horn Row** is a unique ensemble of Georgian-Federal–style early warehouses, dating to around 1811.

City Hall Park
and the
Brooklyn Bridge

S ince New York's early days, the seats of government – federal, state, and municipal – have been located around **City Hall Park**. Though many of the original buildings no longer stand, great examples of the city's finest architecture can still be found here. The park itself contains stately City Hall and Tweed Courthouse, and the Woolworth Building stands by as a venerable onlooker. Meanwhile, the Municipal Building guards Police Plaza and the courthouses that form the center of New York's judiciary, and just south the **Brooklyn Bridge** – which makes for a great walk – zooms eastward over the river to the genteel neighborhood of Brooklyn Heights (see p.160).

City Hall

③

Map 4, E4. Free tours (reservations required in advance) Fri at 2pm; ☎212/788-6865. #N or #R to City Hall, #6 to Brooklyn Bridge/City Hall, or #2 or #3 to Park Place.

Broadway and Park Row form the apex of **City Hall Park**, a noisy, pigeon-splattered triangle of green that marks the center of the jumble of government offices and courts. At the park's northern head stands **City Hall**, whose interior is an elegant meeting of arrogance and authority, with the sweeping spiral staircase delivering you to the precise geometry of the Governor's Room. In 1865, Abraham Lincoln's body lay here in state while 120,000 New Yorkers paid their respects. Later, after the city's 1927 fêting of the returned aviator Charles Lindbergh, it became the traditional finishing point for Broadway tickertape parades given for astronauts, returned hostages, and triumphant sports teams.

This triangular wedge is dotted with **statues**, not least of which is one of Horace Greeley, founder of the *New York Tribune* newspaper, and in front of whose bronzed countenance a farmer's market is held each Tuesday and Friday (April–Dec 8am–6pm). Prize position among the patriotic statues here goes to **Nathan Hale**, who, in 1776, was captured by the British and hanged for spying, but not before he'd spat out his gloriously and memorably famous last words: "I regret that I only have but one life to lose for my country."

The Woolworth Building

Map 4, E4. #N or #R to City Hall, #6 to Brooklyn Bridge/City Hall, or #2 or #3 to Park Place.

At the west side of the park is the esteemed **Woolworth Building**, one of the city's most aesthetically pleasing skyscrapers. Money, ornament, and prestige mingle in this 1913 "Cathedral of Commerce," whose soaring, graceful lines are fringed with Gothic decoration more for fun than any portentous allusion. Within, where high-profile financial service corporations have their offices, vaulted ceilings ooze honey-gold mosaics – even the brass mailboxes are magnificent. On the whole, the building has a well-humored panache more or less extinct in today's architecture. Unfortunately the Woolworth is not open to the public, though you can inspect the ground-floor lobby Monday to Friday 9am to 5pm.

The Municipal Building and around

Straddling Chambers Street, which runs along the top of City Hall Park, the **Municipal Building** (Map 4, F4) stands like an oversized chest of drawers. Built between 1907 and 1914, the building was architects McKim, Mead and White's first skyscraper. Atop it, an extravagant pile of columns and pinnacles signals a frivolous conclusion to a no-nonsense building that houses public records; below, though not apparent, subway cars travel through its foundation.

At 100 Centre St, the 1939 Art-Deco **Criminal Courts Building**, reminiscent of a Babylonian temple, houses the **Manhattan Detention Center of Men**, which is nicknamed "the Tombs," after the funereal Egyptian-style building that once stood across the street. Where "the Tombs" used to be, the White Street Correctional Facility houses up to five hundred maximum-security inmates, and the "bridge of sighs" over White Street (nicknamed thusly for the supposed sighs of prisoners as they pass through) connects the two facilities. The criminal courts are open to the public Monday to Friday 9am to 5pm – just don't expect *Law & Order*–style theatrics.

The Brooklyn Bridge

South along Centre Street from the Municipal Building is the entrance to the **Brooklyn Bridge**, a magnificent, towering piece of engineering that, along with the Staten Island ferry, offers some of the best free views of Manhattan and the Statue of Liberty in the city.

Built by **John Roebling** and his son **Washington**, the bridge was opened in 1883 and was, for twenty years after, the world's largest and longest suspension bridge. To New Yorkers, it was an object of awe, the massively concrete symbol of the Great American Dream, and the painter Joseph Stella called it "a shrine containing all the efforts of the new civilization of America." Indeed, the bridge's meeting of art and function, of romantic Gothic and daring practicality, became a sort of spiritual model for the next generation's skyscrapers.

The bridge's wooden walkway leads across the East River to **Brooklyn Heights** (see p.160) – though many visitors simply walk halfway, turn to admire the beautiful skyline, and walk back to lower Manhattan. It's an undeniably impressive view: the Financial District's giants clutter shoulder to shoulder through the spidery latticework of the cables (with a noticeable gap where the Twin Towers once stood); the East River laps below as cars hum to and from Brooklyn; and the Statue of Liberty is visible in the harbor. It's a glimpse of the twenty-first-century metropolis, and on no account to be missed.

4

SoHo, TriBeCa, and NoLita

This triumvirate of acronym'd neighborhoods represents some of the city's most piquant examples of urban renewal and cultural turnaround, having mutated from working-class wholesale and chiefly immigrant areas into artist spaces and then again into super-chic neighborhoods boasting gourmet eateries, wine and cocktail bars, high-end shopping, and luxury hotel and apartment living. **TriBeCa**, while adversely affected by the economic downturn after 9/11, still boasts great alternative music venues and several good hotels. **SoHo** has lost many of its artists, but its trademark cast-iron buildings still play host to unique stores and eateries as well as several members of the publishing and architectural avant-garde. Lastly, it's **NoLita**, with its tiny boutiques, designer ice-cream stores, and cafés crammed with beautiful people that perhaps best exemplifies the new, moneyed inhabitants of Downtown.

TriBeCa

#1 to Franklin Street.

Just a few blocks' walk northwest from City Hall puts you in **TriBeCa** (Try-beck-ah) – the **Tri**angle **Be**low **Ca**nal Street, an area that was rapidly transformed in the early 1990s from a wholesale garment district to an upscale community that mixes commercial establishments with loft residences, studios, art galleries, and chic eateries. Less a triangle than a crumpled rectangle – the area is bounded by Canal and Murray streets, Broadway, and the Hudson River – it takes in spacious industrial buildings whose upper layers have become the apartments of TriBeCa's new gentry.

Despite rising rents, commercial space in TriBeCa is still less expensive than in SoHo or Greenwich Village, so well-to-do creative industries have been moving to the area en masse. Galleries and recording studios, computer graphics companies, photo labs, and even the film industry have made themselves at home here. The **TriBeCa Film Center**, 375 Greenwich St (Map 4, C2), is a screening facility and production company that is co-owned by Robert De Niro; it is also the nexus of the annual **TriBeCa Film Festival**, founded as an artists' response to the 9/11 terrorist attacks and bringing together directors, actors, and audiences every spring.

Exploring TriBeCa

To get a feel for TriBeCa's mix of old and new, go to **Duane Park**, a sliver of green between Hudson and Greenwich streets. Around the park's picturesque perimeter you'll see the former depots of New York's egg, butter, and cheese distribution center wedged between new residential apartments, where the World Trade Center buildings used to guard the skyline like sentinels.

Take a left out of Duane Park and follow Greenwich toward Canal Street. In this main strip restaurants from the affordable (*Yaffa's T Room*) to the expensive (*TriBeCa Grill*) line the street. Parallel to Greenwich lies Hudson Street, which catches the overflow of fancy restaurants before, in sharp contrast, petering out into still-active warehouses, whose denizens do the same work they have for decades. See p.212 for TriBeCa restaurant reviews.

West Broadway is one of TriBeCa's main thoroughfares and has a few interesting, if nonessential, sites to check out. The most poignant is perhaps **Ladder Company 8**, between Varick and North Moore streets, a turn-of-the-nineteenth-century brick-and-stone firehouse dotted with white stars. The closest firehouse to the World Trade Center, it suffered many casualties during the terrorist attacks of 9/11.

SoHo

#N or #R to Prince Street or #6 to Spring Street.

From the mid-1960s to the late 1980s, **SoHo**, the grid of streets that runs **So**uth of **Ho**uston Street, meant one thing: art. As the West Village increased in price and declined in hipness, artists moved into SoHo's industry-vacated loft spaces. Galleries were established, quickly attracting the city's art crowd, as well as trendy clothes shops and some of the city's best restaurants. Soon the artists who'd settled the district were priced out and moved on to Chelsea, Brooklyn, and beyond. What remains is a mix of chichi antique shops, often overpriced art galleries, and chain clothiers from around the world.

Although SoHo now carries the veneer of the establishment – a loft in the area means money (and lots of it) – no amount of gloss can cover up the neighborhood's quintessential appearance, its sunlit alleys of paint-peeled former garment factories fronted by some of the best cast-iron facades in the country. **Houston Street** (pronounced *How*ston rather than *Hew*ston) marks the top of SoHo's trellis of streets, any exploration of which entails criss-crossing and doubling back. **Greene Street** is a great place to start, highlighted all along by the nineteenth-century cast-iron facades that, in part if not in whole, saved SoHo from the bulldozers. **Prince Street**, **Spring Street**, and **West Broadway** hold the best selection of shops and galleries in the area.

SoHo's cast-iron architecture

The technique of **cast-iron architecture** was used simply as a way of assembling buildings quickly and cheaply, with iron beams rather than heavy walls carrying the weight of the floors. The result was the removal of load-bearing walls, greater space for windows, and remarkably decorative facades. Almost any style or whim could be cast in iron and pinned to a building, and architects created the most fanciful of fronts for SoHo's sweatshops.

The **SoHo Cast-Iron Historic District** runs roughly north–south from Houston to Canal and east–west from West Broadway to Crosby. Have a look at **72–76 Greene Street**, an extravagance whose Corinthian portico stretches its entire five stories, all in painted metal, and at the elaborations of its sister building at **nos. 28–30**. These are some of the best examples, but from Broome to Canal streets most of the fronts on Greene Street's west side are either real (or mock) cast iron.

At the northeast corner of Broome Street and Broadway is the magnificent **Haughwout Building** (Map 5, G7), perhaps the ultimate in cast-iron architecture. Rhythmically repeated motifs of colonnaded arches are framed here behind taller columns in a thin sliver of a mock-Venetian palace. In 1904, Ernest Flagg took the possibilities of cast iron to their conclusion in his "**Little Singer**" Building, 561 Broadway, at Prince (Map 5, F6), a design whose use of wide window frames points the way to the glass curtain wall of the 1950s.

North from Canal Street

Loosely speaking, SoHo's diversions start out grittier down south and get nicer as you move north. Still, **Broome** and **Grand streets**, formerly full of dilapidated storefronts and dusty windows, are home to a small band of boutiques, galleries, cafés, and eclectic restaurants. The ultrachic (and ultra-expensive) *SoHo Grand Hotel* occupies the corner of Canal and West Broadway. If you don't want to fork out the dough for a room, at least look around the lobby or have a cocktail at the sumptuous bar. Marking SoHo's southern entrance and border with TriBeCa, Canal Street links the Holland Tunnel with the Manhattan Bridge, though in truth the street is in look and feel more Chinatown than any other area.

Prince Street

At 112 Prince Street, SoHo celebrates its architecture with Richard Haas's **mural**, a self-referential *trompe l'oeil* affair that reproduces the building's cast-iron facade. Also at this intersection of Prince and Greene streets is one of SoHo's affordable **markets** (there's another at the meeting of Spring and Wooster streets). Many of the clothes and antique shops around here are beyond reasonable budgets, although Prince and the other SoHo streets have their fair share of chain clothing stores you'd find in any mid-size American city. Bargain treasures and pure bric-a-brac can also be found at the **Antique Flea Market**, held every weekend on the southeast corner of Grand Street and Broadway. See Chapter 27, "Shopping," for further options.

What you'll find in SoHo's remaining **galleries** is similarly overpriced, but no one minds you looking in for a while, and doing this is also a sure way of bumping into the more visible eccentrics of the area. Most of the galleries are concentrated on West Broadway and Prince Street, with some on Grand between West Broadway and Broadway. They're generally open Tuesday to Saturday 11am to 6pm, with Saturdays being the most lively. For a greater selection of galleries, as well as the new Chelsea addresses of some former SoHo establishments, see Chapter 28, "Commercial galleries."

NoLita

Map 5, G6. #N or #R to Prince Street.

Just east of Broadway and south of Houston, fashion, style, and nonchalant living have found fertile breeding ground. Lining the streets here are fresh, creative, independent designer boutiques, cafés, and eateries, establishing this area as the latest in chic. Referred to as **NoLita**, this area **no**rth of **Li**ttle **Ita**ly, which extends east from Lafayette, Mott, and Elizabeth streets between Prince and Houston, is great for hip, only-in-New York shopping. NoLita is not cheap by any means, but the young, artsy, and restless hanging around the district's proliferation of trendy stores, bars, and restaurants make it an excellent place for a late-afternoon drink and a spot of beautiful-people watching.

5

Chinatown and Little Italy

With more than 200,000 residents (125,000 of them Chinese and most of the rest other Asian ethnicities), seven Chinese newspapers, twelve Buddhist temples, around 150 restaurants, and over 300 garment factories, **Chinatown** is Manhattan's most populous ethnic neighborhood, one of busy eateries and exotic street markets. In the nineteenth century this contained the notorious **Five Points** district, home to the Irish and Nativist gangs celebrated in Martin Scorsese's *Gangs of New York*, but Chinese culture has predominated here for the last 100+ years. Since the 1980s, Chinatown has pushed its boundaries north across Canal Street into Little Italy and sprawls east into the nether fringes of the Lower East Side around Division Street and East Broadway.

The Chinese community has been careful to preserve its own way of dealing with things, preferring to keep affairs close to the bond of the family and allowing few intrusions into a still-insular culture. And while insularity means that much of Chinatown's character survives relatively unspoilt – especially on streets such as Canal, Pell, Mott, and Bayard

– it has also meant sweatshop labor and poor, overcrowded tenements ill-kept by landlords. However, unless you stay in Chinatown for a considerable length of time it's unlikely you'll see much of this seamier side. Most tourists, like most New Yorkers, come here not to get the lowdown on Chinese politics but to eat excellent **Chinese food** or to hunt for bargains along **Canal Street**.

Just north of Chinatown is **Little Italy**, one of the city's most storied immigrant neighborhoods. Signs made out of red, green, and white tinsel effusively welcome visitors here, a signal perhaps that today's Little Italy is light years from the solid ethnic enclave of old. The neighborhood is a lot smaller and more commercial than it once was, and the area settled by New York's huge nineteenth-century influx of Italian immigrants is encroached upon a little more each year by Chinatown. Walk north from Canal Street along Mulberry or Mott to get here, and the transition from the cultural heart of Chinatown to Little Italy's Big Tomato tourist schmaltz can be a little difficult to stomach. Few Italians live here anymore, and many of the restaurants cater primarily to tourists, with valet parking and by piping the music of New York's favorite Italian son, Frank Sinatra, onto the street.

But that's not to advise missing out on Little Italy altogether. Some original bakeries and *salumerias* (Italian specialty food stores) do survive, and here, amid the imported cheeses, sausages, and salamis hanging from the ceiling, you can buy filling sandwiches made with cured meats and slabs

Chinese New Year

Chinatown bursts open during the **Chinese New Year festival**, held each year on the second full moon after the winter solstice (usually between mid-Jan and mid-Feb) when a giant cloth and papier-mâché dragon runs down Mott Street. The firecrackers that traditionally accompanied the festival are now banned by the city as a fire hazard (much to local chagrin), yet the gutters still run with ceremonial dyes.

of fresh mozzarella or eat slices of homemade focaccia and sip espresso.

The best way to reach Chinatown is to take the #J, #M, #N, #Q, #R, #W, #Z, or #6 train to Canal Street. To access Little Italy, take any of the above trains to Canal Street and walk north on Mulberry.

Mott Street

Mott Street is Chinatown's most obvious-tourist-restaurant row, although the streets around – Canal, Pell, Bayard, Doyers, and Bowery – host a glut of restaurants, tea and rice shops, and grocers as well. Cantonese cuisine predominates, but there are also many **restaurants** that specialize in the spicier Szechuan and Hunan cuisines, along with Fukien, Soochow, and the spicy Chowchou dishes. Just remember that most Chinese restaurants start closing up around 9.30pm – best to go early if you want less-frenzied service and atmosphere. If you're looking for specific recommendations (especially for BYOB lunchtime dim sum), some of the best are detailed in Chapter 22, "Restaurants."

Besides wolfing down Asian delights, the lure of China-town lies in wandering amid the exotica of the shops and absorbing the neighborhood's vigorous street life. Meander-ing is highly recommended, and there are several interesting, vaguely structured routes to take. Mott Street, again, is the obvious starting point: follow it from Worth Street and there's **Chinatown Fair** at the southern end, on the site of the dis-trict's first Chinese shop. Once a bona fide museum, this is now little more than a bizarre and very popular video arcade, where a predominantly male crowd gathers to play anything from pinball to 1950s Test Your Own Strength machines and the most modern interactive video phenomena.

Further north along Mott Street, a rare edifice predat-ing the Chinese arrival dominates the corner of Mott and Mosco streets. It's the early nineteenth-century green-domed

Catholic school and **Church of the Transfiguration** (Map 7, G3), an elegant building that has been newly renovated over the last decade. Masses are held here daily in Cantonese and English, with additional services in Mandarin on Sunday. Just across from the church is picturesquely crooked **Doyers Street**, once known as "Bloody Angle" for its reputation as a dumping ground for dead bodies.

5

Museum of Chinese in the Americas

Map 4, G2. Tues–Sat noon–5pm; $3, children $1; ☎212/619-4785, ⓦwww.moca-nyc.org.

One block west of Mott is Mulberry Street, where, at no. 70, you'll find the double red doors of the community center right on the corner. Two floors up lies the tiny but fascinating **Museum of Chinese in the Americas**. The museum is dedicated to documenting the experiences of Chinese immigrants in the Americas as well as reclaiming and preserving Chinese history in the West. Displays include Chinese photographs, cultural artifacts, and a fascinating collection of "yellow peril" memorabilia that documents prejudice and racial stereotyping of Asian Americans in the US. The collection includes sometimes-shocking movie posters, trading cards, comic books, and cartoons. The museum also offers historical group **tours** of Chinatown ($10, three weeks advance booking required) and sells a **Historic Walking Tour Map**, ideal for touring the neighborhood.

Canal and Grand streets

One block north of the Chinese Museum is **Canal Street**, at all hours a crowded thoroughfare crammed with jewelry shops and kiosks hawking sunglasses, T-shirts, and fake Rolexes. At no. 277, the **Pearl River Department Store**, at the corner of Canal and Bowery, is the closest you'll ever get to a Shanghai bazaar without going to China. Specialties include all sorts of embroidered slippers and silk clothing, rice cookers, pottery, and beautiful lacquered paper umbrellas. East from here, at no. 133, the gilded **Mahayana Buddhist Temple** (daily 8am–6pm; ☎212/925-8787) is a brash religious retreat and certainly worth a peek, at least for the fairy lights, the neon circlets, and the gold Buddha that dominates the main room.

North of Canal, take Mott or Mulberry to **Grand Street**, where outdoor fruit, vegetable, and seafood stands line the curbs, offering a wide array of delectables, much of it still alive, including fish, lobsters, crabs, mussels, and sea urchins, as well as bean curd, fungi, oriental cabbage, and dried sea cucumbers. Here, too, ribs, whole chickens, and Peking ducks glisten in storefront windows: the sight of them can put more than a vegetarian off his food. Perhaps even more fascinating are the Chinese herbalists dotted about: the roots and powders in their boxes, drawers, and glass cases are centuries-old remedies – but for those accustomed to Western medicine they may seem no better than voodoo potions.

Mulberry Street

Little Italy's main strip, **Mulberry Street** is home to many of the neighborhood's cafés and restaurants – and therefore filled with tourists. The street is particularly lively at night, when the lights come on and the sidewalks fill with restaurant hosts who shout menu specials at passersby. Few of the restaurants around here really stand out, but the former site of **Umberto's Clam House**, on the corner of Mulberry and Hester streets, was quite notorious in its time: it was the scene of a vicious gangland murder in 1972, when Joe "Crazy Joey" Gallo was shot dead while celebrating his birthday with his wife and daughter. Gallo, a big talker and ruthless businessman, was alleged to have offended a rival family and so paid the price. *Umberto's Clam House* has since relocated to 386 Broome St.

If you're here in mid-September, the ten-day **Festa di San Gennaro** is a wild and tacky celebration of the day of the patron saint of Naples. Italians from all over the city converge on Mulberry, and the area is transformed by street stalls and numerous Italian fast-food and snack outlets. The festivities center around the **Church of the Most Precious Blood**, just off Canal at 109 Mulberry, and provide a rare chance to see this quaint church and its courtyard, normally closed and protected from the public gaze.

Old St Patrick's Cathedral

Map 5, G6. 263 Mulberry St. Masses in English Mon–Fri 9am & noon, Sat 5.30pm, Sun 9.15am & 12.30pm.

The **Old St Patrick's Cathedral** was the first Catholic cathedral in the city and the parent church to its much more famous offspring on Fifth Avenue and 50th Street (see p.93). The interior has been restored to its former glory and plans are afoot to add spires to its 100-year-old roof (though this has been in the planning stages for over two decades and still hasn't happened). Mass (the only time you can view the cathedral's interior) is still held here and the service is open to the public (see times above), unlike the walled cemetery behind, which is, unfortunately, almost always locked.

Old Police Headquarters

Map 5, G7. Centre St, at Broome.

Reaction to Little Italy's illicit past can be found at the corner of Centre and Broome streets, where you'll find the **Old Police Headquarters**, a palatial 1909 Neoclassical confection meant to cow would-be criminals into obedience with its high-rise dome and lavish ornamentation. Police HQ moved to a bland modern building around City Hall in 1973, with this overbearing palace converted in the late 1980s to upmarket condos.

The Lower East Side

Historically the epitome of the American melting pot, the **Lower East Side** is one of Manhattan's most enthralling downtown neighborhoods. A little-known quarter that began to attract attention toward the end of the nineteenth century when it became an insular slum for over half a million **Jewish immigrants**, the Lower East Side was once the most densely populated spot in the world. Coming here from Eastern Europe, refugees sought a better life, scratching out a living in the neighborhood's sweatshops.

Since then, the area has become considerably depopulated and better maintained. While up until the mid-1990s the inhabitants were largely working-class Puerto Rican or Chinese, these days you're as likely to find students, artsy types, and hipster refugees from the gentrified East Village. Today's Lower East Side – bounded by Houston to the north and Canal to the south, and encompassing everything from the East River to the Bowery – is one of the hippest areas around for shopping, drinking, dancing, and (what else?) food. At the far southeastern edge, around East Broadway and Grand Street, however, it is still a bit seedy.

To reach the Lower East Side, take the #F or #V to Second Avenue or the #F, #J, #M, or #Z to Delancey/Essex Street.

6 Along East Houston

In the first half of the nineteenth century, the streets immediately south of Houston were known as *Kleine Deutschland* ("Little Germany"), home to well-off German merchants and then, as they moved away, the poorest of the Jewish immigrants fleeing poverty and pogroms in Eastern Europe. Even now Houston Street still holds remnants of its Jewish past, such as the area's homemade kosher cuisine and its ritual bathhouse for women who are "unclean." There are a variety of Jewish delicacies available on East Houston: *Russ & Daughters*, at no. 179, specializes in smoked fish, herring, and caviar, while *Yonah Schimmel*, further west at no. 137, has been making some of New York's best knishes since 1910. Meanwhile, some outsiders are drawn to the area for **discount shopping**, as the city's finest vintage clothing and mid-century furniture stores are located here, though the best thing to do around these parts is simply stroll the neighborhood, soaking up the old-world ambience.

Ludlow and Orchard streets

Ludlow Street, where a half-dozen or so bars dot the block, such as the popular *Local 138* (at no. 138, natch) and *Max Fish* at no. 178, sparked the hipster migration south of the East Village. You'll also see a number of secondhand stores offering retro items – especially mid-century furniture – and high-end used-clothing shops that are regularly scoured by fashion designers seeking inspiration for their next collection. Around the intersection of Allen and Stanton streets are several bar/performance spaces. For more on the Lower East Side's excellent bar and nightlife scene, see p.242.

On the corner of Ludlow and East Houston you'll find **Katz's Deli** (Map 5, K5), a delicatessen famous for its assembly-line counter service, stellar pastrami sandwich, and motto "Send a salami to your boy in the army!"; it's lauded by locals as one of the best in New York.

Just one block west of Ludlow is **Orchard Street**, center of the so-called Bargain District, which is filled with stalls and storefronts hawking discounted designer clothes and bags. The best time to visit the Orchard Street Market is Sunday morning, when you'll catch the Lower East Side at its most vibrant.

The Lower East Side Tenement Museum

Map 5, K7. 108 Orchard St (visitors' center); 97 Orchard St (tenement museum). Mon 11am–5.30pm, Tues–Fri 11am–6pm, Sat & Sun 10.45am–6pm; the tenement museum is accessible only by guided tours ($9), which run every half-hour and begin at the visitors' center; ☎212/431-0233, ⓦwww.tenement.org. #F, #J, #M, or #Z to Delancey/Essex Street.

If you haven't got the time to tour the Lower East Side extensively, make sure to visit the **Lower East Side Tenement Museum**, a fully intact and wonderfully preserved 1863 tenement which does an imaginative job of bringing to life the neighborhood's immigrant past and present. Various apartments within the tenement have been renovated with period furnishings to reflect the lives of its tenants, from the mid-nineteenth century when there was no plumbing, electricity, or heating, to the mid-twentieth century when many families ran small cottage industries out of their apartments.

Delancey, Essex, and Clinton streets

Orchard Street leads to **Delancey Street** – once the horizontal axis of the Jewish Lower East Side, now a traffic-choked boulevard – and all the way east to the **Williamsburg Bridge**, which you can walk or bike across to the Williamsburg section of Brooklyn (see p.169). On either side of Delancey sprawls the **Essex Street Market**. Here you'll find all sorts of fresh fruit, fish, and vegetables, along with random clothing bargains and the occasional trinket. At no. 49 is The Pickle Guys, a shop where customers line up to buy fresh homemade pickles and olives from barrels of garlicky brine.

East of Essex Street, the atmosphere changes from a smorgasbord of ethnic treats to an edgy melting pot of artsy post-punk white kids and long-established Latin locals; the neighborhood here is traditionally Puerto Rican and Dominican. **Clinton Street** – a mass of cheap Hispanic restaurants, retailers, and travel agents, punctuated by a good number of upscale, trendy eateries like *Clinton Fresh Food* at no. 71 – is in many ways the central thoroughfare of what remains of *Loisaida*, or the Spanish Lower East Side.

The Bowery

The **Bowery** (from *bouwerij*, the Dutch word for farm) spears north out of Chinatown, running a mile from Chatham Square up to Cooper Square on the edge of the East Village. The city's only thoroughfare never to have been graced by a church, the Bowery is no longer the city's famous Skid Row of the nineteenth century, though it's singularly unattractive regardless, lined as it is with restaurant-equipment dealers, light-bulb depots, and the like. Furthermore, as the demand for apartments continues and the tide of gentrification sweeps its way south through the Lower East Side, the Bowery is slowly being colonized by the upwardly mobile, leading to ever more out-of-place glass-and-steel condo complexes.

Between Delancey and East Broadway

Although the southern half of **East Broadway** is now almost exclusively Chinese, the street used to be the hub of the Jewish Lower East Side. For the old feel of the quarter – where the synagogues remain active – it's best to explore north of here, starting with the 1886 **Eldridge Street Synagogue**, at no. 12 (Map 5, J9), which was in its day one of the neighborhood's grandest, with its brick and terracotta hybrid of Moorish arches and Gothic rose windows. The facade still possesses a certain grandeur, and the majestic sanctuary has been meticulously restored over the past two decades. **Tours** of the synagogue's beautifully restored interiors are offered Sunday and Tuesday to Thursday, hourly from 11am to 3pm ($5).

East Broadway, Essex, and Grand streets frame the pie-slice-shaped complex that comprises **Seward Park** (Map 5, L8) and its neighboring apartment blocks. Constructed in 1899 by the city to provide a bit of green space in the overburdened precincts of the Lower East Side, the park boasted the first public playground in New York and is still surrounded by benevolent institutions set up for the benefit of ambitious immigrants.

A few blocks west, you'll pass the **Church of St Mary**, at 440 Grand St, the third-oldest Catholic church (1832) in the city. It's now a favorite resting spot of elderly Jewish couples, who sit on the benches outside and watch the world go by.

The East Village

L
ike the Lower East Side, which it abuts, the **East Village**, stretching between Houston and 14th streets and Broadway and Avenue D, was once a refuge of immigrants and solidly working class. It became home to New York's nonconformist intelligentsia in the early part of the twentieth century, and ever since has hosted its share of celebrated artists, politicos, and literati. W.H. Auden lived at 77 St Mark's Place, the neighborhood's main artery. In the 1950s, the East Village was the New York haunt of the Beats – Kerouac, Burroughs, Ginsberg, et al – who would get together at Ginsberg's house on East 7th Street for declamatory poetry readings. Later, Andy Warhol debuted the Velvet Underground at the now-defunct *Fillmore East*, which played host to just about every band you've ever heard of – and forgotten. Also in danger of extinction is the infamous **CBGB** (Map 5, H5) club on the **Bowery**, where the likes of the Ramones, Talking Heads, Blondie, and Patti Smith made their indelible marks in the Seventies.

During the Nineties, escalating rents forced many people out, and today the East Village is no longer the hotbed of dissidence and creativity it once was. Nevertheless, the area remains one of downtown Manhattan's most vibrant neighborhoods, with boutiques, thrift stores, record shops, bars, and restaurants aplenty. It's populated by a mix of old-world Ukrainians, Puerto Ricans, students, punks, artists, hipsters, and burn-outs feeding continuous energy through the streets 24 hours a day. Despite the vaudevillian circus of **St Mark's Place** and corporate attempts to turn the whole neighborhood into a *Starbucks*, principled resistance to the status quo can still be found.

To reach the East Village, take the #6 train to Astor Place, or the #N or #R to 8th Street/NYU, and walk east.

St Mark's Place, Cooper Square, and around

Most begin their tour of the East Village on **St Mark's Place** between Second and Third avenues, where discount record and video stores struggle for space amid hippie-chic clothiers, head shops, and chain restaurants in a somewhat contrived atmosphere of grunge cool. Below St Mark's, **7th Street** boasts used-clothing stores as well as several original boutiques, while 6th Street, between First and Second avenues – also known as "**Indian Row**" – offers endless choices of all things curry.

On **Cooper Square** (Map 5, H3), a busy crossroads formed by the intersection of the Bowery, Third Avenue, and Lafayette Street, countless teenage style-gods and out-of-town punks mill around. The square is dominated by the seven-story brownstone mass of **Cooper Union**, erected in 1859 by the wealthy industrialist/inventor Peter Cooper as a college for the poor, and the first New York structure to be hung on a frame of iron girders. It's best known as the place where, in 1860, Abraham Lincoln wowed an audience of top New Yorkers with his so-called "might makes right" speech, in which he criticized the pro-slavery policies of the Southern states, helping to propel himself to the White House later that year.

Astor Place and around

Just west of Cooper Square lies **Astor Place**, named after John Jacob Astor and, during the 1830s, just before high society moved west to Washington Square, one of the city's most desirable addresses. The old-fashioned kiosk of the Astor Place subway station, bang in the middle of the junction, discreetly remembers Astor on the platforms, its colored mosaic reliefs depicting beavers, recalling Astor's first big killings in the fur trade. The orange-brick with arched windows **Astor Building** is where John Jacob Astor III conducted business. It now houses a *Starbucks* and luxury loft apartments, and faces a giant black cube sculpture, *Alamo* by Tony Rosenthal, that's stood squat in the center of Astor Place since 1968. Typically surrounded by young punks and daredevil skateboarders, the sculpture can be rotated at its base if you have enough people to give it an initial push.

Lafayette Street and Broadway

Astor Place is hardly the stuffy, upper-crust residential district that it was during Astor's life. The last real traces of the time when **Lafayette Street**, which cuts along the edge of the East Village and down into SoHo, was a millionaire's row of residential mansions is **Colonnade Row**, just south of Astor Place. This strip of four 1832 Greek Revival houses with a Corinthian colonnade is now home to the Colonnade Theater. The **Public Theater**, at no. 425 (Map 5, H3), is legendary both as a forerunner of Off-Broadway theater and as the original venue of hit musicals like *Hair*. For years it was run by the director Joseph Papp, who pioneered Shakespeare in the Park. On the ground floor you'll find the celeb-studded music venue/restaurant/bar, *Joe's Pub*, named in Papp's honor; for details on seeing a show at the Public or *Joe's*, see pp.261 & 268, respectively.

Head one block west to Broadway and look north: filling a bend in the street is the lacy marble of **Grace Church**, on the corner of 10th Street (Map 5, G2), which was built and designed in 1846 by James Renwick (of St Patrick's Cathedral fame) in a delicate neo-Gothic style. Dark and aisled, with a flattened, web-vaulted ceiling, it's one of the city's most successful churches – and, in many ways, one of its most secretive escapes. The grounds and sanctuary are open to all during daylight hours, and free **tours** of the church are available each Sunday after the 11am worship service.

East toward Tompkins Square Park

Head east along 10th Street until you reach **St Mark's-in-the-Bowery** (Map 5, I2), a box-like church on the corner of Second Avenue originally built in 1799 but with a Neo-classical portico added half a century later. In the 1950s, the Beat poets gave readings here, and it remains an important literary rendezvous, with regular readings, dance perform-ances, and music recitals, where you can often catch the likes of Lou Reed, Patti Smith, and Sonic Youth's Lee Ranaldo doing their thing.

Continue along 10th, past the old red-brick **Tenth Street Russian and Turkish Bath**, whose steam and massage services have been active back into the nineteenth century. Venture further east and you'll catch up with Avenue A, which will lead you south to **Tompkins Square Park** (Map 5, K3), a large, scenic neighborhood greenspace which buzzes at its edges with thrift stores and trendy bars.

Alphabet City

In the late 1980s and early 1990s, the lettered avenues form-ing **Alphabet City** formed a notoriously unsafe corner of town, run by drug pushers and gangsters. Most of this was brought to a halt with "Operation Pressure Point," a massive police campaign to clean up the area and make it a place where people would want to live. Crime is way down, the old buildings have been renovated and supplemented by ugly new ones, and today the streets have become the haunt of moneyed twenty-somethings and tourist youth.

Go beyond Avenue C and you may get hassled, but – during the day at least – you're unlikely to run into any trouble, and avenues A, B, and C have some of the coolest bars, cafés, and shops in the city. One definite cultural highlight is the **NuYorican Poets Café**, 236 E 3rd St (☎212/505-8183), where you can catch some of the biggest stars of the spoken-word scene.

Community gardens

Over the past three decades, East Village residents have reclaimed neglected and empty lots of land, turning burnt-out rubble into some of the prettiest and most verdant **community gardens** in lower Manhattan and providing a focus for residents in what was traditionally a down-at-heel part of town. Though the city decreed that these spaces should be used for real estate, several have survived. In summer, there is no nicer way to while away an evening than to relax, eat a sandwich, or read a book surrounded by lush trees and carefully planted foliage.

Of particular note is the 6th Street and Avenue B affair, overgrown with wildflowers, vegetables, trees, and roses, and home to a spectacular four-story-high sculpture (which will be familiar to those who have seen the East Village–set Broadway musical *Rent*). Other gardens nearby include the very serene **6BC Botanical Garden**, on 6th St between B and C; **Miracle Garden**, on 3rd St between A and B; **El Sol Brillante**, on 12th St between A and B; and the **Liz Christie Garden**, on Houston St and 2nd Ave.

8

The West Village

W hen the *Village Voice*, NYC's most venerable alternative weekly newspaper, began life as a chronicler of Greenwich Village nightlife in 1955, "the Village" really had, since World War II, a dissident, artistic, vibrant voice. While the nonconformist image of Greenwich Village, more commonly known today as the **West Village**, survives to an extent, the description is no longer truly accurate. Though still one of the more progressive neighborhoods in the city, the West Village has attained a moneyed status over the last four decades and is now firmly for those who have Arrived.

There's still a European quaintness here that makes for a great day of walking through a grid of cobblestone streets and elegant brownstones that doesn't even attempt to conform to the rest of the city's established numbered pattern. **Washington Square** is a hub of enjoyably aimless activity throughout the year, and a natural place to start your exploration. This portion of the West Village has been somewhat taken over by **New York University**, and during the fall and spring semesters the streets here teem with young would-be filmmakers, actors, and writers. Cafés and bars in these parts are priced to attract the student population, and if you're on a budget may offer some of the best deals around.

West of Sixth Avenue, the Village is more quiet and residential, although much of the area still has a busy streetlife that lasts late into the night. There are more restaurants per capita here than any other neighborhood, and stylish bars and cute local eateries serving super-fresh cuisine, though rarely cheap in these moneyed reaches, abound. **Christopher Street**, meanwhile, is the main artery of gay New York, and north from here the **Meatpacking District**, which once functioned as its name suggests, now serves primarily as a nightlife playground for the well-off and well-coiffed.

The West Village is easily reached by taking the #1 to Christopher Street/Sheridan Square or the #A, #C, #E, #D, #B, #F, or #V to West 4th Street/Washington Square.

Washington Square

Map 5, E3.

The ideal way to see the Village is to walk, and the best place to start is its natural center, **Washington Square**, commemorated in the 1880 novel of that title by Henry James and haunted by many of the Village's illustrious past residents. It is not an elegant-looking place – too large to be a square, too small to be a park – but it does retain its northern edging of red-brick row-houses (the "solid, honorable dwellings" of James's novel). More imposing is Stanford White's impossible-to-miss **Triumphal Arch**, built in 1892 to commemorate the centenary of George Washington's inauguration as president; it's recently been cleaned and jazzed up with fancy lighting.

Washington Square is undergoing a general **clean-up** scheduled for completion in the spring of 2006; the project calls for moving the fountain 23 feet in order to align it with the arch, and for landscaping significant portions. Whatever these niceties may do in terms of aesthetics, it's unlikely they'll increase the park's overwhelming charm. As soon as the weather gets warm, the place becomes a running track, performance venue, chess tournament, and social club, boiling over with life as skateboards flip, dogs run, and acoustic guitar notes crash through the urgent cries of performers calling for the crowd's attention. At times like this, there's no better square in the city.

Around Washington Square

Eugene O'Neill, one of the Village's most acclaimed residents, lived (and in 1939 wrote *The Iceman Cometh*) at 38 Washington Square South, and consumed vast quantities of ale at *The Golden Swan Bar*, which once stood on the corner of Sixth Avenue and West 4th Street. It was nearby, also, that he got his first dramatic break, with a company called the **Provincetown Players** who, on the advice of author John Reed, had moved down here from Massachusetts and set up shop at 177 MacDougal St.

At Washington Square East and Washington Place lies the **Grey Art Gallery** (Map 5, F4; Tues, Thurs & Fri 11am–6pm, Wed 11am–8pm, Sat 11am–5pm; $2.50; ☎212/998-6780, ⓦwww.nyu.edu/greyart), an excellent example of NYU putting their real estate to good use. The world-class exhibitions here usually last a couple of months and range from extensive investigations of Eastern European Modernism to a survey of illustrations for sixteenth-century books.

From the southwest corner of the park, follow MacDougal Street south, pausing for a detour down Minetta Lane until you hit **Bleecker Street**, a vibrant junction with mock-European sidewalk cafés that have been literary hangouts since the 1920s. The **Café Figaro**, made famous by the Beats in the 1950s, is always thronged: it's still worth the price of a cappuccino to people-watch for an hour or so. Afterwards, you can follow Bleecker Street one of two ways – east toward the solid towers of Washington Square Village, or west right through the hubbub of West Village life.

Sixth Avenue and west

Sixth Avenue itself is mainly tawdry stores and fast-food joints, but on its west side, across Father Demo Square and up Bleecker, are some of the Village's prettiest residential streets. Turn left on **Leroy Street** and cross over Varick Street, where, confusingly, Leroy Street becomes St Luke's Place for a block. The houses here, dating from the 1850s, are among the city's most graceful, one of them (recognizable by the two lamps of honor at the bottom of the steps) is the ex-residence of **Jimmy Walker**, mayor of New York in the 1920s. Walker was for a time the most popular of mayors, a big-spending, wisecracking man who gave up his work as a songwriter for the world of politics and lived an extravagant lifestyle that rarely kept him out of the gossip columns.

Bedford and Grove streets

Retrace your steps across Varick Street and take a left on **Bedford Street**, pausing to peer into **Grove Court**, a typical secluded West Village mews. Along with nearby Barrow and Commerce streets, Bedford is one of the quietest and most desirable Village addresses – Edna St Vincent Millay, the poet and playwright, lived at no. 75 1/2, said to be the narrowest house in the city, nine feet wide and topped with a tiny gable. Built in 1799, the clapboard structure next door claims to be the **oldest house** in the Village, but much renovated since and probably worth a considerable fortune now. Further down Bedford, at no. 86, the former speakeasy *Chumley's* (see "Drinking," p.243) is recognizable only by the metal grille on its door – a low profile useful in Prohibition years that makes it hard to find today.

Turn right off Bedford onto **Grove Street**, following it towards Seventh Avenue and looking out for **Marie's Crisis Café** at no. 59. Now a gay bar, it was once home to Thomas Paine, English by birth but perhaps *the* most important and radical thinker of the American Revolutionary era, and from whose *Crisis Papers* the café takes its name. Grove Street meets Seventh Avenue at one of the Village's busiest junctions, **Sheridan Square** (Map 5, C3) – not in fact a square at all unless you count Christopher Park's slim strip of green, but simply a wide and hazardous confluence of several busy streets. The square was named after General Sheridan, cavalry commander in the Civil War, and holds a pompous-looking statue to his memory. It is better known, however, as the scene of one of the worst and bloodiest of New York's Draft Riots (see "History," p.319), when in 1863 a marauding mob assembled here and attacked members of the black community, several of whom were lynched.

Christopher Street and around

Christopher Street, one of the main thoroughfares of the West Village, leads off from Sheridan Square – the traditional heartland of the city's gay community. Scenes of violence also erupted in 1969, when the **gay community** wasn't as readily accepted as it is now. The violence on this occasion was provoked by the police, who raided the *Stonewall* gay bar, and started arresting its occupants – for the local gay community the latest in a long line of harassment from the police. Spontaneously, word went around to other bars in the area, and before long the *Stonewall* was surrounded, resulting in a siege that lasted the better part of the night and sparked up again the next two nights. The riot ended with several arrests and a number of injured policemen. Though hardly a victory for their rights, it was the first time that gay men had stood up en masse to the persecutions of the city police and, as such, formally inaugurated the gay rights movement. Both this clash and the gay rights movement are honored by the annual **Gay Pride March** (held on the last Sun in June).

Nowadays, the gay community is a huge part of West Village life; in fact, the neighborhood would seem odd without it. From Seventh Avenue down to the Hudson River is a tight-knit enclave – focusing on Christopher Street – of bars, restaurants, and bookstores used largely, but not exclusively, by gay men. The scene along the Hudson River itself, along and around West Street and the river piers, is considerably raunchier at night. However, on the eastern stretch of Christopher things lighten up, with the accent less on sex and more on excessive, fun camp. Among the more accessible gay bars here are *The Monster*, on Sheridan Square itself, and *Marie's Crisis Café*, on Grove Street. See Chapter 26, "Gay and lesbian New York," for more nightlife options.

Patchin Place

At the eastern end of Christopher Street, Sixth Avenue is met by **Greenwich Avenue**, one of the neighborhood's major shopping streets. Look out for **Patchin Place** (Map 5, C2) – opening onto West 10th Street by the Jefferson Market Courthouse – a tiny mews whose neat, gray row-houses are yet another Village literary landmark. No. 5 was home to the reclusive Djuna Barnes for more than forty years, and Barnes' longtime neighbor e.e. cummings, at no. 4, used to call out to her "just to see if she was still alive." Patchin Place was at various times also home to Marlon Brando, John Masefield, Theodore Dreiser, John Reed, and Eugene O'Neill.

The Meatpacking District

Stretching from the Hudson River to Eighth Avenue and from West 14th Street to Gansevoort, the **Meatpacking District** was recently granted historic district status as the city's last remaining market area. The dozen or so blocks encompassed here have undergone many metamorphoses over the centuries, from Native American trading village to Dutch tobacco planatation, and from nineteenth-century fort to the city's major wholesale meat market for most of the last century. The majority of the meat dealers have now moved to the Bronx, making room for an influx of European bistros, luxury food stores, rooftop bars, boutique hotels, and cutting-edge fashion design. Yet the area's history still seems to seep out of the cobblestones, perhaps because its topography has changed little over the last 150 years, with renovated warehouse spaces and narrow streets endowing it with enchanting atmosphere and stylish European-style streetlife.

9

Chelsea

A low-built grid of tenements, row-houses, and ware-houses between 14th and 23rd streets to the west of Broadway, **Chelsea** was never considered an interesting or desirable neighbourhood until the 1990s, which saw the area boosted by spillover from SoHo and the Village and the arrival of affluent gay and artistic communities – followed by the inevitable wave of yuppies. There is one small **historic district** that boasts a row of beautiful nineteenth-century townhouses, but Chelsea as a whole was given over to industry from the nearby industrial piers and meatpacking facilities, and was therefore considered an appropriately unenviable spot on which to place several public housing projects which stand to this day. These days, though, trendy stores, chichi restaurants, and a few notable tourist attractions pepper the scene, along with upmarket real estate. The district's main sight is the storied **Chelsea Hotel**, in which many artists, musicians, and writers have holed up to live – or, in many cases, burn out – in New York. After taking a look at this historic hotel, check out the neighborhood's cutting-edge **art scene**.

Chelsea can be reached by taking the #1 to either 18th Street or 23rd Street (both at Seventh Ave), or by taking the #C or #E to 23rd Street (at Eighth Ave).

The Chelsea Hotel

Map 6, F7. 222 23rd St. ☎212/243-3700, ⊛www.hotelchelsea.com.

Double back east along 23rd Street past Eighth Avenue to find one of the neighborhood's major claims to fame – the **Chelsea Hotel** at no. 222. Constructed in 1883 and at that time the city's tallest building, these days it's not much to look at, though it does possess a certain down-at-heel Edwardian grandeur all its own, with its weather-beaten neon Art Deco sign and wrought-iron balconies lining the facade.

Regardless, the hotel has served as undisputed watering hole of the city's (often hard-up) **literati**. It has lodged Mark Twain and Tennessee Williams, while Brendan Behan and Dylan Thomas staggered in and out during their New York visits; in fact, Thomas famously collapsed from alcohol poisoning while climbing the hotel's front steps, expiring later at a local hospital. Thomas Wolfe assembled *You Can't Go Home Again* from thousands of pages of manuscript he had stacked in his room; in 1951, Jack Kerouac, armed with a specially adapted typewriter (and a lot of Benzedrine), typed the first draft of *On the Road* nonstop onto a 120-foot roll of paper. William Burroughs completed *Naked Lunch* and Arthur C. Clarke wrote *2001: A Space Odyssey* while in residence.

In the 1960s, the *Chelsea* entered a wilder phase. Andy Warhol and his doomed protégées Edie Sedgwick and Candy Darling walled up here and made the film *Chelsea Girls* as a twisted homage. It also served as a waystation for some of America's most influential **musicians**: Patti Smith, Bob Dylan, Janis Joplin, Leonard Cohen, and Nico called it home for extended periods, and Hendrix, Zappa, Pink Floyd, and various members of the Grateful Dead passed through. Dylan, Smith, Cohen, and even Jon Bon Jovi have written songs extolling their time here. Of course these days the *Chelsea* is most firmly rooted in the popular imagination as the spot where Sid Vicious stabbed Nancy Spungen to death in their suite in 1978, and a fair percentage of today's clientele consists of punked-out twentysomething Sid & Nancy wannabes.

With this sort of pedigree it's easy to forget that the *Chelsea* is still a functioning hotel – and a fairly affordable one, at that. For a more accommodation-oriented review, see p.189.

Eighth, Ninth, and Tenth avenues

Eighth, **Ninth**, and **Tenth avenues** are for the most part none too attractive, essentially noisy, one-way highways dividing this otherwise pretty residential district. If Chelsea has a main drag it's broad, frenetic **Eighth Avenue**, which has a vibrant retail energy to rival the fast-moving traffic in the street. A spate of bars, restaurants, health-food stores, gyms, bookstores, and clothing shops line the route, and while it's not exactly picturesque, a few minor diversions into the crosstown streets will suffice to restore faith in the architectural beauty of New York.

Further north, the cross streets between Ninth and Tenth avenues, specifically 20th, 21st, and 22nd streets, constitute the **Chelsea Historic District**. Though the label "district" is a bit grand for an area of three blocks, it boasts a great variety of predominantly Italianate and Greek Revival row-houses in brick and various shades of brownstone; past denizens include the poet Wallace Stevens, who lived at 441 W 21st St. At the corner of 22nd Street and Tenth Avenue, the nineteenth century meets the Art Deco era in the **Empire Diner**, built in the 1930s and resembling an old-style railroad dining car done up with metal siding pilfered from the Chrysler Building.

Between Ninth and Tenth avenues and 20th and 21st streets lies one of Chelsea's secrets: the **General Theological Seminary** (Map 6, D7). Clement Clarke Moore donated this land to the institute where he formerly taught, and today the harmonious assembly of ivy-clad Gothicisms surrounding a restive green feels like part of an elite college campus. Though the buildings, most of which were completed in the nineteenth century, still house a working seminary, it's possible to explore the park on weekdays and

Saturday lunchtimes, as long as you sign in and keep quiet (the entrance is via the modern building on Ninth Avenue). If you're at all interested in theological history, you should check out their collection of Latin Bibles – it's one of the largest in the world.

The Chelsea Piers

Map 6, A8. Ⓦ www.chelseapiers.com.

Head west along 23rd Street and brave crossing the West Side Highway to one of Manhattan's most ambitious waterfront projects, **Chelsea Piers**, a $100 million, 1.7-million-square-foot development along four Hudson River piers. Opened in 1910, these piers were where the great transatlantic liners would disembark their passengers – the *Titanic* was en route when it sank in 1912. In the 1960s, the piers fell into disuse

---

The Chelsea Art Scene

Back over the West Side Highway and along 22nd Street are the galleries and warehouse spaces that house the core of New York's **art scene**, by far the largest in the United States. You'll find an especially strong presence along West 22nd Street between Tenth and Eleventh avenues. The **Dia Center for the Arts** (Ⓦ www.diacenter.org), a Chelsea pioneer, with space here since 1987, has its main exhibition gallery at 548 W 22nd St, featuring a dramatic open-air space on top. There are also dozens of other **galleries** in residence here, and the area is especially lively on Friday nights, when many venues host wine-and-cheese openings for their new shows. Aside from openings, all galleries are typically open Tues–Sat 10am–6pm. Among the best are **Metro Pictures**, 519 W 24th St, between 10th and 11th (☎212/206-7100, Ⓦ www.metropicturesgallery.com); **Cohan and Leslie**, 138 Tenth Ave, at 19th (☎212/206-8710, Ⓦ www.cohanandleslie.com); and the extremely upscale **Jim Kempner**, 501 W 23rd St, at 10th, 2nd floor (☎212/206-6872). See Chapter 28, "Commercial galleries," for more listings.

and decay, but a recent infusion of money has transformed them into a thriving sports complex, with ice rinks and a landscaped golf driving range (see Chapter 29, "Sports and outdoor activities"). Perhaps the best part of the development is its emphasis on **public spaces**, including a waterfront walkway and bike path that extends from Chelsea Piers all along the Hudson waterfront in both directions.

North Chelsea

Heading north above 23rd Street, away from Chelsea's heart, the city's largest **antiques market** (and surrounding junk sales) takes place on weekends in a few open-air parking lots centered around Sixth Avenue and 26th Street (see Chapter 27, "Shopping"). The area around 28th Street is Manhattan's **Flower Market**: not really a market as such, but rather a collection of warehouses where potted plants and cut flowers are stored before brightening offices and atriums across the city; walking down this street is like taking a detour through some fragrant, forgotten jungle district of Manhattan.

⑩

Union Square and Gramercy Park

oisy, traffic-choked 14th Street forms the divide between downtown and midtown Manhattan. North of 14th, Broadway forms a dividing line between Chelsea to the west and, to the east, the area that comprises **Union Square** and **Gramercy Park**. It is here, between the great avenues – Third, Park, and Fifth – that midtown Manhattan's skyscrapers begin to rise from the low-lying buildings. Before heading on to those jaw-droppers, like the Empire State Building (see p.86), it's certainly worth a jaunt around the more genteel parts of these two neighborhoods, which offer some decent architecture themselves, like the **Flatiron Building**, and some great streetlife, especially in Union Square itself.

The #L, #N, #Q, #R, #W, #4, #5, and #6 trains all stop at 14th Street–Union Square.

Union Square

Once the elegant center of the city's theatrical and shopping scene, **Union Square**, where Broadway, Fourth, and Park avenues meet between 14th and 18th streets, invites you to stroll its paths, feed the squirrels, and gaze at its array of statuary, including an equestrian figure of George Washington. Unfortunately, the proliferation of chain cafés and superstores hereabouts makes it impossible to forget you are on the fringes of the most commercial part of New York. Still, the park is a welcome respite from the crazed taxi drivers and rushed pedestrians. On the plaza at the park's south end there invariably will be an array of breakdancers, skateboarders, and vaguely coherent activists making a ruckus; sitting on the steps here and watching the scene is fine free entertainment.

The Farmers' Market

On Mondays, Wednesdays, Fridays, and Saturdays from 7am until 6pm, Union Square plays host to the city's best and most popular **greenmarket** on its northern edge. Farmers and other food producers from upstate New York, Long Island, New Jersey, and as far as Pennsylvania Dutch Country sell fresh fruit and vegetables, baked goods, cheeses, eggs, meats, fish, plants, and flowers. The quality of the produce is generally very high and buying picnic fodder from the market to concoct a feast is one of the finest things you can do here on a spring or summer's day.

Irving Place and around

Just one block east of Union Square, the six graceful blocks of **Irving Place** lead north toward Gramercy Park. The street is named for *The Legend of Sleepy Hollow* author Washington Irving, who lived for a short time here at no. 56. Before reaching the park, digress on 20th Street, where, at no. 28, you will find **Theodore Roosevelt's birthplace** (Map 6, I8; Wed–Sun 9am–5pm; $2; ☎212/260–1616), or at least a reconstruction of it: in 1923, the house was rebuilt as it would have been when Roosevelt was born there in 1858. The rather somber mansion contains many original furnishings, some of Teddy's hunting trophies, and a small gallery documenting the president's life, viewable on an obligatory guided tour.

Gramercy Park

Map 6, K7.

Manhattan's clutter suddenly breaks into ordered open space at **Gramercy Park**, a former swamp between 21st and 22nd streets that divides Irving Place and Lexington Avenue. Gramercy is one of the city's prettiest squares, its center beautifully planted and completely empty for much of the day; it is the city's last private park and the only people who can gain access are those rich or fortunate enough to live here. Famous past key-holders have included Mark Twain and Julia Roberts, never mind all those Kennedys and Roosevelts.

Have a walk around the square to get a look at the many early nineteenth-century townhouses. **The Players**, at 16 Gramercy Park South, was created in 1888 when actor Edwin Booth turned his home into a private social club for theater types, at a time when they were considered morally suspect and thus not accepted into regular society. Some famous club members were Irving Berlin, Frank Sinatra, and Winston Churchill – women were not admitted until 1989. Next door, at no. 17, the **School of Visual Arts** occupies the former home of Joseph Pulitzer.

At the northeastern corner of the square, no. 38 is the mock-Tudor building in which John Steinbeck, then a struggling reporter, lived between 1925 and 1926. At 52 Gramercy Park North stands the imposing 1920s bulk of the **Gramercy Park Hotel**, whose early elite residents counted among their numbers Mary McCarthy, a very young John F.

Kennedy, and Humphrey Bogart. Once a fairly stodgy, old-fashioned affair, it's recently been renovated by entrepreneur Ian Schrager and turned into a minimalist interior-design masterpiece; hotel guests also get access to Gramercy Park. Lastly, lining Gramercy Park West is a splendid row of brick Greek Revival townhouses dating from the 1840s.

Madison Square and the Flatiron Building

Map 6, I7. #N, #R, or #W to 23rd Street.

Northwest of Gramercy Park, where Broadway and Fifth Avenue meet, lies **Madison Square**. Though a maelstrom of cars, cabs, buses, and dodging pedestrians is all around, the grandiose architectural quality of the surrounding buildings and the newly renovated park-space in the square's center lend it a neat seclusion that Union Square has long since lost. According to some baseball historians (other accounts place the game's origin elsewhere), baseball as we know it was invented here in 1845, when the Knickerbocker Base Ball Club played the first game to adhere to Alexander Cartwright's rules.

The lofty, elegant, yet decidedly anorexic **Flatiron Building** (originally the Fuller Construction Company, later renamed in honor of its distinctive shape), set on a triangular plot of land on the square's southern side, is one of the city's most well-known buildings. It's now hard to believe that this was the city's first true skyscraper, hung on a steel frame in 1902, its full twenty stories dwarfing all the other structures around.

On Madison Square's east side, at no. 1 Madison Ave, stands the tiered, stately **Met-Life Building**, which became the city's tallest tower in 1909, and is still visible from blocks away. Just north of the Met-Life Building, at no. 27, is the Corinthian-columned marble facade of the Appellate Division of the **New York State Supreme Court**, resolutely righteous with its statues of *Justice*, *Wisdom*, and *Peace*. The grand structure next to that, the **New York Life Building** proper, was the work of Cass Gilbert, creator of the Wool-worth Building downtown (see p.44). It went up in 1928 on the site of the original **Madison Square Garden**, heart of the former theater district.

North of Madison Square

Lexington Avenue begins its long journey north at Gramercy Park: if you're heading uptown on the East Side from here, you'll pass the lumbering **69th Regiment Armory** at 25th Street. This was the site of the celebrated Armory Show of 1913, which brought modern art to New York. It is now a venue for antiques shows and art fairs.

Midtown East

Rolling eastward from Fifth Avenue, the grand sight-and store-studded spine of Manhattan, from the 30s through the 50s, is the largely corporate and commercial area known as **Midtown East**. Here you'll find the city's sniffiest boutiques, best Art-Deco facades, and exemplary Modernist skyscrapers scattered primarily along **Fifth**, **Park**, and **Madison avenues**. Known for their neck-cricking vistas and impossible traffic, the streets in this part of town choke with yellow cabs and office workers during the day – activity that comes to a screeching halt after-hours when corporate nine-to-fivers go home.

Anchored by Cornelius Vanderbilt's Beaux-Arts train station, **Grand Central Terminal**, Midtown East is a trove of architectural and cultural treasures that include that soaring symbol of New York City, the **Empire State Building**; the renovated **Museum of Modern Art**; **Rockefeller Center**, a masterpiece of urban planning; the **Seagram Building**; the automobile-inspired 1930s Deco delight of the **Chrysler Building**; and the rambling geometric bulk of the **United Nations** complex.

The Empire State Building

Map 6, H4. Daily 8am–midnight, last trip up 11.15pm; $14, seniors and kids 12–17 $13, kids 5–12 $9, under-5s free; combined tickets for New York SKYRIDE and the observatory $28, or $20 for under-12s; ☎212/736-3100, ⊛www.esbnyc.com. #6 to 33rd Street.

With the destruction of the World Trade Center, the **Empire State Building** is once again the city's tallest skyscraper. Occupying a whole city block on Fifth Avenue between 33rd and 34th streets, it is easily the most potent and evocative symbol of New York, and has been since its completion in 1931. Its 103 stories and 1454 feet – toe to TV mast – rank the Empire State Building in height behind only the Sears Tower in Chicago and the Petronas Towers in Kuala Lumpur, Malaysia, but its height is deceptive, rising in stately tiers with steady panache.

Standing on Fifth Avenue below, it's easy to walk right past the ESB without even realizing it's there; only the crowds serve as an indicator of what stretches above. Skip the eight-minute simulated flight **NEW YORK SKYRIDE** (daily 10am–10pm; $23, under-12s $16, seniors and kids 12–17 $18; ☎212/299-4922 or 1-888/SKY-RIDE, ⊛www.skyride.com), which purports to soar above skyscrapers and among other New York landmarks, but will leave the weak-hearted merely dizzy and the strong-willed wondering why they wasted their cash.

The first elevators up whisk you to the 80th floor in under one minute, and then more (rather old and rickety) elevators take you to the observation deck on the 86th floor, summit of the building before the radio and TV mast was added. The views from the outside walkways here are as stunning as you'd expect; on a clear day you can see as far as Connecticut. If you're feeling brave – and can stand the wait for the tight squeeze into the single elevator – you can go up to the building's last reachable zenith, a small cylinder at the foot of the TV mast that was added as part of a harebrained scheme to erect a mooring post for airships.

Skyscrapers

Manhattan is one of the best places in the world in which to view **skyscrapers**, its puckered, almost medieval skyline of towers the city's most familiar and striking image. In fact, there are only two main clusters of skyscrapers, but they set the tone for the city – the Financial District, where the combination of narrow streets and tall buildings forms slender, lightless canyons, and midtown Manhattan, where the big skyscrapers, flanking the wide central avenues between the 30s and the 60s, have long competed for height and prestige.

New York's first skyscraper was Madison Square's 1902 **Flatiron Building**, so-called because of the obvious way its triangular shape made the most of the new iron-frame construction technique that had made such structures possible. In 1913, the sixty-story **Woolworth Building** on Broadway gave New York the world's tallest building, and the city later produced such landmarks as the **Chrysler Building**, the **Empire State Building**, and, before 9/11, the World Trade Center's **Twin Towers**.

Styles have changed over the years, perhaps most influenced by the stringency of the city's zoning laws, which, early in the century, placed restrictions on the types of building permitted. At first skyscrapers were sheer vertical monsters, maximizing the floor space possible from any given site with no regard to how this affected neighboring buildings. City authorities later invented the concept of "air rights," limiting how high a building could be before it had to be set back from its base. This constraint forced skyscrapers to be designed in a series of steps – a law most elegantly adhered to by the Empire State Building, which has no less than ten steps in all – and forms a pattern you will see repeated all over the city.

It's important to allow at least **two hours** for visiting the ESB, as lines can be very long, especially on clear days. You have to queue for the security checkpoint first of all, but the second line (for tickets) can be avoided by buying tickets in advance at the website listed above. The third and fourth lines – one for elevators to the 80th floor, and the other, much longer, for one of the two elevators to the 86th-floor observation deck – are unfortunately unavoidable. Very early mornings and mid-afternoon are the **best times** to visit, while sunset and late-at-night trips tend to be the most crowded.

⑪ The Morgan Library

Map 6, J3. 29 E 36th St, at Madison Ave. ☎212/685-0610, ⓦwww .morganlibrary.org. #6 to 33rd Street.

When Madison Avenue was on a par with Fifth as the place to live, Murray Hill came to be dominated by the Morgan family, the crusty old financier J.P. and his offspring, who at one time owned a clutch of property here. The **Morgan Library** was built for the old crustacean in 1906. A gracious Italian Renaissance–style mansion, it houses one of New York's best small museums. Though the Morgan was closed at the time of writing while undergoing a comprehensive expansion, it's set to reopen in the spring of 2006. For up-to-date information on the expansion, hours, and admission prices, call or visit the library on the Web.

As for the **collection**, the museum, which originated with Morgan's own impressive holding of manuscripts, has grown to include nearly ten thousand drawings and prints (including works by Rembrandt, da Vinci, Degas, and Dürer), and an extraordinary array of historical, literary, and musical manuscripts. The exhibits change so frequently that it's impossible to catalogue what visitors will see – but a copy of the 1455 Gutenberg Bible (the museum owns a magnificent three out of the eleven surviving books) is always on display. There are also original scores by Mahler, Beethoven, Schubert, and Gilbert and Sullivan; the only complete copy of Thomas Malory's *Morte d'Arthur*; letters from the likes of Vasari, Mozart, and George Washington; and the literary manuscripts of Dickens, Jane Austen, and Thoreau.

Bryant Park

Map 6, H1. ⓦwww.bryantpark.org. #B, #D, #F, or #V to 42nd Street/ Bryant Park or #7 to Fifth Avenue.

One block east of Times Square, **Bryant Park**, between Fifth and Sixth avenues and 40th and 42nd streets, is a lush grassy square filled with slender trees and inviting green chairs. As well as free jazz and outdoor movies in summer months (visit ⓦwww.bryantpark.org for the schedule), there's also a rather aggressive happy-hour singles scene at the pricey *Bryant Park Café*. Additionally, plans are in the works to turn Bryant Park in the winter into an ice-skating rink, larger than the one at Rockefeller Center but not as big as the one at Central Park. Also of note, just across from the park at 40 W 40th St, the **Radiator Building**, designed in 1924 for the American Radiator Company, commands attention for its Gothic tower and polished, black-granite facade.

The New York Public Library

Map 6, H1. Tues & Wed 11am–7.30pm, Thurs–Sat 10am–6pm; ☏212/870-1630, ⓦwww.nypl.org. #B, #D, #F, or #V to 42nd Street/ Bryant Park or #7 to Fifth Avenue.

Bryant Park forms the backyard of the **New York Public Library**, whose Fifth-Avenue entrance is guarded by two majestic lion statues. The library boasts 88 miles of books, which are stored on eight levels of stacks – a collection that makes this the largest research library with a circulation system in the world. Free one-hour tours of the building are available Tuesday to Saturday at 11am & 2pm, the highlight of which is the large, coffered **Reading Room**.

Grand Central Station

Map 6, J1. ⓦwww.grandcentralterminal.com. #4, #5, #6, #7, or #S to Grand Central/42nd Street.

A masterful piece of urban planning, the 1903 **Grand Central Station**, between Madison and Lexington avenues, mainly serves commuters speeding out no further than Connecticut or Westchester County. A Beaux-Arts monument to the power of the railways, Grand Central was the symbolic gateway in the nineteenth century to an undiscovered continent. Today, the most spectacular aspect of the building is its size. The main concourse is one of the world's finest and most imposing open spaces, 470 feet long and 150 feet high, the barrel-vaulted ceiling speckled like a Baroque church with a painted representation of the winter night sky. Stand in the middle and you realize Grand Central represents a time when stations were humbling preludes to great cities. For those with a special interest in the magnificent building, the Municipal Arts Society sponsors a **free tour** of Grand Central every Wednesday at 12.30pm. Meet at the center information booth on the main concourse.

The Chrysler Building

Map 6, K1. #4, #5, #6, #7, or #S to Grand Central/42nd Street.
Just east of Grand Central, occupying the block between Lexington and Third avenues and 42nd and 43rd streets, the **Chrysler Building** dates from an era (1930, though renovated in 2000 by Philip Johnson) when architects carried off prestige with grace and style. The building was for a fleeting moment the world's tallest – until it was surpassed by the Empire State Building in 1931 – and is easily one of Manhattan's best loved. Its car-motif friezes, a spire resembling a car radiator grill, and hood-ornament gargoyles jutting from the setbacks all recall the golden age of motoring. The **lobby**, once a car showroom, has opulently inlaid elevators, walls covered in African marble, and on the ceiling a realistic, if rather faded, study showing airplanes, machines, and the brawny builders who worked on the tower, which, unfortunately, is not open to the public.

East of the Chrysler Building

Flanking Lexington Avenue on the south side of 42nd Street are two more buildings that repay consideration. On the west side, the **Chanin Building** is another Art-Deco monument, cut with terracotta carvings of leaves, tendrils, and sea creatures. More interestingly, the design on the outside of the weighty **Mobil Building** across the street is deliberately folded in such a manner that it can be cleaned automatically by the movement of the wind.

East of here is the somber yet elegant former **Daily News Building**, whose stone facade fronts a surprising Deco interior. The most impressive remnant of the original 1923 decor is a large globe encased in a lighted circular frame (with updated geography), made famous by the film *Superman*, in which the Daily News Building housed the *Daily Planet*.

Further east still, 42nd Street grows more tranquil. Between Second and First avenues, the **Ford Foundation Building** provides one of the most peaceful spaces of all. Built in 1967, this was the first of the atriums that are now commonplace across Manhattan, and it is certainly the most lush. Essentially it's a giant greenhouse, with two walls of offices visible through the windows; 42nd Street is no more than a murmur outside.

At the east end of 42nd Street, steps lead up to the 1925 ensemble of **Tudor City**, which rises behind a tree-filled parklet. With its coats of arms, leaded glass, and neat neighborhood shops, it is the very picture of self-contained residential respectability, and an official historic district. Trip down the steps from here and you're plum opposite the **United Nations**.

The United Nations

Map 7, L9. First Ave, at 46th St. One-hour tours leave every 30min from General Assembly Lobby, Mon–Fri 9.30am–4.45pm, weekends & holidays 10am–4.30pm, closed weekends Jan & Feb; $11.50, $7.50 students; ☏212/963-8687, ⓦwww.un.org. #4, #5, #6, #7, or #S to Grand Central Station.

Some see the **United Nations** complex as one of the major sights of New York; others, usually those who've been there, are not so complimentary. Whatever the symbolism of the UN, there can be few buildings that are quite so dull to walk around. What's more, as if to rationalize years of UN impotence in war and hunger zones worldwide, the (obligatory) guided **tours** emphasize that the UN's main purpose is to promote dialogue and awareness rather than enforcement.

For the determined, the complex consists of three main buildings – the thin glass-curtained slab of the Secretariat, the sweeping curve of the General Assembly Building, and, just between, the low-rise, connecting Conference Wing. Tours take in the main conference chambers of the UN and its constituent parts, the foremost of which is the General Assembly Chamber itself.

Rockefeller Center

Map 7, H8. #B, #D, #F, or #V to 47th–50th streets/Rockefeller Center.
Filling the whole block west of Fifth Avenue between 49th and 50th streets, **Rockefeller Center** was built between 1932 and 1940 by John D. Rockefeller, son of the oil magnate. It's one of the finest pieces of urban planning anywhere – office space with cafés, a theater, underground concourses, and rooftop gardens work together with a rare intelligence and grace.

You're lured into the center from Fifth Avenue down the gentle slope of the **Channel Gardens** to the **GE Building**, focus of the center. Rising 850 feet, this monumental structure is softened by symmetrical setbacks. At its foot, the **Lower Plaza** holds a sunken restaurant and bar in the summer months, linked visually to the downward flow of the building by Paul Manship's sparkling *Prometheus* sculpture; in winter the sunken area becomes an ice rink, giving skaters a chance to show off their skills to passing shoppers. Inside the GE Building's lobby are José Maria Sert's murals, *American Progress* and *Time*, which, while faded, are eagerly in tune with the 1930s Deco ambience.

NBC Studios

Among the many office ensembles in the GE Building is **NBC Studios**, home of the network's long-established late-night comedy show *Saturday Night Live*, which simply refuses to die, among other programs. Get a backstage look on the **NBC Experience Tour** (every 30min Mon–Thurs 8.30am–5.30pm, every 15min Fri & Sat 8.30am–5.30pm and Sun 9.30am–4.30pm; $18, seniors and children $15.50, under-6s not allowed on tour; ☏212/664-7174). The tour includes the NBC History Theatre, where a televised Katie Couric and Matt Lauer present the history of the network, and the opportunity to visit the various studios (provided they are not in use) that serve as home for shows such as *Saturday Night Live*, *Late Night with Conan O'Brien*, *Dateline NBC*, *NBC Nightly News*, and *NBC Sports*. Tours leave from the NBC Experience Store on 49th Street between Fifth and Sixth avenues; reservations are recommended (call ☏212/644-7174 or reserve a specific tour online at ⊛www.tickets.com).

For a free, early-morning TV thrill, you can gawk at NBC's *Today Show*, which broadcasts live from 7am to 10am weekday mornings from glass-enclosed studios in the new NBC News Building on the southwest corner of 49th Street and Rockefeller Plaza.

St Patrick's Cathedral

Map 7, H7. Fifth Ave, between 50th and 51st sts. #E or #V to 5th Avenue/53rd Street.

Bone-white **St Patrick's Cathedral** sits among the glitz of Fifth Avenue like a misplaced bit of moral imperative, and seems the result of a painstaking academic tour of the Gothic cathedrals of Europe: faultless in detail, lifeless in spirit. In the peaceful **Lady Chapel** at the back of the cathedral, however, the graceful, simple altar captures the spirituality that its big sister lacks. Nevertheless, St Patrick's is an essential part of the midtown landscape, and perhaps the most important Catholic church in America, serving as a premier religious contact point for generations of Italian, Irish, and other practising immigrants. The Gothic details are perfect and the cathedral is certainly striking – made all the more so by the sunglass-black **Olympic Tower** behind, which serves as a dramatically neutral backdrop to this work of art. Across the street, at 611 Fifth Ave, are the striped awnings of **Saks Fifth Avenue**, one of the last of New York's premier department stores.

Museum of Television & Radio

Map 7, H7. 25 W 52nd St, between 5th and 6th aves. Tues & Wed, Fri–Sun noon–6pm, Thurs noon–8pm; $10, students $8, under-14s $5; ☎212/621-6800, ⍟www.mtr.org. #E or #V to 5th Avenue/53rd Street.

The Museum of Television & Radio holds an archive of 100,000 mostly American TV shows, radio broadcasts, and commercials, any of which are available for your personal viewing. The museum's excellent computerized reference system allows you to research news, public affairs, documentaries, sporting events, comedies, advertisements, and other aural and visual selections. Note that the MTR becomes unbearably crowded on weekends, so plan to visit at other times.

Museum of American Folk Art

Map 7, F6. 45 W 53rd St, between 5th and 6th aves. Tues–Sun 10.30am–5.30pm, Fri until 7.30pm; $9, students and seniors $7, Fri after 5.30pm free; ☎212/265-1040, ⍟www.folkartmuseum.org. #E or #V to 5th Avenue/53rd Street.

The **Museum of American Folk Art** stands in an exceptionally intimate, prize-winning building designed by Tod Williams and Billie Tsien. Its highly sculptural eight-floor facade is based on traditional folk-art techniques and clad in tombasil, a white bronze alloy, while a giant skylight atop the structure allows natural light to filter down through all the galleries. Visitors are encouraged to wander freely, and the greatest part of the structure is designed to be public space as well as gallery. The museum houses interesting (if a little recondite) exhibitions of multicultural folk art from all over the US, with a permanent collection that includes over 3500 works from the seventeenth to twentieth centuries.

North toward Central Park

Here comes the glitz: **Cartier**, **Gucci**, and **Tiffany and Co.** are among many gilt-edged storefronts that will jump out at you along Fifth Avenue between 53rd and 59th streets. If you're keen to do more than merely window-shop, Tiffany's, at no. 727, is worth a perusal, its soothing green marble and weathered wood interior best described by Truman Capote's fictional Holly Golightly: "It calms me down right away. . . nothing very bad could happen to you there."

Topping all this off is **F.A.O. Schwarz**, a block north at no. 767, a colossal emporium of children's toys. Fight the kids off and there's some great stuff to play with – once again, the best (and biggest, including gas-powered cars, life-sized stuffed animals, and Lego creations) that money can buy. Across 58th Street, Fifth Avenue broadens into **Grand Army Plaza** and the southeast fringes of Central Park. Looming impressively on the plaza is, aptly enough, the copper-edged **Plaza Hotel** (Map 7, H6), recognizable from its many film appearances. Wander around to soak in the (slightly faded) gilt-and-brocade grandeur; the snazzy **Oak Room** bar is worth a snoop too.

Madison Avenue

Madison Avenue shadows Fifth to the east, offering some of its sweep but less excitement. Madison is a little removed from its 1960s and 1970s prime, when it was internationally recognized as the advertising industry's epicenter. A few good stores – notably those specializing in men's haberdashery, shoes, and cigars – can still be found here.

Madison's most interesting buildings come in a four-block strip above 53rd Street. The **Sony Building** (Map 7, H6), between 55th and 56th streets, followed the postmodernist theory of eclectic borrowing from historical styles: it's a modernist skyscraper sandwiched between a Chippendale top and a Renaissance base. The building has its fans, but in popular opinion the tower doesn't work, and it's unlikely to stand the test of time. The first floor is well worth ducking into to soak in the brute grandeur, though.

The **IBM Building**, next door at no. 590, has a far more inviting plaza, the calm glass-enclosed atrium and tropical foliage making for a far less ponderous experience. Across 57th Street, as the first of Madison's clothing stores appear, the **Fuller Building** is worth catching: black-and-white Art Deco, with a fine entrance and tiled floor. Cut east down 57th Street to find the **Four Seasons Hotel**, notable for its I.M. Pei–designed foyer and lobby, ostentatious in its sweeping marble.

Park Avenue

"Where wealth is so swollen that it almost bursts," wrote Collinson Owen of **Park Avenue** in 1929, and things aren't much changed: corporate headquarters jostle for prominence in a triumphal procession to capitalism, pushed apart by Park's broad avenue that was built to support elevated rail tracks. Whatever your feelings, it's one of the city's most awesome sights. Looking south from anywhere above 42nd Street, everything progresses to the high altar of the New York Central Building (now renamed the **Helmsley Building**; Map 7, I8), a delicate, energetic construction with an excessive Rococo lobby.

Despite Park Avenue's power, an individual look at most of the skyscrapers reveals the familiar glass box, and the first few buildings to stand out do so exactly because that's what they're not. Wherever you placed the solid **Waldorf-Astoria Hotel** (between 49th and 50th sts; Map 7, I8), it would hold its own, a resplendent statement of Art Deco elegance. Duck inside to stroll through the sweeping marble and hushed plushness. Crouching across the street, **St Bartholomew's Church** is a low-slung Byzantine hybrid that by contrast adds immeasurably to the street scene, giving the lumbering skyscrapers a much-needed sense of scale. The spiky-topped **General Electric Building** (Map 7, I7) behind, at the southwest corner of Lexington Avenue and 51st Street, seems like a wild extension of the church, its slender, carved red-marble shaft rising to a meshed crown of abstract sparks and lightning strokes that symbolizes the radio waves used by its original owner, RCA. The lobby with its vaulted ceiling (entrance at 570 Lexington Ave) is yet another Art Deco delight.

The Seagram Building

Map 7, I7. #E or #V to Lexington Ave/53rd Street.

Among all this it's difficult at first to see the originality of the **Seagram Building** between 52nd and 53rd streets. Designed by Mies van der Rohe and built in 1958, this was the seminal curtain-wall skyscraper, the floors supported internally rather than by the building's walls, allowing a skin of smoky glass and whiskey-bronze metal, now weathered to a dull black. It was the supreme example of modernist reason, deceptively simple and cleverly detailed, and its opening was met with a wave of approval. The **plaza**, an open forecourt designed to set the building apart from its neighbors and display it to advantage, was such a success as a public space that the city revised its zoning laws to encourage other high-rise builders to supply plazas.

Across Park Avenue between 53rd and 54th, **Lever House** (Map 7, I7) was the building that set the modernist ball rolling on Park Avenue in 1952. Then, the two right-angled slabs that form a steel and glass bookend seemed revolutionary compared to the traditional buildings that surrounded it.

Lexington Avenue and Citicorp Center

Lexington Avenue is always active, especially around the mid-40s, where commuters swarm around Grand Central Station and the **post office** on the corner of 50th Street. Just as the Chrysler Building dominates the lower stretches of the avenue, the chisel-topped **Citicorp Center** (Map 7, J7) anchors and governs the 50s. Finished in 1979, the building, now one of New York's most conspicuous landmarks, looks as if it is sheathed in shiny graph paper, while the slope of tower resembles a linear representation of a mathematical equation. The slanted roof was designed to house solar panels and provide power, but the idea was ahead of the day's technology and Citicorp had to content itself with adopting the distinctive top as a corporate logo. The atrium of stores known as **The Market** is pleasant enough, with some enticing food options.

Third, Second, and First avenues

Third Avenue remained mainly undeveloped until the old elevated railway that ran here was dismantled in 1955. Until then Third had been a strip of earthy bars and run-down tenements, in effect a border to the more salubrious Midtown district. After Citicorp went up, other office buildings sprouted, revitalizing the flagging fortunes of midtown Manhattan in the late 1970s. The best section is between 44th and 50th streets – look out for the sheer marble monument of the **Wang Building** between 48th and 49th, whose cross-patterns reveal the structure within.

All this office space hasn't totally removed interest from the street, but most life, especially at night, seems to have shifted across to **Second Avenue** – on the whole lower, quieter, more residential, and with any number of bars to crawl between. The area from Third to the East River in the upper 40s is known as **Turtle Bay**, and there's a scattering of brownstones alongside chirpier shops and industry that disappear as you head north.

First Avenue has a certain raggy looseness that's a relief after the concrete claustrophobia of Midtown, and **Beekman Place**, from 49th to 51st streets between First Avenue and the East River, is quieter still, a beguiling enclave of garbled styles. Similar, though not quite as intimate, is **Sutton Place**, a long stretch running from 53rd to 59th between First and the river. Originally built for the lordly Morgans and Vanderbilts in 1875, Sutton increases in elegance as you move north and, for today's *crème de la crème*, **Riverview Terrace** (Map 7, L5) is a very private enclave of five brownstones.

Museum of Modern Art

 New York City's **Museum of Modern Art** – **MoMA** to its friends – reopened in November 2004, just in time for its 75th anniversary, after a massive renovation that took over two years. The overhaul was clearly necessary: it has doubled the gallery space available, and Yoshio Taniguchi's design has created new and vibrant public spaces while expanding the galleries into larger and more accessible venues for the museum's extraordinary collection. The building is complex and clever, easy to navigate but constantly and deliberately giving glimpses of other levels – down into the sculpture garden, into the lobby and the second-floor landing where Monet's large *Waterlilies* study is displayed.

Yet those familiar with the museum may wonder what has really changed: it is still divided broadly into the same categories, and the principal exhibits – in the core **Painting and Sculpture** galleries at least – are displayed in much the same chronological order as before, albeit with some thematic detours. What is different is the museum's ability to display its peripheral material – its drawings, photography, and more – to show more art from the present day, and to mount temporary exhibitions without cutting into the permanent space.

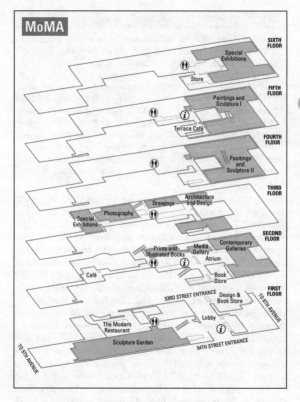

Painting and Sculpture 1

The core of MoMA is the Painting and Sculpture galleries, and if this is your priority you should head straight for the fifth floor – to **Painting and Sculpture 1**. The starting

Museum practicalities

Map 7, G7. 11 W 53rd St, between 5th and 6th. Wed–Mon 10.30am–5.30pm, Fri open until 8pm, closed Tues, Thanksgiving Day & Christmas Day; $20, seniors $16, students $12, free Fri 4–8pm; tickets can be booked in advance through Ticketmaster on ☏212/220-0505 or ⊛www.ticketmaster.com; general info ☏212/708-9400, ⊛www.moma.org. #E or #V to 5th Avenue/53rd Street or #B, #D, #F, or #V to 47–50 Streets/Rockefeller Center.

If you need to **take a break** while touring MoMA, the second-floor *Café 2* does very good and slickly presented Italian **food**. There's also a more formal option, *Terrace 5*, on the fifth floor, with nice views over the sculpture garden, and a very swanky full-service restaurant, *The Modern*, on the ground floor.

point here is the post-Impressionists of the late nineteenth century, with works by Cézanne, Seurat, Van Gogh, and Gauguin mixed in with vivid early paintings by Derain, Braque, and James Ensor that already hint at a more Modernist perspective. This is developed in the next room by **Picasso**, most notably with his seminal *Demoiselles d'Avignon*, and other later, more Cubist offerings by Picasso and Braque. Later works by these two men and Léger follow, while beyond you'll find the big swirling colors of Boccioni and the Italian Futurists.

Straight on takes you into an exploration of color, with paintings by Chagall, Kandinsky, and Kirchner predominating, and an entire room devoted to **Matisse**, with the *Red Studio*, the *Piano Lesson*, and other paintings, as well as his lumpy series of sculpted heads of *Jeanette*. After Matisse is the so-called "Crossroads" gallery, which houses some of the most recognizable works of the modern age – Picasso's *Three Women at the Spring* and *Three Musicians* as well as Léger's *Three Women*, all painted the same year (1921). Here too are some haunting works by de Chirico.

Off this room lead galleries devoted to Duchamp, Malevich, and the paintings of the Dutch *De Stijl* movement, tracing the development of its leading light, **Mondrian**, from his tentative early work to the pure color abstract of *Broadway Boogie Woogie*, painted in New York in 1943. Oddly enough, Matisse's muscular back studies occupy a room with Bonnard's soft domestic scenes; while further on are paintings by Diego Rivera and another room devoted to the Surrealists – much of it familiar from popular reproductions: Miró's *Dutch Interiors*, Magritte's *The Menaced Assassin*, and Dalí's *Persistence of Memory*, among others. Finally there are a few **American** paintings to round things off: Wyeth's *Christina's World*, a couple of typically atmospheric Hoppers, and one of Charles Scheeler's American industrial landscapes.

Painting and Sculpture 2

Painting and Sculpture 2, the next floor down, displays work from the 1940s to the 1960s and inevitably has a more American feel, starting with works by Pollock, Rothko, and De Kooning. Further on, Dubuffet's challenging paintings sit with Giacometti's sticklike figures and paintings by Bacon (*Study of a Baboon*) and Picasso (*The Charnel Room*), the latter inspired by the horrors of the Second World War. Beyond here the Abstract Expressionists hold sway, with vast canvases by Barnett Newman, Rothko, and Pollock – all at the height of their powers in the 1950s, when these paintings were done. Later rooms contain lots of work familiar from the modern canon: Jasper Johns' iconic *Flag*, Robert Rauschenberg's mixed-media paintings, Warhol's soup cans and Marilyn Monroes, Lichtenstein's postmodern cartoons, and Oldenburg's soft sculptures.

Photography, and Architecture and Design

The other parts of the museum are just as impressive as the Painting and Sculpture galleries and shouldn't be missed if you have the time. On the third floor, the **Photography** galleries are also chronological in their layout, and begin with a European slant – photos of Paris by Atget, Brassaï, and Cartier-Bresson – before moving on to Robert Franck's and Robert Capa's stunning pictures of the USA, their realism mirrored by the hypernaturalism of the later, more contemporary, works in the collection.

Architecture and Design, on the same floor, shows classic designs of the last century: examples of modern buildings and town planning by key innovators like Frank Lloyd Wright; interior design with chairs by Rietveld, Arne Jacobsen, Charles Rennie Mackintosh; and lots of glass and ceramics. There is also a series of neat large-scale objects like a 1946 Ferrari, a British motorcycle, and signage from the New York subway – the latter perhaps the best illustration you could find of the subliminal nature of the best design.

Drawing, Contemporary Art, and film

The **Drawing** galleries, also on the third floor, show works on paper by a glittering array of twentieth-century artists – Lucien Freud, Jackson Pollock, Robert Rauschenberg, and his old roommate Willem De Kooning, along with studies by Warhol, Jasper Johns, and Lichtenstein. Finally, the second-floor galleries give MoMA the chance to show its **Contemporary Art** in all media, and basically consists of works from the 1970s onwards, including work by Bruce Nauman, Jeff Koons, and other stellar names from the contemporary art world. Finally, MoMA hosts regular screenings of mainly arthouse and foreign-language **films**, every evening during the week and on afternoons and evenings at weekends. Check the website for details; this can be a good opportunity to view some rarely screened gems.

⑬

Midtown West

M uch of the midtown Manhattan district that runs
between West 30th and 59th streets to the west
of Sixth Avenue is an enthralling, noisy, hurly-
burly of garish attractions meant to entertain the
tourists staying in the area's dense concentration of hotels.
The southern reaches of **Midtown West** encompass the
bustling, business-minded **Garment District** – an area of
several blocks filled with fabric store after fabric store, many
of them wholesale but others open to the public – whose
main attractions are Madison Square Garden and Macy's
department store. The real heart of the district, though, is
Times Square, an exploded version of the East Side's more
tight-lipped monuments to capitalism. It's at this nexus,
where jostling crowds and flashing signs (some many stories
high) make for an exhilarating assault on the senses, that
New York City reaches its commercial zenith. Just north
of the once "naughty, bawdy 42nd Street," the **Theater
District** offers the most impressive concentration of live
theater in the world.

For glimpses of vintage seediness, keep heading west to
Eighth Avenue and beyond to **Hell's Kitchen** – though
keep in mind that the forces of gentrification are fully
entrenched in this buzzing part of town, where shiny open-
air eateries are far more common these days than peep-show
pavilions. There aren't many tourist attractions per se in this

direction, though if you head all the way over to the Hudson River, you'll come upon the massive **Intrepid Sea, Air & Space Museum**, based in a retired aircraft carrier.

The Garment District can be reached by taking the #A, #C, #E, #1, #2, or #3 to 34th Street/Penn Station or by taking the #B, #D, #F, #N, #Q, #R, #V, or #W to 34th Street/Herald Square. Times Square can be reached by taking the #N, #Q, #R, #S, #W, #1, #2, #3, or #7 to Times Square/42nd Street.

Madison Square Garden and around

Map 6, E4.

The most prominent landmark of the Garment District is the **Pennsylvania Station and Madison Square Garden complex**, a combined box-and-drum structure that swallows up millions of commuters into its train station belly while housing Knicks basketball and Rangers hockey games (for ticket info, see p.291). There's nothing memorable about the railway station, which has incurred a fair amount of resentment because the original Penn Station, demolished in 1963 to make way for it, is now hailed as a lost masterpiece, one that brought an air of dignity to the neighborhood. As 1960s architectural historian Vincent Scully lamented following the passing of the original, "through it one entered the city like a god... one now scuttles in like a rat."

A whimsical reminder of the old days is the **Hotel Pennsylvania**, on Seventh Ave at 33rd St, which was built in 1919. A main venue for Glenn Miller and other big swing bands of the 1940s, it keeps the phone number that made it famous – ☏212/736-5000 (under the old system, "PENNsylvania 6-5000") the title of Miller's affectionate hit. It has recently been refurbished, and now bravely claims to offer "New York's newest rooms."

Greeley and Herald squares

One block east of Penn Station, Sixth Avenue collides with Broadway at seedy **Greeley Square**. Perhaps Horace Greeley, founder of the *Tribune* newspaper, deserves better than this triangle. Known for his rallying call to the youth of the nineteenth century to explore the continent ("Go West, young man!"), he also supported the rights of women and trade unions, denounced slavery and capital punishment, and commissioned a weekly column from Karl Marx. His paper no longer exists and the square named after him is one of those bits of Manhattan that looks ready to disintegrate at any moment, despite recent attempts to spruce it up.

Herald Square, at the intersection of 34th Street, Broadway, and Sixth Avenue, is perhaps best recognized as the one George M. Cohan asked to be remembered to in his 1904 hit song. These days its grimy mediocrity wouldn't inspire anyone to sing about it, and the area's unkempt and seedy nature is tempered by that temple of commercialism, **Macy's** (Map 6, G3), the world's largest department store (see Chapter 27, "Shopping," for more).

The General Post Office

Map 6, D4.

Immediately west of Penn Station, the **General Post Office** is a 1913 structure that survived from an era when municipal pride was all about making statements – though to say that the Post Office is monumental in the grandest manner still seems to underplay it. The old joke is that it had to be this big to fit in the sonorous inscription above the columns – "Neither snow nor rain nor heat nor gloom of night stays these couriers from the swift completion of their appointed rounds" – a highly incredible claim. In 2004, the architecture and engineering firm HDR won the highly contested and much-delayed contract to create a new Penn Station for Amtrak in the General Post Office building. Slated to be the largest transportation hub in the world, the new structure is set to open sometime in 2008.

Port Authority and around

The **Port Authority Terminal Building** (Map 6, E1), at 40th Street and Eighth Avenue, has a tawdry reputation as a hangout for the destitute and mentally deranged, and despite recent improvements, it does little to combat these accusations. Greyhound leaves from here, as do regional services out to the boroughs, and buses tend to run regularly and on time. You'll need to arrive early to assure yourself a seat on some departures – and this, unfortunately, can mean spending more time than you might like to with the various winos and weirdos that haunt the stalls.

To the west of Port Authority, at 330 W 42nd St, is the **McGraw-Hill Building** (Map 6, D1), a greeny-blue radiator built in 1972 that architects raved over at the time: "proto-jukebox modern," the critic Scully called it. The lobby, festooned with opaque Carrera glass and stainless steel, should definitely be seen.

Times Square and around

Times Square, tourist destination *ne plus ultra* for many visitors to New York, occupies the streets between 42nd and 47th, where Seventh Avenue and Broadway collide. This is the center of the Theater District, where the pulsating neon suggests a heart for the city itself. Traditionally a melting pot of debauch, depravity, and fun, the area used to be quite edgy, a place where out-of-towners supplied easy pickings for petty criminals, drug dealers, and prostitutes. Now, though, almost all of the peep shows and sex shops have disappeared, making Times Square a largely sanitized universe of consumption. This isn't to say that the area is without charm, though: if you've never seen Times Square, plan to visit at night, when the place hums with an excited electricity fueled in large part by tourists oohing and aahing over the the bright advertisements they've seen so often on TV.

At the square's southernmost edge, **Times Tower** was originally headquarters of the *New York Times*, the city's (and America's) most respected newspaper. It's here that the alcohol-fueled masses gather for New Year's Eve, to witness the giant sparkling ball drop from the top of the Tower. The newspaper itself has long since moved around a corner to a handsome building with globe lamps on 43rd Street; walk past in the early hours of the morning and you'll see the newspaper coming hot off the presses.

Dotted around Times Square are most of New York's great **theaters**, such as the majestic 1927 clock-and-globe-topped **Paramount Building** at 1501 Broadway, between 43rd and 44th streets; it now serves as office space. The **New Amsterdam** and the **New Victory**, both on 42nd Street between Seventh and Eighth avenues, have been refurbished to their original splendor, one of the truly welcome results of the massive changes here. The **Lyceum**, at 149 W 45th St, has its original facade, while the **Shubert** Theater, which hosted *A Chorus Line* during its twenty-odd-year run, occupies its own small space at 225 W 44th St. At 432 W 44th St is the **Actors' Studio**, where Lee Strasberg, America's leading proponent of Stanislavski's method-acting technique, taught his students. Among the oldest is the **Belasco**, on 111 W 44th St, between Sixth and Seventh avenues, which was also the first of Broadway's theaters to incorporate machinery into its stagings.

Tickets for shows at these theaters can be purchased at the nifty canvas-and-frame stand of the **TKTS booth**, located in **Duffy Square**, the northernmost island of Times Square. The booth, which sells half-price, same-day tickets for many (though never the newest or most popular) Broadway shows, is always mobbed, though the line moves more quickly than you might think. **Duffy Square** itself offers an excellent panoramic view of the lights, megahotels, theme stores, and theme restaurants metastasizing daily. Above the square, a lifelike statue of Broadway's doyen **George M. Cohan** looks on – though if you've ever seen the film *Yankee Doodle Dandy* it's impossible to think of him as other than a swaggering Jimmy Cagney.

Hell's Kitchen

To the west of Times Square lies **Hell's Kitchen**, an area centered on (and really only worth visiting for) the engaging slash of restaurants, bars, and ethnic delis of **Ninth Avenue** and around; for eating and drinking reviews in this neighborhood, see pp.224 & 246, respectively. Extending down to the Garment District and up to the low 50s, this was once one of New York's most violent and lurid neighborhoods, made up of soap and glue factories, slaughterhouses, and the like. Gangs roamed the streets, and though their rule ended in 1910 after a major police counteroffensive, the area remained somewhat dangerous until fairly recently, when musicians, Broadway types, and young professionals began moving in.

Head to Hell's Kitchen from Eighth Avenue (which now houses the porn businesses expelled from Times Square) down 46th Street – the so-called **Restaurant Row** that is the area's preferred haunt for pre- and post-theater dining. Here you can begin to detect a more pastoral (or at least less frenetic) feel, which only increases on many of the side streets around Ninth and Tenth avenues.

Intrepid Sea, Air & Space Museum

Map 7, A8. April–Sept Mon–Fri 10am–5pm, Sat & Sun 10am–6pm; Oct–March Tues–Sun 10am–5pm, last admission 1 hour prior to closing; $16.50, children 6–17 $11.50, children 2–5 $4.50, under 2 years free; ☎212/245-0072, ⓦ www.intrepidmuseum.org.

Continue west down 46th Street until you hit the Hudson River at Pier 86 and you'll spot the grey hulk of the USS *Intrepid*, which houses the **Intrepid Sea, Air & Space Museum**. This old aircraft carrier has a long and distinguished history, including hauling capsules out of the ocean following *Mercury* and *Gemini* space missions. It holds an array of modern and vintage air and sea craft including the A-12 *Blackbird*, the world's fastest spy plane, and the USS *Growler*, a guided-missile submarine.

North to Central Park

Heading north from Times Square, the **West 50s** between Sixth and Eighth avenues are also emphatically tourist territory. Edged by Central Park in the north and the Theater District to the south, and with Fifth Avenue and Rockefeller Center in easy striking distance, the area has been invaded by overpriced restaurants and cheapo souvenir stores.

A couple of sights worth searching out, however, are the **Equitable Center** (Map 7, F7) and the **Ed Sullivan Theater** (Map 7, F7). In the case of the former, the building itself, at 757 Seventh Ave, is dapper if not a little self-important, with Roy Lichtenstein's 68-foot *Mural with Blue Brushstroke* poking you in the eye as you enter. The Ed Sullivan Theater, on the other hand, is more famous for what's gone on inside rather than for any particular architectural merit. This 1920s theater, at 1697 Broadway, at West 53rd St, currently serves as the studio for *The Late Show with David Letterman*, and was the site of the Beatles' well-remembered first television performance in America.

Carnegie Hall

Map 7, F6. 154 W 57th St, at 7th. Tours Oct–June Mon, Tues, Thurs & Fri 11.30am, 2pm & 3pm; $6, students $5; ☎212/903-9765. #N, #Q, #R, #W to 57th Street/Seventh Ave.

Stately **Carnegie Hall** is one of the world's greatest concert venues, whose superb acoustics ensure full houses most of the year. Tchaikovsky conducted the program on opening night and Mahler, Rachmaninov, Toscanini, Frank Sinatra, and Judy Garland all played here. If you can't attend a performance, try and catch one of the engaging tours (see above for details).

Sixth Avenue

Sixth Avenue is properly named **Avenue of the Americas**, though no New Yorker ever calls it this: the only manifestation of the tag are lamppost flags of Central and South American countries. If nothing else, Sixth's distinction is its width, a result of the elevated railway that once ran along here, now replaced by the Sixth Avenue subway. In its day the Sixth Avenue "El" marked the border between respectability to the east and shadier areas to the west, and in a way it's still a dividing line separating the glamorous strips of Fifth, Madison, and Park avenues from the brasher western districts. At 1133 Sixth Ave, at 43rd St, is the **International Center of Photography** (Map 7, G9; Tues–Thurs 10am–5pm, Fri 10am–8pm, Sat & Sun 10am–6pm; $9, students $6, free Fri 5–8pm; ☏212/857-0000, ⊛www.icp.org), whose glassy confines generally present interesting exhibits. The permanent collection is particularly strong in twentieth-century documentary photography, and boasts more than 100,000 pictures, including classics by the likes of Henri Cartier-Bresson and Robert Capa. Further up Sixth, in the **AXA Financial Building** at no. 1290, look out for Thomas Hart Benton's *America Today* murals, which dynamically and magnificently portray ordinary American life in the days before the Depression.

Diamond Row

One of the best things about New York City is the small hidden pockets abruptly discovered when you least expect them. West 47th Street between Fifth and Sixth avenues is a perfect example: **Diamond Row** is a strip of shops chock-full of gems and jewelry, largely managed by Hasidic Jews who seem only to exist in the confines of the street. Maybe they are what gives the street its workaday feel – Diamond Row seems more like the Garment District than Fifth Avenue, and the conversations you overhear on the street or in the nearby delicatessens are memorably Jewish.

By the time Sixth Avenue reaches midtown Manhattan, it has become a dazzling showcase of corporate wealth. Following the **Time & Life Building** at 50th Street, three near-identical blocks went up in the 1970s, and if they don't have the romance of their predecessors they at least possess some of their monumentality. At street level, things can be just as interesting – the broad sidewalks allow peddlers of food and handbills, street musicians, mimics, and actors to do their thing.

Radio City Music Hall

Map 7, G7. Tours daily 11am–3pm; $17, $14 seniors, children under 12 $10; ☎212/307-7171, ⓦwww.radiocity.com. #B, #D, #F, or #V to 47th–50th Streets/Rockefeller Center.

By far the most spectacular attraction on Sixth is **Radio City Music Hall**, at 50th Street, just northwest of Rockefeller Center (see p.92). This Art-Deco jewel box represents the last word in 1930s luxury: inside, the staircase is regally resplendent with the world's largest chandeliers and the huge auditorium looks like an extravagant scalloped shell or a vast sunset. Believe it or not, Radio City was nearly demolished in 1970; the outcry this caused resulted in its being designated a National Landmark. Tours here are highly recommended.

14

Central Park

"All radiant in the magic atmosphere of art and taste." So raved *Harper's* magazine on the opening of **Central Park** in 1876, and though that was a slight overstatement, today few New Yorkers could imagine life without it. At various times and places, the park functions as a beach, theater, singles' scene, athletic activity center, and animal-behavior lab, both human and canine. In bad times and good New Yorkers still treasure it more than any other city institution.

In spite of the advent of motorized traffic, the sense of disorderly nature the park's nineteenth-century designers, Frederick Law Olmsted and Calvert Vaux, intended largely survives, with cars and buses cutting through the park in the sheltered, sunken transverses originally meant for horse-drawn carriages, mostly unseen from the park itself. The Midtown skyline, of course, has changed, and buildings thrust their way into view, sometimes detracting from the park's original pastoral intention, but at the same time adding to the sense of being on a green island in the center of a magnificent city.

Getting around and orientation

At 840 acres, Central Park – which runs from 59th to 110th streets and is flanked by Fifth Avenue and Central Park

West – is so enormous that it's almost impossible to miss and nearly as impossible to cover in one visit. Nevertheless, the intricate **footpaths** that meander with no discernible organization through the park are one of its greatest successes; after all, the point here is to lose yourself . . . or at least to feel like you can. To figure out exactly **where you are**, find the nearest **lamppost** – the first two digits on the post signify the number of the nearest cross street.

The **Reservoir** divides Central Park in two. The larger and more familiar **southern park** holds most of the attractions (and people), but the **northern park** (above 86th St) is worth a visit for its wilder natural setting and its dramatically different ambience.

As for **safety**, you should be fine during the day, though always be alert to your surroundings and try to avoid being alone in an isolated part of the park.

Bicycle rental

One of the best ways to see the park is to **rent a bicycle** from the Loeb Boathouse (see p.118). Bikes cost $9–15 an hour and require a (refundable) $250 cash or credit card deposit, along with a passport or driver's license.

After dark, it's safer than it used to be but still not advisable to walk around. The exception to this rule is in the case of a public evening event such as a concert or Shakespeare in the Park; just make sure you leave when the crowds do.

The southern park

Entering at **Grand Army Plaza** (Fifth Ave and 59th St), to your left lies the **Pond** and a little further north you'll find the **Wollman Memorial Rink**. Sit or stand above the rink to watch skaters and contemplate the view of Central Park South's skyline emerging above the trees. Or **rent skates** of your own, available here in season (Nov–March). In summer, the place plays host to a mini-**amusement park** for kids (entry $6, then $10 for ten rides, or $12 for unlimited rides).

Northeast of the skating rink lies a small zoo, at 64th Street and Fifth Avenue, the **Central Park Wildlife Center** (April–Oct Mon–Fri 10am–5pm, Sat, Sun & holidays 10am–5.30pm; Nov–March daily 10am–4.30pm; $6, ages 3–12 $1, under-3s free; ☎212/439-6500). Its collection is based on three climatic regions – the Tropic Zone, the Temperate Territory, and the Polar Circle, and the complex also boasts the **Tisch Children's Zoo**, with interactive displays and a petting zoo.

The next point to head for is the **Dairy**, at mid-park and 65th Street, a kind of Gothic, toy ranch building constructed in 1870 and originally stocked with cows (and milkmaids) for the purpose of selling milk and other dairy products to mothers with young children. It now houses one of the park's **visitor centers** (Tues–Sun 10am–5pm; ☎212/794-6564), which distribute free leaflets and organize weekend walking tours.

Just west of the Dairy stands the **Carousel**, at mid-park and 64th Street (April–Oct Mon–Fri 10am–6pm, Sat & Sun 10am–7pm; Nov–Dec daily 10am–dusk; Jan–March weekends & holidays only 10am–dusk; $1), where kids of all ages can ride on hand-carved jumping horses to the accompaniment of a military band organ. Built in 1903 and moved from Coney Island to the park in 1951, this handmade carousel is one of fewer than 150 left in the country; one of the others is at Coney Island (see p.167).

Straight ahead and north past the Dairy, you'll come to the **Mall**, the park's most formal stretch, where you'll witness every manner of street performer. To the west, between 66th and 69th streets, lies **Sheep Meadow**, fifteen acres of commons where sheep grazed until 1934; today the area is usually crowded with picnickers, sunbathers, families, and Frisbee players.

On warm weekends, an area between the Sheep Meadow and the north end of the Mall is filled with colorfully attired rollerbladers and rollerskaters dancing to loud funk, disco, and hip-hop music – one of the best free shows around. Meanwhile, just west of Sheep Meadow, at 67th Street and Central Park West, is the once exclusive (and still expensive) but now rather tacky landmark restaurant and finishing point of the annual New York City Marathon, **Tavern on the Green**.

At the northernmost point of the Mall lie the 1920s **Naumburg Bandshell**, the **Rumsey Playfield**, site of the free SummerStage performance series (see box, p.267), and the excellent-for-people-watching two-story **Bethesda Terrace and Fountain**, at the heart of the park at 72nd Street. Bethesda Terrace overlooks the lake; beneath it is **Bethesda Arcade**, whose Minton-tiled ceilings are currently being restored.

Take a break from your wanderings on the lake's eastern bank at the **Loeb Boathouse**. Here, you can go for a gondola ride or rent a rowboat, enjoying the serenity of this patch of water in the center of the city, with the skyscrapers of Midtown reaching up all around (rowboats: March–Nov daily 10am–6pm, weather permitting; $10 for the first hour, $2.50 each 15min after, with a refundable $30 deposit; gondola rides: summer Mon–Fri 5–9pm, Sat & Sun 2–9pm; $30 per half-hour; reservations required; ☎212/517-2233).

The Great Lawn and around

Continuing north will bring you to the backyard of the **Metropolitan Museum of Art**, to the east at 81st Street (see p.122), and the **Obelisk** to the west, an 1881 gift from Egypt that dates back to 1450 BC. Also nearby is the **Great Lawn**, a perfect spot for an early evening picnic. The Lawn hosts free summer shows by the New York Philharmonic and the Metropolitan Opera, as well as the occasional major rock concert, or speech by world-famous dignitaries such as the Dalai Lama. In addition, the Lawn boasts eight softball fields and, at its northern end, basketball and volleyball courts, plus a short jogging track.

Strawberry Fields

At 72nd Street and Central Park West, **Strawberry Fields** is a peaceful region of the park dedicated to the memory of John Lennon, who in 1980 was murdered in front of his home at the **Dakota Building**, across the street on Central Park West (see p.147). Strawberry Fields draws people here to remember Lennon, as well as picnickers and seniors resting on the park benches. Near the West 72nd Street entrance to the area is a round Italian mosaic with the word "Imagine" at its center, donated by Yoko Ono and invariably covered with flowers, photos, and other sentimental knickknacks. Every year on December 8th, the anniversary of Lennon's murder, Strawberry Fields is packed with his fans, singing Beatles songs and sharing their grief, even after all these years.

Southwest of the Great Lawn is the **Delacorte Theater**, site of the annual free Shakespeare in the Park productions (see the box on p.120 for ticket information). Next door, the tranquil **Shakespeare Garden** claims to hold every species of plant mentioned in the Bard's plays. East of the garden is **Belvedere Castle**, a mock medieval citadel first erected in 1869 as a lookout, but now the home of the Urban Park Rangers (who provide walking tours and educational programs). The highest point in the park, and a wonderful viewpoint, the castle also houses the NY Meteorological Observatory's weather center, which provides the "official" Central Park temperature of the day, and makes for a lovely backdrop for the Delacorte's performances.

The northern park

There are fewer attractions, but more open space, north of the Great Lawn. Much of this area is taken up by the **Reservoir**, at mid-park between 86th and 96th streets (main entrance at 90th St and Fifth Ave), around which disciplined New Yorkers faithfully jog. The raised track is a great place to get breathtaking 360-degree views of the skyline – just don't block any jogger's path or there will be hell to pay. The reservoir once provided New York City's water (a duty now filled by a series of reservoirs in upstate New York) but now serves as a steady water supply to three interlaced Central Park water features: the Harlem Meer, the Pool, and the Loch.

If you see nothing else in the park above 86th Street, don't miss the **Conservatory Garden**, between East 103rd and 106th streets along Fifth Avenue. A great spot to pause for a picnic, this pleasing, six-acre space comprises three formal terraced gardens filled with flowering trees and shrubs, planted flower beds, fanciful fountains, and shaded benches. The main iron-gated entrance at 104th Street and Fifth Avenue is a favorite spot for weekend wedding-party photographs.

Seasonal events and activities

SummerStage concerts are held at the Rumsey Playing Field near 72nd St and 5th Ave (Ⓣ212/360-2777, Ⓦwww.summer-stage.org). **Shakespeare in the Park** takes place at the open-air Delacorte Theater, near the West 81st Street entrance to the park, where tickets are distributed daily at 1pm for that evening's performance – though you'll probably have to get in line well before then. Tickets are also distributed downtown at the Public Theater (425 Lafayette St) between 1pm and 3pm on the day of the performance. Call the Shakespeare Festival (Ⓣ212/539-8750) or visit Ⓦwww.publictheater.org for more information.

New York Philharmonic in the Park (Ⓣ212/875-5709) and **Metropolitan Opera in the Park** (Ⓣ212/362-6000) hold several evenings of classical music in the summer.

Claremont Riding Academy, 175 W 89th St Ⓣ212/724-5100. Mon–Fri 6.30am–10pm, Sat & Sun 6.30am–5pm. Horseback riding lessons are available, as are rentals for riders experienced in the English saddle. $42 for a 30min lesson, $35 for a ride on Central Park's bridlepaths.

The Harlem Meer Festival, 110th St between Fifth and Lenox avenues Ⓣ212/860-1370. Fairly intimate and enjoyable free performances of jazz and salsa music outside the Dana Discovery Center on Sundays from 4 to 6pm throughout the summer.

At the northeast corner of the park is the **Charles A. Dana Discovery Center** (Tues–Sun 10am–5pm, 4pm in winter; Ⓣ212/860-1370), an environmental education and visitor center, with free literature, changing visual exhibits, bird walks every Saturday at 11am in July and August, and multicultural performances (see box, above). Crowds of locals fish in the adjacent **Harlem Meer**, an eleven-acre lake which also serves as home to many of the city's swans and grebes. The center provides free bamboo poles and bait, though you have to release whatever you might catch.

General information

General Park Information ☎212/360-3444; also ☎1-888/ NYPARKS for special events information.

Founded in 1980, the Central Park Conservancy is a nonprofit organization dedicated to preserving and managing the park. It operates four **visitor centers**, with free maps and other helpful literature, as well as special events. All visitor centers are open Tues–Sun from 10am to 5pm: The Dairy (mid-park at 65th St; ☎212/794-6564); Belvedere Castle (mid-park at 79th St; ☎212/772-0210); North Meadow Recreation Center (mid-park at 97th St; also open Mon; ☎212/348-4867); and the Dana Discovery Center (110th St off Fifth Ave; ☎212/860-1370).

Restrooms are available at Heckscher Playground (currently undergoing renovation and due to open again in 2007), the Boat Pond (Conservatory Water), Mineral Springs House (northwest end of Sheep Meadow), Loeb Boathouse, the Delacorte Theater, the North Meadow Recreation Center, The Conservatory Garden, and the Dana Discovery Center.

In case of emergency, use the **emergency call boxes** located throughout the park and along the crosstown vehicle streets that traverse the park (they provide a direct connection to the Central Park Precinct), or dial ☎911 at any pay phone.

15

The Metropolitan Museum of Art

The **Metropolitan Museum of Art**, or the Met, as it's usually called, is the foremost art museum in America. It started in a brownstone downtown before decamping to a larger site in Central Park that Frederick Law Olmsted and Calvert Vaux had initially tagged for a ball field. The building unveiled in 1880 was designed in Gothic Revival–style brick, contrasting with the prevailing notion of the day that a museum should be a magnificent, daunting structure.

The collection takes in over two million works of art and spans the cultures of America, Europe, Africa, the Far East, and the classical and Islamic worlds. Broadly, the museum breaks down into **seven major collections**: European Art – Painting and Sculpture; Asian Art; American Painting and Decorative Arts; Egyptian Antiquities; Medieval Art; Ancient Greek and Roman Art; and the Art of Africa, Oceania, and the Americas. We have also provided an overview of the Met's often-overlooked but nevertheless impressive **modern art** holdings.

The museum also features, at any one time, several **special exhibitions**, usually of very high quality (depending on

METROPOLITAN MUSEUM OF ART

SECOND FLOOR

Modern Art

The American Wing

The American Wing

European Paintings

Musical Instruments

19th Century European Paintings & Sculpture

Drawing, Prints & Photographs

Shop

Japanese Art

Cypriot Art

Asian Art

Chinese Art

Chinese Art

Korean Art

Islamic Art

Ancient Near Eastern Art

Great Hall Balcony

South Asian Art

Chinese Garden Court

Southeast Asian Art

FIRST FLOOR

Elevator to roof garden (seasonal)

The Robert Lehman Collection

CENTRAL PARK

Modern Art

European Sculpture & Decorative Arts

The American Wing

Medieval Art

European Sculpture & Decorative Arts

European Sculpture & Decorative Arts

Arms & Armor

Temple of Dendur

Arts of Africa, Oceania & the Americas

Library

Shop

Grace Rainey Rogers Auditorium

The Sackler Wing

Bar & Café Restaurant Cafeteria

Shop

Greek & Roman Art

Great Hall

Egyptian Art

Egyptian Art

FIFTH AVENUE

FIFTH AVENUE

MAIN ENTRANCE

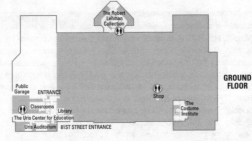

GROUND FLOOR

The Robert Lehman Collection

Public Garage

ENTRANCE

Shop

Classrooms

Library

The Costume Institute

The Uris Center for Education

Uris Auditorium

81ST STREET ENTRANCE

the exhibit, admission may or may not be included in the Met's suggested admission price). The exhibits range from single-artist retrospectives to intelligently curated surveys of the permanent collection. Recent and forthcoming exhibits include retrospectives of surrealist Max Ernst, romantic landscape painter Samuel Palmer, and medieval man of the cloth Fra Angelico, as well as sculptures by architect Santiago Calatrava and drawings by Van Gogh.

There is one **main entrance** to the museum, and once you've passed through it you find yourself in the **Great Hall**, a deftly lit Neoclassical cavern where you can consult plans, check tours, and pick up info on the Met's excellent lecture listings. Directly ahead is the Grand Staircase, which leads to, for many visitors, the single greatest attraction – the European Painting galleries. Make sure you pick up the detailed room-by-room gallery maps for the European Painting and Nineteenth-Century Painting collections, available at the **main information desk** in the Great Hall.

Note that the Met is currently undergoing some major **renovations**, mostly centered on the Neoclassical interior courtyard on its southern edge facing Fifth Avenue. This spot served as a restaurant until 2003, when the eatery was moved elsewhere; now, the space is set for conversion into a sculpture space to display much of the museum's Roman holdings and is set to open in 2007.

Museum practicalities

Map 8, H8. Fifth Ave, at 82nd, set into Central Park. Tues–Thurs & Sun 9.30am–5.30pm, Fri & Sat 9.30am–9pm; suggested admission $15, seniors $10, students $7 (includes admission to the Cloisters on the same day; see p.157); audio guide tours of the major collections and visiting exhibitions $6; free conducted tours, "Highlights of the Met," daily; also highly detailed tours of specific galleries; several restaurants and excellent book and gift shops; ☏212/879-5500 or 535-7710 for recorded information; ⓦwww.metmuseum.org. #4, #5, or #6 to 86th Street.

European Art

The Met's **European Art** galleries, located on the second floor, are at their best in the Dutch painting section, with major works of Rembrandt (a superb *Self-Portrait*), Hals, and especially Vermeer, whose *Young Woman with a Water Jug* and *A Girl Asleep* display the artist at his most complex and the Met at its most fortunate. Continue on, and as you loop back to the entrance to the painting galleries you'll pass through another smattering of works by Spanish, French, and Italian painters, most notably Goya and Velázquez. The latter's piercing and somber *Portrait of Juan de Pareja* shouldn't be missed. A whole room is dedicated to the formidable works of El Greco. His extraordinary *View of Toledo* – all brooding intensity as the skies seem about to swallow up the ghost-like town – is perhaps the best of his works anywhere in the world.

The **Italian Renaissance** isn't spectacularly represented, but there's a worthy selection from the various schools; these works consist largely of narrative panels or altarpieces, and gold paint is often used, either for the background or for the haloes of the religious figures. Highlights include an early tempera on wood by Raphael, *Madonna and Child Enthroned with Saints*; a late Botticelli (the crisply linear *Three Miracles of Saint Zenobius*); Filippo Lippi's grandiose, fresco-inspired *Madonna and Child Enthroned with Two Angels*; and Michele de Verona's handsome *Madonna and Child with the Infant John the Baptist*, in which the characters are almost sculpturally rendered.

Impressionist and Post-Impressionist painting

On its second floor the Met has a stunning array of **Impressionist** and **Post-Impressionist** art. Chief works include Manet's *Young Lady in 1866*, an eerie, sepia-toned rendering of a maniacal-looking woman with her parrot; Courbet's crisply pastoral *Young Ladies of the Village*; and one of Degas' beautiful, shadowy ballet works, *Dancers Practicing at the Bar*. Three superb works by Monet – *Rouen Cathedral*, where the same subject was painted at different hours of the day; his rendering of a quintessentially urban Albion, *The Houses of Parliament (Effect of Fog)*; and, done in oils, his watery, ethereal *The Doge's Palace Seen from San Giorgio Maggiore* – show the beginnings of his final phase of near-abstract Impressionism.

Renoir is perhaps the best represented among the remaining Impressionists, though his most important work here dates from 1878, when he began to move away from the mainstream techniques he'd learned while working with Monet. *Mme Charpentier and Her Children* is a likeable enough piece, one whose affectionate tone manages to sidestep the sentimentality of Renoir's later work. Finally, also here is Cézanne's masterpiece **The Card Players**, the second in a series of five paintings all dealing with the same scene. Yet all of this scratches little more than the surface of the galleries. Look out as well for major works by Van Gogh (including **Irises**, **Woman of Arles**, and **Sunflowers**), Rousseau, Bonnard, Pissarro, and Seurat.

Modern Art

The Met's **modern art** collection, housed on the second-floor Lila Acheson Wallace Wing, is a fascinating and relatively compact group of paintings. Picasso's *Portrait of Gertrude Stein*, a labor of love that took ninety sittings and almost two years to complete, and his blue-period *The Blind Man's Meal* are here, alongside works by Klee, Modigliani, Braque, and Klimt. Other highlights include O'Keeffe's sumptuous, erotic *Black Iris*, Pollock's disorienting, layered *Autumn Rhythm (Number 30)*, and Warhol's *Last Self-Portrait*, which dates from 1986.

The Cantor Roof Garden

From May through October, you can ascend to the **Cantor Roof Garden** (accessible by elevator from the first floor) on top of the Wallace Wing, which displays **contemporary sculpture** against the dramatic backdrop of New York's Midtown skyline. In October this is a great place to see the colorful fall foliage in Central Park. Drinks and snacks are available, perhaps on the expensive side, though the breathtaking views make up for it.

Asian Art

The second floor's **Asian Art** galleries gather an impressive and vast array of Chinese, Japanese, Indian, and Southeast Asian sculpture, painting, ceramics, and metalwork, as well as an indoor replica of a Chinese garden. Fourteen recently renovated and expanded galleries showcase Chinese painting, calligraphy, jade, lacquer, and textiles, making this collection one of the largest in the world. It has incredible Edo-period works, including a beautiful pair of gold-leaf folding screens by Kôrin (*Eight Planked Bridge*); Sansetu's *The Old Plum*; and Hokusai's *The Great Wave at Kanagawa*, rumored to have been a major source of inspiration for both Debussy and Rilke. Much more ancient beauty is to be found in the fourth-century Buddhist shrine from Pakistan and in the tenth-century Indian *Standing Pavarti* statue.

The highlight is the **Chinese Garden Court**, a serene, minimalist retreat enclosed by the galleries, and the adjacent **Ming Room**, a typical salon decorated in Ming-period style with wooden lattice doors. The naturally lit garden is representative of one found in Chinese homes – a pagoda, small waterfall, and stocked goldfish pond landscaped by limestone rocks, trees, and shrubs conjure up a palpable sense of peace.

American Painting

The **American Painting** galleries, on the second floor of the American Wing, begin in a maze of rooms filled with eighteenth-century portraits (look out for the heroics of Leutzes's *Washington Crossing the Delaware*) and continues with West's allegorical *The Triumph of Love* and the nineteenth-century landscape painters of the Hudson Valley School, who glorified the land in their vast lyrical canvases. Cole, the school's doyen, is represented by *The Oxbow*, his pupil Church by an immense *Heart of the Andes*, combining the mountains' grand sweep with minutely depicted flora. Also here are several striking portraits by Sargent including the magnificent *Portrait of Madam X*.

Winslow Homer is allowed most of a gallery to himself – fittingly for a painter who so greatly influenced the late nineteenth-century artistic scene in America. Homer began his career illustrating the day-to-day realities of the Civil War – there's a good selection here that shows the tedium and sadness of that era. His talent in recording detail carried over into his late, quasi-Impressionistic studies of seascapes, of which the explosive, spuming **Northeaster** is one of the finest.

Medieval Art

Although you could move straight to the **medieval art** from the American Wing, you'd miss out on the museum's carefully planned approach. Instead, enter these galleries via the corridor from the western end (or rear) of the Great Hall on the left of the main staircase. There you'll see displays of sumptuous Byzantine metalwork and jewelry, donated by financier J.P. Morgan. At the end of the corridor is the main sculpture hall, piled high with religious statuary and carvings like a tremendous *St Nicholas Saving Three Boys in the Brine Tub*; it's divided by a 52-foot-high *reja* – a decorative, open-work iron altar screen – from Valladolid Cathedral.

To the right of the hall, the **medieval treasury** has a magnificent and all-embracing display of objects religious, liturgical, and secular. And beyond are the **Jack and Belle Linski Galleries**: Flemish, Florentine, and Venetian painting, porcelain, and bronzes.

Ancient Greek and Roman Art

This is one of the largest collections of **ancient art** in the world, which is set to decamp to new quarters at the museum's southeastern corner by 2007. In the meantime, the collection is exhibited in eight galleries on the first floor. Enter from the southern end of the museum's Great Hall, and you'll soon find yourself in the **Belfer Court**, a sort of preamble to the exhibit. The court displays prehistoric and early Greek art, such as a fanciful **Minoan vase** in the shape of a bull's head from around 1400 BC. The central hall, which displays sixth- to fourth-century BC marble sculpture including several large sphinxes, is flanked by three rooms on either side, each with exhibits arranged by theme, medium, and chronology. You'll find everything from large **funerary monuments** to tiny terracotta figures to intricately carved gold jewelry in the same room.

Egyptian Antiquities

The **Egyptian Antiquities** collection, to the north end of the Great Hall, holds 35,000 objects and nearly all are on lavish display. The large statuary are the most immediately striking of the exhibits, but it's the smaller sculptural pieces that hold the attention longest. Look out for the dazzling collection of Princess Sit-hathor-yunet's jewelry, a pinnacle in Egyptian decorative art that dates from around 1830 BC. Most striking of all is the Temple of Dendur, a complete fifteenth-century (BC) temple; marvelously lit up at night, it was moved here during the construction of the Aswan High Dam in 1965.

Arts of Africa, Oceania, and the Americas

The Rockefeller Wing holds the Met's comprehensive collection of art from **Africa, Oceania, and the Americas**. It's a superb set of galleries, the muted, understated decor throwing the exhibits into sharp and often dramatic focus. The African exhibit has a particularly awe-inspiring display of art from the Court of Benin in present-day Nigeria: tiny carved-ivory statues and vessels, created with astonishing detail. The Oceanic collection covers the islands of Melanesia, Micronesia, Polynesia, New Zealand, and Australia, and contains a wide array of objects such as wild, somewhat frightening wooden masks with piercing, all-too-realistic eyes. Lastly, highlights of the American works include thousands-of-years-old masks, ancestor figures, and other statues from Mexico, exquisitely-crafted pendants from Colombia and Panama, and bottles, drums, and tunics from Peru.

16

The Upper East Side

The defining characteristic of Manhattan's **Upper East Side**, a two-square-mile grid scored with the great avenues of **Madison**, **Park**, and **Lexington**, is wealth. While other neighborhoods are affected by incursions of immigrant groups, artistic trends, and the like, this remains primarily an enclave of the well-off, with tony shops, clean and safe streets, and well-preserved buildings and landmarks. It also has some of the city's finest museums, all in a compact strip running on or near **Fifth Avenue**, known as **Museum Mile**: the Frick Collection and the Guggenheim are the best (and best known), though the Whitney Museum of American Art, the Jewish Museum, the Neue Galerie, and the Museum of the City of New York each command attention.

Along Fifth Avenue

Fifth Avenue – which, as it progresses northward, becomes the aforementioned Museum Mile – has been the haughty patrician face of Manhattan since the opening of Central Park in 1876 lured the Carnegies, Astors, Vanderbilts,

Whitneys, and other notable New York capitalists up from lower Fifth Avenue and Gramercy Park to build their fashionable Neoclassical residences along the park's eastern edge. A great deal of what you see along this stretch, though, is third- or fourth-generation construction. Through the latter part of the nineteenth century, fanciful mansions were built at vast expense, to stand only ten or fifteen years before being demolished for even wilder extravagances or, more commonly – as rocketing land values made the chance of selling at vast profit irresistible – grand apartment blocks.

Grand Army Plaza to the Frick

Grand Army Plaza (Map 7, H5) is the southernmost point of introduction to all this, an oval at the junction of Central Park South and Fifth Avenue that marks the division between Fifth as a shopping district to the south and a residential boulevard to the north. This is one of the city's most dramatic public spaces, boasting a fountain and a gold statue of Civil War victor General Sherman, and flanked by the extended copper-lined chateau of the **Plaza Hotel**, which is undergoing renovations until 2007. The darkened, swooping, television-screen facade of the **Solow Building** and two more hotels, the high-necked *Sherry Netherland* and the *Pierre*, luxuriate nearby. Many of the rooms here have permanent guests; needless to say, they're not on welfare.

Up six blocks from Grand Army Plaza, on the corner of Fifth Avenue and 65th Street, America's largest Reformed synagogue, the **Temple Emanu-El** (Map 7, H4; Mon–Fri & Sun 9am–5pm) strikes a sober aspect, a brooding Romanesque–Byzantine cavern that manages to be bigger inside than it seems out. Once within, the interior melts away into mysterious darkness, making you feel very small indeed.

The Frick Collection

Map 7, H3. 1 E 70th St. Tues–Sat 10am–6pm, Sun 1–6pm; $12, seniors $8, students $5, under-10s not admitted; ☎212/288-0700,

ⓦ www.frickcollection.org. A 22min AV presentation is given every hour on the half-hour. #6 to 68th Street/Hunter College.

Housed in Henry Clay Frick's eighteenth-century-style former mansion, the immensely enjoyable **Frick Collection** comprises the art treasures hoarded by this most ruthless and hated of New York's robber barons. However, the legacy of Frick's ill-gotten gains is a superb collection of works, and as good a glimpse of the sumptuous life enjoyed by New York's early industrialists as you'll find.

Opened in the mid-1930s, the museum has been largely kept as it looked when the Fricks lived there. Much of the furniture is heavy eighteenth-century French, but the nice thing about the place – and many people rank the Frick as their favorite New York gallery for this reason – is that it strives hard to be as unlike a museum as possible. The furnishings and pictures create an intimate interior, making the visitor feel like a high-class voyeur, peeping into private lives from another era. This intimacy is carried over into the architecture, with Frick's collection stretching from the grandiose, English country-house style of the West Gallery to the airy Fragonard Room and the richly wooded Living Hall, filled with masterpieces by the likes of Titian and Holbein.

There's a magnificent array of works here by Rembrandt (including a set of piercing *Self-Portraits*), Goya, and Whistler, as well as an early (and suggestive) Vermeer, *Officer and Laughing Girl*, and one of van Eyck's last works, a *Virgin and Child*. The **West Gallery**, where the former two paintings are located, is the Frick's major draw, holding some of its finest works in a truly magnificent setting, a long, elegant room with a concave glass ceiling and ornately carved wood trim. Two Turners, views of Cologne and Dieppe, hang opposite one another, each a blaze of orange and creamy tones; van Dyck pitches in with a couple of uncharacteristically informal portraits of Frans Snyders and his wife – two paintings reunited only when Frick purchased them; there are several austere, somewhat generic portraits by Frans Hals; and El

Greco dazzles with *Vincenzo Anastagi*, a stunning portrait of a Spanish soldier resplendent in green velvet and armor. Lastly, Piero della Francesca's enormous *St John the Evangelist* presides over the space, framed by the arched entryway to the Enamel Room.

The Neue Galerie

Map 8, H7. 1048 5th Ave, at 86th. Sat, Sun & Mon 11am–6pm, Fri 11am–9pm; $15, seniors and students $10, under-12s not admitted; ☎212/423-3500, ⊛www.neuegalerie.org. #4, #5, or #6 to 86th Street.

A Museum Mile newcomer, the small **Neue Galerie** is an elegant, two-tiered celebration of early twentieth-century German and Austrian art and design housed in a landmark building by architects Carrère and Hastings (who designed the New York Public Library). A welcome addition to the city's museums, it boasts an exceptional collection of turn-of-the-century Viennese fine and decorative arts on the second floor, with work such as Klimt's beautifully complex *The Dancer* and Schiele's terrifyingly stark *Self Portrait with Arm Twisted above Head*, as well as works by Hofmann and Wagner. The Germans get their turn on the third floor, where the collection features new objectivist masterworks like Max Beckmann's profound and upsetting *Self-Portrait in Front of Red Curtain*, which disturbed one contemporary viewer so much that he stabbed the painting with a knife. Rounding out the third-floor German collection are pieces by Klee, Kandinsky, and Dix, as well as a stunning representation of the various incarnations of Bauhaus.

The Guggenheim Museum

Map 8, H7. 1071 5th Ave, at 89th. Sat–Wed 10am–6pm, Fri 10am–8pm; $15, seniors and students $10, under-12s free, Fri 6–8pm pay what you wish; ☎212/423-3500, ⊛www.guggenheim.org. #4, #5, or #6 to 86th Street.

Whatever you think of the **Guggenheim Museum**'s collection of paintings, it's the upturned beehive building designed by Frank Lloyd Wright that steals the show, looking wildly out of place amid Fifth Avenue's solemn facades. Based on an inverted ziggurat, or Babylonian temple, the museum was commissioned in 1934 but was not finished until 1959, after the architect's death. Whereas most other museums sweep visitors in and immediately barrage them with visuals, ushering them from gallery to gallery, Wright's Guggenheim was designed for the leisurely contemplation of art.

In the first half of the twentieth century, the museum's founder, Solomon Guggenheim, was one of America's richest men and a frenetic collector of modern painting who bought wholesale the works of Kandinsky, Chagall, Klee, Léger, and others, exhibiting them as his Museum of Non-Objective Painting to a bemused American public. Subsequent additions include masterworks by Cézanne, Degas, Gauguin, Manet, Toulouse-Lautrec, Van Gogh, and Picasso, greatly enhancing the museum's Impressionist and Post-Impressionist holdings. Much of the Kandinsky is usually on display, along with hefty selections of Picasso, Chagall, and Cézanne. Two hundred photographs by Robert Mapplethorpe, meanwhile, are housed in the fourth floor's Mapplethorpe Gallery.

Since the circular galleries increase upward at a not-so-gentle slope, you should start at the top of the museum and work your way down; most of the temporary **special exhibits** are planned that way. These include historical and single-artist retrospectives such as Matthew Barney's *Cremaster* cycle and 2005's Russia!, the most comprehensive showing of Russian art ever in the US, as well as thematic collections, nation-specific modern art, and more.

The Jewish Museum

Map 8, H6. 1109 5th Ave, at 92nd. Sun–Wed 11am–5.45pm, Thurs 11am–9pm, Fri 11am–3pm; $10, students and seniors $7.50, under-12s free, free Tues 5–9pm; ☎212/423-3200, ⓦwww.jewishmuseum .org. #4, #5, or #6 to 96th Street.

The centerpiece of the **Jewish Museum**, the largest museum of Judaica outside of Israel, is a permanent exhibition that seeks to answer the question, "What constitutes the essence of Jewish identity?" via a presentation of the people's basic ideas, values, and culture as developed over four thousand years. A collection of Hanukkah lamps is one highlight, though more vibrant are the changing displays of works by major international artists and theme exhibitions. Forthcoming shows include the first-ever major museum exhibit devoted to Sarah Bernhardt, featuring painting, sculpture, stage design, costumes, jewelery, and other personal effects. The Jewish Museum also sponsors a varied media program, including a **film festival**, which takes place for two weeks each mid-January and highlights new and exciting work by up-and-coming filmmakers alongside screenings of digitally restored historical prints. See the museum's website for more information on the festival.

Museum of the City of New York

Map 8, H3. 1220 5th Ave, at 103rd. Tues–Sun 10am–5pm, Tues 10am–2pm for pre-registered tour groups only; suggested donation $7, students $4, families $12; ⓣ212/534-1672, Ⓦwww.mcny.org. #6 to 103rd Street.

Spaciously housed in a neo-Georgian mansion, the permanent collection of the **Museum of the City of New York** provides a thorough, fascinating history of the city from Dutch times to the present. Prints, photographs, costumes, and furniture are displayed across four floors, and a film about the city's history runs continuously. Permanent exhibits include "New York Toy Stories," an engaging trip from the late-1800s to today that consists of all manner of motion toys, board games, sports equipment, and dollhouses. Covering the same timeframe is an intriguing collection of costumes, screenplays, props, and more that form the John Golden Archive of theater history. Casual, time-pressed visitors may choose to skip this museum in favor of the bigger names, but for those interested in the city's mythology, the MCNY is a must-see.

Museo del Barrio

Map 8, H3. 1230 5th Ave, at 104th. Wed–Sun 11am–5pm, closed Mon & Tues; suggested donation $6, students and seniors $4, Thurs seniors free; ℡212/831-7272, Ⓦwww.elmuseo.org. #6 to 103rd Street.

Literally translated as "the neighborhood museum," the **Museo del Barrio** was founded in 1969 by a group of Puerto Rican parents, educators, and artists from Spanish Harlem who wanted to teach their children about their roots. Initially settled by Italians, Spanish Harlem has more recently become a nexus of expat Puerto Rican and Mexican life. The area, which stretches for thirty blocks uptown from 100th Street, and across town from Central Park to the Harlem River, has seen it all, from riots in the 1960s and 70s to the crack epidemic of the 1980s, and the panic around the initial outbreak of AIDS.

Even as the neighborhood currently experiences white yuppie overflow from the Upper East Side, the museum remains popular and largely Puerto Rican, though it now embraces the whole of Latin America and the Caribbean. Each year there are five major loan exhibitions of painting, photographs, and crafts, by both traditional and emerging artists. The permanent collection, on the other hand, boasts a particularly impressive history of the Puerto Rican print industry, early pre-Columbian Caribbean ceremonial objects, an outstanding collection of *santos de palo* (carved wooden saints used for prayer), and more recent sculpture and multimedia work.

Along Madison Avenue

Immediately east of Fifth Avenue lies **Madison Avenue**, a strip that was entirely residential until the 1920s. Today it's mainly an elegant shopping and advertising street, lined with top-notch designer clothes stores, some of whose doors are kept locked, and high-powered ad execs huddled in think-tanks on the floors above. The only key sight along its Upper East Side stretch is the **Whitney Museum of American Art**.

Whitney Museum of American Art

Map 7, I2. 945 Madison Ave, at 75th. Wed, Thurs, Sat & Sun 11am–6pm, Fri 1–9pm; $12, seniors and students $9.50, Fri 6–9pm pay what you wish; ☎212/570-3600, ⓦwww.whitney.org. Excellent free gallery talks Wed–Sun, call for times. #6 to 77th Street.

Located in a heavy, arsenal-like building, the **Whitney Museum of American Art** is a great forum for one of the pre-eminent collections of twentieth- and twenty-first-century American art. The museum owns over 12,000 paintings, sculptures, photographs, and films, the best overview of which is contained in the "Highlights of the Permanent Collection," situated in the Lauder Galleries on the fifth floor and the Lee Galleries on the second.

The collection is particularly strong on Hopper, and several of his best paintings are here: *Early Sun Morning* is typical, a bleak urban landscape, uneasily tense in its lighting and rejection of topical detail. Other major bequests include a significant number of works by Avery, Demuth, and O'Keeffe (don't miss her spectacular small watercolor *Morning Sky*), and a major collection of Calder, including his perennially popular *Calder's Circus*, a replica of a real circus complete with animals and acrobats, in the artist's typically whimsical wire style. The Abstract Expressionists are featured strongly, with great works such as Pollock's deeply textured *Number 27, 1950*, Louise Bourgeois' haunting postwar sculpture *Quarantania*, and De Kooning's catastrophically coherent *Woman and Bicycle*. Somewhat calmer are pieces by Warhol, Johns (the deceptively simple nationalist dissent of *Three Flags* is a standout), and Oldenburg, whose *Soft Sculptures* are vinyl-type material reconstructions of everyday objects.

Finally, every other year there is an exhibition – the **Whitney Biennial** – designed to give a provocative overview of what's happening in contemporary American art. It is often panned by critics (sometimes for good reason) but always packed with visitors. Catch it if you can between March and June in even-numbered years.

Along Park Avenue

A block east from Madison, **Park Avenue** is stolidly comfortable and often elegant. Where Park runs through the Upper East Side, it's especially known for the dozens of swish apartment blocks that line each side – look for the uniformed doormen dotting the sidewalk, the sleek black town cars idling with their drivers still inside, and the Chanel-suited women who periodically emerge. Aside from such glimpses of Manhattan's moneyed elite, it's worth wandering down Park for the sweeping view south, where it coasts down to the hulking New York Central and Met Life buildings.

Park's twin arteries sandwich a lush green median – in the low 90s, look for the large black shapes of the Louise Nevelson **sculptures** dotted on the traffic islands. Just above 96th Street the neighborhood rather joltingly transitions from blocks of quiet, moneyed apartment buildings to **Spanish Harlem** at the point where the subway line emerges from underground.

Lower down on Park, the hulking, fortress-like **Seventh Regiment Armory** (Map 7, I4) dominates a full square block between 66th and 67th streets. Built in the 1870s with pseudo-medieval crenellations, it's the only surviving building from the era before the New York Central's railroad tracks were roofed over and Park Avenue became an upscale residential neighborhood. There are two surviving nineteenth-century interiors here, and they are amongst the finest in the US. These are the Veterans' Room and the

Library, both designed by a group of artists working under Louis Comfort Tiffany and featuring an amalgam of Greek, Moresque, Celtic, Persian, and Japanese influences. The glasswork is exquisite and there are no fewer than five Tiffany stained-glass windows; particularly of note is the peacock-blue of the fireplace wall, standing out as a testament to the play of fire and light. To see inside the armory, which today plays host to frequent art and antique shows, you must call ahead to arrange a **tour** (℡212/744-8180).

Asia Society Museum

Map 7, I3. 725 Park Ave, at 70th. Tues–Sun 11am–6pm, Fri until 9pm (except July–Sept); $10, seniors $7, students $5, free Fri 6–9pm; ℡212/288-6400, ⓦwww.asiasocietymuseum.org . #6 to 68th Street.

A prominent educational resource on Asia founded by John D. Rockefeller III, the **Asia Society** offers an exhibition space dedicated to both traditional and contemporary art from all over Asia; in addition to the usually worthwhile temporary exhibits, intriguing performances, political round-tables, lectures, films, and free events are frequently held. The permanent collection features a relatively small but highly impressive trove of treasures from Korea, Japan, Southeast Asia, China, Mongolia, and the Himalayas. Highlights include late sixth- and eighth-century Buddhas and a first-century Shiva from India, along with Tibetan, Thai, Japanese, and Nepalese Bodhisattvas, sublime Japanese earthenware from the Edo period, and Ming vases from China.

Lexington Avenue and east

Lexington Avenue – or just "Lex" – is Madison Avenue without the class; as the west became richer, property developers rushed to slick up real estate in the east. Much of the East 60s and 70s now house young, unattached, and upwardly mobile professionals, as the number of "happening" singles bars along Second and Third avenues will attest.

Bloomingdale's, a much more upscale version of Macy's in Midtown, provides retail therapy for those in sartorial need, while culture, of a rarefied kind, can be found under the auspices of the **Mount Vernon Hotel Museum and Garden** and the **Gracie Mansion**.

The Mount Vernon Hotel Museum and Garden

Map 7, L5. 421 E 61st St, between York and First. Tues–Sun 11am–4pm, Tues in June & July until 9pm, closed Aug; $8, students and seniors $5, under-12s free; ☎212/838-6878, ⓦwww.mvhm.org. #N, #R, #W, #4, #5, or #6 to Lexington Avenue/59th Street.

Several long blocks east of Lex, the **Mount Vernon Hotel Museum and Garden** is a Federal-period structure that has been restored by the Colonial Dames of America, a society founded by women in 1890 to preserve American cultural heritage and history, and to commemorate the original thirteen colonies. The furnishings, knickknacks, and the serene little park out back are more engaging than the house itself, but there's an odd sort of pull to the place if you're lucky enough to be guided around by a chattily urbane Colonial Dame.

Gracie Mansion

Map 8, N7. East End Ave, at 88th. Tours on Wed only; $7, seniors $4, afternoon tea $25; ☎212/570-4751. #4, #5, or #6 to 86th Street.

Much further north and a good hike from the subway, nearly all the way to the East River, **Gracie Mansion** was built in 1799 as a country manor house. It is one of the best-preserved colonial buildings in the city, and today features several objects on loan from MoMA and the New-York Historical Society. As the official residence of the mayor of New York City from 1942 to 2002, its residents have included everyone from Fiorello LaGuardia to Rudy Giuliani. No longer, though: Gracie is now known as the "Peoples' House," meaning that both the public and visiting dignitaries can make use of what was, for a long time, the mayor's private home. Gracie is open for tours (which must be booked well in advance) every Wednesday at 10am, 11am, 1pm, and 2pm, when visitors will be treated to New York lore and detailed information about the design and artisanship of the mansion's many fine examples of nineteenth-century craftsmanship: cabinetry, furniture, lighting fixtures, and so on, mostly in the Federal architectural style.

17

The Upper West Side and Morningside Heights

The **Upper West Side** has always had a more unbuttoned vibe than its counterpart across the park. It is one of the city's most desirable addresses, and tends to attract what might be called New York's cultural elite and new-money types – musicians, writers, journalists, curators, and the like – though there is also a small but visible homeless presence.

The Upper West Side is bordered by Central Park to the east, the Hudson River to the west, Columbus Circle at 59th Street to the south, and 110th Street (the upper boundary of Central Park) to the north. The main commercial artery is

Broadway and, generally speaking, the further you stray east or west the more wealthy (and residential) things become, until you reach the pinnacle of prosperity, the historic apartment buildings of Central Park West and Riverside Drive. **Lincoln Center**, New York's most prestigious palace of performing arts, lies in the region's southern streets, and along with the superlative **American Museum of Natural History**, are the Upper West Side's greatest attractions. North of 110th Street finds you in the neighborhood of **Morningside Heights**, home to the Cathedral Church of St John the Divine and Columbia University.

Columbus Circle and around

Map 7, E5. #A, #B, #C, #D, or #1 to 59th Street/Columbus Circle.

Columbus Circle, at the intersection of Broadway, Central Park West, and 59th Street, is a pedestrian's worst nightmare but a good place to start investigating the Upper West Side nonetheless. Once here, you'll immediately spy the glittering *Trump International Hotel* – touted as "The World's Most Prestigious Address," it's just one of the more recent examples of Donald Trump's extraordinary hubris.

Also soaring skyward from Columbus Circle is the controversial **Time Warner Center**, the gleaming twin-towered edifice that replaced the former Coliseum in 2004. It now houses Lincoln Center's jazz facilities, luxury apartments, Time Warner's HQ, a great Whole Foods supermarket, and the *Mandarin Oriental Hotel* (see review, p.193), whose 35th-floor lobby proffers one of the best views of Midtown. The building is also home to a New York specialty: very exclusive restaurants. Highlights include Thomas Keller's (of California's *French Laundry* fame) *Per Se* and the tiny Japanese restaurant *Masa*, with tasting menus from $300–500 per person.

For relief from all this high-rise glitz, go west a few blocks and contemplate the **Church of St Paul the Apostle**, on Ninth Avenue between 59th and 60th, a beautiful Old Gothic structure with Byzantine basilica features.

Lincoln Center

Map 7, D4. 9th Ave, betwen 63rd and 66th. ☎212/875-5456, Ⓦwww
.lincolncenter.org. #1 to 66th Street/Lincoln Center.

Broadway continues north from Columbus Circle to the
Lincoln Center for the Performing Arts, an imposing group of buildings arranged around a large plaza and
fountain. Built in the mid-1960s on a site that formerly held
some of the city's poorest slums, Lincoln Center is home to
the Metropolitan Opera and the New York Philharmonic, as
well as a host of other smaller companies. See pp.265–266 for
ticket information. Lincoln Center also hosts a variety of free
entertainment, ranging from the Autumn Crafts Fair in early
September to folk and jazz bands at lunchtime throughout
the summer; call the phone number listed above for details.

The New York State Theater and Avery Fisher Hall

On the south side of Lincoln Center's plaza, the spare and
elegant **New York State Theater** (☎212/870-5570) is home
to the New York City Ballet, the New York City Opera, and
the famed annual December performances of *The Nutcracker
Suite*. The ballet season runs from late November through
February, and from early April through June; the opera season
starts in July and runs through mid-November.

Avery Fisher Hall (☎212/875-5030), on the north side
of the plaza, does not possess the magnificence of the auditorium across the way, and the most exciting thing about the
hall is its foyer, dominated by a huge hanging sculpture. The
New York Philharmonic performs here from September
through May; the less expensive Mostly Mozart concerts
take place here in July and August.

The Metropolitan Opera House

Tours daily Oct–June at 3.30pm, also Sat at 10.30am; $10, $5 for students; ☎212/362-6000, Ⓦwww.metoperafamily.org.

Like the museum (see p.122), the **Metropolitan Opera House** is also known as "the Met." Home to one of the best opera companies in the world, this is the focal point of Lincoln Center's plaza, with enormous crystal chandeliers and red-carpeted staircases designed for grand entrances in gliding eveningwear. Behind two of the high-arched windows hang **murals** by Marc Chagall, adding to the opera house's elegant, opulent interior.

The rest of Lincoln Center

To the south of the Met lies Damrosch Park, a large space with rows of chairs facing the Guggenheim Bandshell, where you can catch free summer lunchtime concerts and various performances. To the north, you'll find a lovely, smaller plaza facing the Vivian Beaumont Theater, where top Broadway musicals and plays are performed. Across 66th Street is Alice Tully Hall, a recital hall that houses the Chamber Music Society of Lincoln Center, and the Walter E. Reade Theater, which features foreign films and retrospectives and, together with Avery Fisher and Alice Tully halls, hosts the annual **New York Film Festival** in September (see p.305). The famed Juilliard School of Music is in an adjacent building.

Broadway

On Broadway at 72nd, tiny, triangular Verdi Square (featuring a craggy statue in the likeness of the composer) makes a fine place to take a break from Lincoln Center's modernist marvels. From the square, you can fully appreciate the ornate balconies, round corner towers, and cupolas of the **Ansonia Hotel**, 2109 Broadway, at West 73rd. Never actually a hotel (it was planned as upscale apartments), the Ansonia was completed in 1904; the dramatic Beaux-Arts building is still today the artsy *grand dame* of the Upper West Side.

The turnover of commercial establishments in this neighborhood is often astounding, but one stalwart is **Zabar's**, at

2254 Broadway, between 80th and 81st streets (Map 8, B9). The Upper West Side's principal gourmet shop, this area landmark offers more or less anything connected with food.

A couple of blocks north, at 212 W 83rd St, between Broadway and Amsterdam, the **Children's Museum of Manhattan** (Map 8, C8; June to early Sept 10am–5pm, Sept to mid-June Wed–Sun 10am–5pm; children and adults $5, under-1s free; ☎212/721-1234, ⊛www .cmom.org) offers interactive exhibits that stimulate learning, in a fun, relaxed environment for kids (and babies). The Dr. Seuss exhibit and the storytelling room (filled with books from which kids can choose) are perennial winners. For more on what to do with children in New York, see Chapter 31, "Kids' New York."

Central Park West

All along **Central Park West** there are monolithic, mansion-inspired apartment complexes, mostly dating from the early twentieth century, which rim the edge of the park and hog the best of the views. Between 71st and 72nd streets, you'll find the fittingly named **Majestic** (Map 7, E2). Thrown up in 1930, this gigantic Art-Deco landmark is best known for its twin towers and avant-garde brickwork.

The next block north houses the most famous apartment building of all: the **Dakota**, 1 W 72nd St (Map 7, E2), with its turrets, gables, and other odd details, was built in 1884 to persuade wealthy New Yorkers that life in an apartment could be just as luxurious as in a private house. Over the years there have been few residents here not publicly known in some way: big-time tenants included Lauren Bacall and Leonard Bernstein, and in the 1960s the building was used as the setting for Roman Polanski's film *Rosemary's Baby*. But perhaps the most famous resident of the Dakota was **John Lennon**, who was murdered outside the building on the night of December 8, 1980, by Mark David Chapman. His wife, Yoko Ono, still lives here, and Lennon himself is remembered in a memorial plaza just across the street in Central Park; see p.118.

Continue north to the **San Remo**, 145–146 Central Park West, at 74th (Map 7, E2). Another apartment complex, this one dates from 1930 and is one of the most significant components of the skyline here: its ornate twin towers topped by columned, mock-Roman temples are visible from most points in the park.

New-York Historical Society

Map 7, E1. 170 Central Park West, at 77th. Tues–Sun 10am–6pm; $10, students and seniors $5, children free; ☎212/873-3400, Ⓦwww .nyhistory.org. #B or #C to 81st Street–Museum of Natural History.

The often-overlooked **New-York Historical Society** is more a museum of American than New York history, and its temporary exhibitions are more daring than you'd expect, mixing high and low culture with intelligence and flair. On the second floor, **James Audubon**, the Harlem artist and naturalist who specialized in lovingly detailed watercolors of birds, is the focus of one room (the collection holds all 432 original watercolors of Audubon's *Birds of America*); other galleries hold a broad sweep of nineteenth-century American painting.

The American Museum of Natural History

Map 8, E9. Central Park West, at 79th. Museum open daily 10am–5.45pm, Rose Center open Mon–Thurs 10am–5.45pm, Fri until 8.45pm; suggested donation (including the Rose Center) $13, students/seniors $10, children $7.50; IMAX films, the Hayden Planetarium, and certain special exhibits cost extra; ☎212/769-5100, Ⓦwww.amnh.org. #B or #C to 81st Street–Museum of Natural History.

An enormous complex of buildings full of fossils, gems, skeletons, and other natural specimens, along with a wealth of man-made artifacts from indigenous cultures worldwide, the **American Museum of Natural History** is one of the best and largest museums of its kind, with 32 million items on display. There's a fantastic amount to see, but be selective: depending on your interests, anything from a highly discriminating couple of hours to half a day should be ample.

On the second (entry-level) floor are the Hall of Asian People and Hall of African People, each filled with fascinating art and artifacts. Another highlight of this floor is the lower half of the **Hall of African Mammals** – don't miss (though how can you?) the life-sized family of elephants in the center of the room.

The fourth floor is almost entirely taken up with the wildly popular **Dinosaur Exhibit**; covering five spacious, well-lit, and well-designed halls, it is the largest collection in the world, with more than 120 specimens on display.

On the first floor, the Hall of Gems and Minerals includes some strikingly beautiful crystals – not least the Star of India, the largest blue sapphire ever found. More captivating, however, is the new **Hall of Biodiversity**, whose centerpiece is a living re-creation of a Central African rainforest that you can walk through, to the sounds of birdcalls and other critters.

Across from the Hall of Biodiversity lies the first installation of the **Rose Center for Earth and Space**: the Hall of Planet Earth, containing the Dynamic Earth Globe, where visitors seated below the globe are able to watch the earth via satellite go through its full rotation. Don't miss the 400-foot-long Scales of the Universe walkway, which cleverly illustrates the immensity of the universe and our relative insignificance within it. On the floor below is the Hall of the Universe, a permanent exhibition about mankind's astrophysical discoveries and the evolution of everything.

Lastly, one of the museum's greatest attractions is the **Hayden Planetarium**, which includes a state-of-the-art space theater with highly sophisticated interstellar simulations, narrated by Hollywood stars (Tues–Sun last show 4.30pm, Fri last show 7pm; $22, students/seniors $16.50, children $13). In the space below is the Big Bang Experience, a laser and lighting show that illustrates the beginnings of the universe, and a walkable journey down the Cosmic Pathway, which depicts thirteen billion years of evolution in the skies.

Riverside Park and Riverside Drive

At the western edge of 72nd Street, Riverside Park and Riverside Drive begin. **Riverside Drive** winds north, flanked by palatial townhouses and multistory apartment buildings put up in the early part of the twentieth century by those not quite rich enough to compete with the folks on Fifth Avenue. A number of landmarked districts lie along it, particularly in the mid-70s, mid-80s, and low-100s.

One of only eight designated scenic landmarks in New York City, **Riverside Park** is not as imposing or spacious as Central Park, though it was designed by the same team of architects and took 25 years to complete. The park is at its most narrow between 72nd and 79th streets, and not as scenic as it becomes farther north. A delightful place for a break along this stretch is the **79th Street Boat Basin** in Riverside Park, with paths leading down to it located on either side of 79th Street at Riverside Drive. There's also a great café, with basic grill food, good beer, and lots of atmosphere. It's one of the city's loveliest locations, with views of New Jersey across the Hudson River.

Further north on Riverside Drive, between 105th and 106th streets, is a lovely block of historic apartments. It begins with 330 Riverside Drive, now the **Riverside Study Center**, a glorious five-story Beaux-Arts house built in 1900 – note the copper mansard roof, stone balconies, and delicate iron scrollwork.

Morningside Heights

Morningside Heights, just north of the Upper West Side, is the last gasp of Manhattan's wealth before Harlem. Marked at its edge by the monolithic **Cathedral of St John the Divine**, the area is filled with an ethnic hodgepodge of longtime residents and middle-class families of every color, alongside students and professors from the nearby, Ivy League **Columbia University**.

The Cathedral Church of St John

Map 8, D1. Amsterdam Ave, at 112th. Tours Tues–Sat at 11am, Sun 1pm; tours $5, students and seniors $4; ℡212/932-7347. #1 to Cathedral Parkway (110th Street).

The Cathedral Church of St John the Divine rises from the urban landscape with a sure, solid kind of majesty – far from finished, but still one of New York's most impressive sights.

Work on the Episcopal church began in 1892 to the specifications of a Romanesque design that, with a change of architect in 1911, became French Gothic. Work progressed quickly for a while but stopped with the outbreak of war in 1939 and only resumed again in the mid-1980s. The church declared bankruptcy in 1994, fraught with funding difficulties and hard questioning by people who thought the money might be better spent on something of more obvious benefit to the local community. Since then, a massive international fund-raising drive has been launched in the hope of resuming building work soon.

The cathedral appears complete at first glance (despite the ever-present scaffolding), but when you gaze up into its huge, uncompleted towers, you realize how much is left to be done. Only two-thirds of the cathedral is finished, and completion isn't due until around 2050 – even assuming it goes on uninterrupted. Still, if finished, St John the Divine will be the largest cathedral structure in the world, its floor space – at 600 feet long and at the transepts 320 feet wide – big enough to swallow both the cathedrals of Notre Dame and Chartres whole.

Walking the length of the **nave**, you can see the melding of the Romanesque and Gothic styles. This blending is particularly apparent in the choir, which rises from a heavy arcade of Romanesque columns to a high, light-Gothic vaulting, the temporary dome of the crossing to someday be replaced by a tall, delicate Gothic spire.

Columbia University and north

Map 9, B9. #1 to 116th Street/Columbia University.

The **Columbia University** campus fills six blocks between Broadway and Morningside Drive from 114th to 120th streets, with its main entrance at Broadway and 116th Street (**tours** of the campus leave from the information office here Mon–Fri; call ☎212/854-4900 for information). It is one of the most prestigious academic institutions in the country, ranking with the other Ivy League colleges and boasting a campus laid out in grand Beaux Arts style. Of the buildings, the domed and colonnaded **Low Memorial Library** (built in 1902) stands center-stage at the top of a wide flight of stone steps, a focus for somewhat violent demonstrations during the Vietnam War.

Riverside Church (Map 9, B8), on Riverside Drive between 120th and 121st streets (daily 9am–4.30pm, Sun service 10.15am), has a graceful French Gothic Revival tower. Take the elevator to the 20th floor and ascend the steps around the carillon (the largest in the world, with 74 bells) for some classic spreads of Manhattan's skyline, New Jersey, and the hills beyond.

Up the block from the church at 122nd Street is **Grant's Tomb** (Map 9, B8; daily 9am–5pm; free), a Greek-style memorial and the nation's largest mausoleum in which conquering Civil War hero and blundering President Grant really is interred with his wife, in two black-marble Napoleonic sarcophogi.

18

Harlem and northern Manhattan

The most famous African-American community in America (and, arguably, the bedrock of twentieth-century black culture), **Harlem** in the 1920s experienced a musical and literary explosion now known as the Harlem Renaissance. Local legends such as Billie Holiday and Langston Hughes were at their prime during this time, and their achievements still linger, inseparable from the place even today. During the postwar years, however, Harlem declined, languishing as a low-rent, high-crime neighborhood, justly earning a reputation for racial tension and urban decay. Today, it's a far less dangerous area than its reputation suggests – indeed, pockets of it are among Manhattan's more up-and-coming places. Many local observers worry, however, that the price for this influx of money and investment may prove too high.

Continuing northwest, **Hamilton Heights** is largely residential; the old Federalist mansion of Alexander Hamilton is the one sight worth going out of your way to visit here. Further uptown, **Washington Heights** is a residential Dominican neighborhood with little in the way of attractions. You may still want to pass through, though, to see **The Cloisters**, a mock-medieval monastery at the top end of Manhattan that holds the Metropolitan Museum's superlative collection of medieval art.

⑱ 125th Street

125th Street between Broadway and Fifth Avenue is the working center of Harlem and serves as its main commercial and retail drag. The #2 and #3 trains let you out here at 125th Street and Lenox Avenue, and the **Adam Clayton Powell, Jr. State Office Building** on the corner of Seventh Avenue provides a looming concrete landmark. Walking west along 125th, you'll encounter the **Studio Museum in Harlem**, at no. 144 (Map 9, D8; Wed–Fri noon–6pm, Sat 10am–6pm, Sun noon–6pm; suggested donation $7, students and seniors $3, under-12s free; ☏212/864-4500, ⊛www.studiomuseum.org), an exhibition space dedicated to contemporary African-American painting, photography, and sculpture. The permanent collection is displayed on a rotating basis and includes works by Harlem Renaissance-era photographer James Van Der Zee, and paintings and sculpture by postwar artists. Just west is the **Apollo Theater** (Map 9, D8; ☏212/531-5300, ⊛www.apollotheater.com) at no. 253, which, though not much to look at from the outside, was, from the 1930s to the 1970s, the center of black entertainment in New York City and northeastern America. Almost all the great figures of jazz and blues played here along with singers, comedians, and dancers. Past winners of its renowned Amateur Night have included Ella Fitzgerald, Billie Holiday, The Jackson Five, Sarah Vaughan, Marvin

Gaye, and James Brown. The Apollo offers daily 45-minute tours (call ☎212/531-5337), but it's far less interesting than seeing an actual talent night or concert here (see p.252 for show info).

Powell Boulevard and around

Above 125th Street, Seventh Avenue is also known as **Adam Clayton Powell, Jr. Boulevard**, a broad sweep pushing north between low-built houses that allow the sky to break through. As with the rest of Harlem, Powell Boulevard shows years of decline in its graffiti-splattered walls and storefronts punctuated by demolished lots. However, the recent sky-rocketing of real estate prices throughout Manhattan has led to some renovation along the boulevard, though much work remains to be done.

At 132 W 138th St stands the **Abyssinian Baptist Church** (Map 9, D6), noted primarily because of its long-time minister, the ubiquitous **Reverend Powell**, who was instrumental in the 1930s in forcing the white-owned stores of Harlem to employ the blacks who ensured their economic survival. Later, he became the first African American on the city council, then New York's first black representative in Congress, sponsoring the country's first minimum-wage law.

18

Sunday gospel

Gospel music tours (see p.23) are big business in Harlem, often pricey yet usually covering transportation uptown and brunch afterwards. You can, however, easily go it on your own. The choir at the Abyssinian Baptist Church is arguably the best in Harlem, but others of note include **Metropolitan Baptist Church**, 151 W 128th St, at Powell Blvd (☎212/663-8990), and **Mount Nebo Baptist Church**, 1883 7th Ave (Powell Blvd), at 114th (☎212/866-7880). Keep in mind that worship is taken seriously here, so dress accordingly.

Strivers Row

Map 9, D6. #B or #C to 135th Street.

Near the Abyssinian Baptist Church at 138th Street between Powell and Eighth (aka Frederick Douglass Boulevard) are what many consider the finest blocks of row-houses in Manhattan – **Strivers Row**. Commissioned during the 1890s housing boom, Strivers Row constitutes a uniquely harmonious, dignified Renaissance-derived strip that's an amalgam of simplicity and elegance. At the turn of the nineteenth century, this came to be *the* desirable place for ambitious professionals to reside – hence its nickname. None of the houses are open for public viewing, but it's a stunningly beautiful block to see from the outside; past residents have included musicians Eubie Blake, Scott Joplin, and Fletcher Henderson.

Hamilton and Washington Heights

Running down Convent Avenue to City College in the 130s, the **Hamilton Heights Historic District** was populated during the Depression (a period also known locally as the **Harlem Renaissance** for the flowering of African-American literature and visual art that occurred) by black professionals, who looked down on lesser Harlemites. The Heights' greatest historic lure is the 1798 house of Alexander Hamilton, flamboyant first Secretary to the Treasury (and face on the $10 bill). **Hamilton Grange National Memorial**, 287 Convent Ave, at 142nd (Map 9, C6; daily 9am–5pm; free; ☎212/666-1640), may soon be moved to a site in nearby St Nicholas Park. For now, the Federal-style mansion sits awkwardly between the fiercely Romanesque St Luke's Church and an apartment building.

Washington Heights is the rather overarching name given to most of the northern tip of Manhattan; though it spans the majority of ground between 145th and 200th streets, it offers only a couple of stop-offs. The **Hispanic Society of America**, on Audubon Terrace between 155th and 156th (Map 9, B4; Tues–Sat 10am–4.30pm, Sun 1–4pm;

free; (T)212/926-2234), contains one of the largest collections of Spanish art outside of Spain, with works by masters such as Goya, El Greco, and Velázquez, and more than 6000 decorative works of art. The **Morris–Jumel Mansion**, at 65 Jumel Terrace, between 160th and Edgecombe (Map 9, C3; Wed–Sun 10am–4pm; $4, students and seniors $3; (T)212/923-8008), is another uptown surprise. Cornered in its garden, the mansion, with its proud Georgian outlines faced with a later Federal portico, forms a sharp contrast to the low-end tenement housing that surrounds it.

The Cloisters

Tues–Sun: March–Oct 9.30am–5.15pm, Nov–Feb 9.30am–4.45pm; suggested donation $10, students $5; includes same-day admission to the Metropolitan Museum; (T)212/923-3700. #A to 190th Street.

The Cloisters, the Metropolitan Museum's collection of medieval art, is housed in a beautiful ersatz monastery in Fort Tryon Park. Unequivocally, this is a must, and if you're game for riding up on the subway you'll find an additional reward in the park itself, the stone-walled promenade overlooking the Hudson and English-style garden making for a sweepingly romantic spot.

Starting from the entrance hall and working counterclockwise, the collection is laid out in roughly chronological order. First off is the simplicity of the **Romanesque Hall**, featuring French remnants such as an arched limestone doorway dating to 1150 and a thirteenth-century portal from a monastery in Burgundy. The frescoed Spanish **Fuentidueña Chapel** is dominated by a huge, domed twelfth-century apse from Segovia that immediately induces a reverential hush. Hall and chapel form a corner on one of the prettiest of the five cloisters here, **St Guilhelm**, ringed by strong Corinthian-style columns topped by busily carved capitals with floral designs from thirteenth-century southern France.

The highlight of the collection, however, are the **Unicorn Tapestries** (c.1500, Netherlands), which are brilliantly alive with color, observation, and medieval allegory, as all seven have been repaired, restored, and rehung in a refurbished gallery with new lighting. The tapestries depict a hunt for the mythical unicorn that is killed and then magically brought back to life, meant to symbolize both the resurrection of Christ and the courtly transformation of a lover into a bridegroom – presumably after having been hunted down and tamed by his lady.

19

The outer boroughs

Manhattan is a hard act to follow, and the four outer boroughs – **Brooklyn**, **Queens**, **the Bronx**, and Staten Island – inevitably pale in comparison to one of the most famous cities in the world. But while they lack the glamour of Manhattan, and life in them, essentially residential, is less obviously dynamic, they all offer uniquely unexpected and refreshing perspectives on the city.

Most visitors never set foot off Manhattan, but if you have more than a few days there's much out here to be recommended. In Brooklyn, there's salubrious **Brooklyn Heights** and beautiful **Prospect Park**, along with the evocatively run-down, carnival-esque seaside resort of **Coney Island**. Queens features the bustling Greek community of **Astoria** and **Flushing Meadows**, a vast park that played host to the 1939 and 1964 World's Fairs. The Bronx has in recent years begun to conquer its reputation as a vast danger zone; the notorious **South Bronx** – whose highlight is **Yankee Stadium** – has been largely rehabilitated, and the borough contains one of the country's best zoos and botanical gardens. For information on taking a trip on the **Staten Island**

19

Subways and buses

Be warned that the outer boroughs are much larger than Manhattan, and to get to some of the highlights you'll have to take various **subways and buses** in succession. It can be a long haul, but you'll grow to appreciate the MTA's ability to connect vastly separated areas. Make sure you're familiarized with the transit system by studying "City transportation" (see p.17) before you set out. **Taxi cabs** can be taken to and from any borough, though remember they are harder to find the farther you are from Manhattan, when a **car service** might be your best bet. For car service numbers, dial ☎411 or consult ⓦwww.magicyellow.com.

ferry, which affords a grand view of New York Harbor as well as the downtown skyline, see p.30.

Brooklyn

Brooklyn's most visited and most attractive neighborhood is **Brooklyn Heights**, whose tree-lined streets seem a world away from Manhattan's hustle and bustle. More specific reasons to come to Brooklyn are the **Museum of Art** and the **Botanical Gardens**, a half-dozen subway stops past Brooklyn Heights to the east. There's also Frederick Law Olmsted's and Calvert Vaux's **Prospect Park**, which for many is an improvement on their more famous bit of landscaping in Manhattan, Central Park. Aficionados of seedy seaside resorts will love the tacky – and thoroughly fun – **Coney Island**.

Brooklyn Heights

Brooklyn Heights, Brooklyn's original city and maybe the most coveted section of the borough, is one of New York City's stateliest neighborhoods, composed of brown-

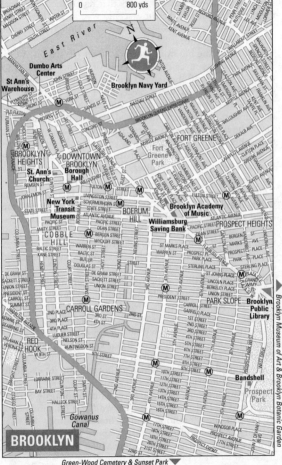

Greenpoint, Williamsburg & Queens ▲

East River

0   800 yds

N

Dumbo Arts Center

St Ann's Warehouse

Brooklyn Navy Yard

FORT GREENE

Fort Greene Park

BROOKLYN HEIGHTS

DOWNTOWN BROOKLYN

St Ann's Church

Borough Hall

New York Transit Museum

BOERUM HILL

Brooklyn Academy of Music

Williamsburg Saving Bank

PROSPECT HEIGHTS

COBBLE HILL

CARROLL GARDENS

RED HOOK

PARK SLOPE

Brooklyn Public Library

Bandshell

Prospect Park

Gowanus Canal

BROOKLYN

Green-Wood Cemetery & Sunset Park ▼

stone houses along narrow streets that reveal the occasional cobblestoned mews. The most scenic way to get here is by walking from lower Manhattan over the Brooklyn Bridge; see p.45 for directions.

Walking up the hill from the York Street #F station at Old Fulton Street, you can take Everett or Henry streets into the oldest part of Brooklyn Heights proper. It's easy and enjoyable to wander these streets lined with a plethora of Federal-style brick buildings; 24 Middagh St, at Willow, is an unassuming but perfectly preserved wooden house dating to 1824, the neighborhood's oldest. Two blocks east, on Orange Street, between Hicks and Henry, you'll see the simple **Plymouth Church of the Pilgrims**, the one-time preaching base of **Henry Ward Beecher**, abolitionist and campaigner for women's rights.

Retrace your steps one block and follow Henry Street to Clark, home to the **Hotel St George** at no. 51. One of the oldest and once one of the largest hotels in the United States, the *St George* was famed for its huge indoor saltwater pool with mirrored ceiling and its celebrity clientele. It served as a setting for *The Godfather* before becoming the student and youth residence it is today.

One block further along, on the corner of Pierrepont, you'll find the **Herman Behr House**, a chunky Romanesque Revival mansion that has been, successively, a hotel, brothel, Franciscan monastery (it was the brothers who added the horrific canopy), and, currently, private apartments. Further down Pierrepont, look in if you can on the **Brooklyn Unitarian Church** – originally known as the Church of the Savior – which is notable for its exquisite neo-Gothic interior.

Walk just one more block and you'll hit **Montague Street**, celebrated by Dylan in his song *Tangled Up in Blue* and home to unchanging storefronts and a literary history to rival that of the West Village. Truman Capote lived here, as did Norman Mailer; playwright Arthur Miller resided at no. 62.

The Promenade

Walk west on any of the streets between Clark and Remsen and you'll reach the **Promenade** (aka, "the Esplanade"), a boardwalk with one of the most spectacular – and renowned – views in all of New York. It's hard to take your eyes off the skyline, the water, the Brooklyn Bridge, and the Statue of Liberty in the distance, but do turn around and notice between the trees the monstrous homes set back modestly from the walkway.

Follow State Street back from the Promenade and onto Boerum Place, where, housed in an abandoned 1930s subway station at the corner of Schermerhorn, you'll find the New York Transit Museum (Tues–Fri 10am–4pm, Sat & Sun noon–5pm; $5, children and seniors $3; ☎718/694-1600, ⓦwww.mta.nyc.ny.us/mta/museum). The museum holds more than 100 years' worth of transportation history and memorabilia, with a gallery dedicated to surface transportation that has some wonderful trolleys and buses dating from the early 1800s. An exhibition on the city's hundred-year-old subway system, meanwhile, proffers photographs, maps, wonderfully refurbished vintage subway cars, and a working signal tower. Be sure to check out the jewelry and accessories fashioned from old subway tokens in the gift shop.

The Brooklyn Academy of Music

30 Lafayette Ave, between Ashland Place and St Felix. ☎718/636-4100, ⓦwww.bam.org. #B, #Q, #2, #3, #4, or #5 to Atlantic Avenue or #D, #M, #N, or #R to Atlantic Avenue–Pacific Street.

The **Brooklyn Academy of Music** (or just "**BAM**" to its fans, who come from all over the city) is the oldest performing arts center in America (1859) and one of the borough's most famous institutions. Located on the edge of Fort Greene, a trendy but well-manicured residential neighborhood dominated by brownstones, BAM has played host over the years to a glittering – and innovative – array of artists, from Charles Dickens and Booker T. Washington to Sergei Rachmaninoff and Philip Glass. These days, world-renowned orchestras, dance troupes, and theater companies still draw visitors from all over the city – which is no small feat, motivating Manhattanites to come over the river to Brooklyn. BAM also has a state-of-the-art four-screen cinema that features art films, international retrospectives, and the occasional new release. Check the website for what's on and when.

Prospect Park and around

Brooklyn really asserts itself – architecturally, at any rate – in the area surrounding **Prospect Park**. A cab ride from downtown Manhattan (about $12; or you can take the #2 or #3 train to Grand Army Plaza) is well worth the price to see some excellent urban planning and a lovely greenspace in the middle of it all. There's an excellent bike path, and lots of spots for a picnic between sightseeing destinations.

Grand Army Plaza

Laid out in the late nineteenth century, Central Park architects Robert Law Olmsted and Calvert Vaux designed **Grand Army Plaza** as a dramatic approach to their newly completed Prospect Park. The triumphal **Soldiers and Sailors' Memorial Arch**, which you can climb during spring and autumn (weekends only; free), was designed in 1892 by John Duncan, also the architect of Grant's Tomb, in tribute to the triumph of the North in the Civil War.

Inside the arch are bas reliefs, including one of *Abraham Lincoln* by Thomas Eakins and one of *General Ulysses S. Grant* by William O'Donovan, both installed in 1895. **The Victory Quadriga** (1898), a fiery sculpture atop the arch designed by Frederick William MacMonnies, depicts a rider, chariot, four horses, and two heralds.

Prospect Park

☎718/965-8951, ⊛www.prospectpark.org.

Energized by their success with Central Park, Olmsted and Vaux landscaped **Prospect Park** in the early 1890s, completing it just as the finishing touches were being put to Grand Army Plaza outside. The park itself is large and lovely, a regular meeting-place for dogs, babies, and their respective parents out for a Sunday stroll. There's a lake on the east side for pedal and electric boating; a ninety-acre open meadow on the west side; and a 3.5-mile, two-lane road that surrounds the park and is primarily reserved for runners, cyclists, rollerbladers, and the like.

From **The Audubon Center** at the Boathouse (April–June & Sept–Dec Thurs–Sun noon–5pm; July–Sept Thurs–Sun noon–6pm; Jan–March weekends only noon–4pm; free), visitors can walk a mile-long nature trail through the park's restored natural environment; less enthusiastic travelers can take electric boat trips ($5, children $3) on the placid Lullwater Lake to get closer to nature. **The Prospect Park Zoo** (Nov–March daily 10am–4.30pm; April–Oct Mon–Fri 10am–5pm, Sat & Sun 10am–5.30pm; $5, seniors $1.25, under-12s $1) is not a bad place to while away the time, with its richly restored 1912 carousel (rides $1). The park's highlight, however, is the ninety-acre **Long Meadow**, which cuts through the center of the park. On warm weekends you can find soccer and volleyball matches, families hosting picnics, and couples reading or romantically entwined.

Brooklyn Museum of Art

200 Eastern Parkway. Wed–Fri 10am–5pm, Sat & Sun 11am–6pm, first Sat of every month 11am–11pm; $8, students and seniors $4; ☎718/638-5000, ⊛www.brooklynmuseum.org. #2 or #3 to Eastern Parkway/Brooklyn Museum.

Though the second-largest art museum in New York City, the **Brooklyn Museum of Art** seems forever doomed to stand in the shadow of the Met (see p.122). That said, the Brooklyn Museum is a jewel in and of itself and well worth a visit, especially for its renowned collection of **Egyptian art**. Recent renovations have added a beautiful sunlit lobby and a plaza with seating, trees, and water features – a lovely spot to ponder the great works you'll have just seen.

A trip through the museum, one of the largest in the US, with 1.5 million objects in its collection and five floors of exhibits, requires considerable selectivity. The permanent collection includes Egyptian, Classical, and Ancient Middle Eastern Art; Arts of Africa, the Pacific, and the Americas; Decorative Arts; Costumes and Textiles; Painting, Sculpture, Prints, Drawings, and Photography; and 28 evocative **period rooms**, ranging from an early American farmhouse to a nineteenth-century Moorish castle.

The world-renowned **Egyptian collection** is particularly noteworthy, its redesigned display putting the works, including objects from tombs and temples, statues, and a 2600-year-old mummy, in their contemporary cultural context. Also worth a look are the newly reopened Kevorkian Galleries, which feature twelve Assyrian reliefs from a Nimrud palace in what is now known as Iraq.

Look in on the American and European Painting and Sculpture galleries on the top story, which progress from eighteenth-century portraits – including one of George Washington by Gilbert Stuart – and bucolic paintings by members of the **Hudson River School** to works by Winslow Homer and John Singer Sargent to pieces by Charles Sheeler and Georgia O'Keeffe. A handful of lesser paintings by European masters – Degas, Cézanne, Toulouse-Lautrec, Monet, and Dufy, among others – are also displayed, plus a large collection of Rodin sculptures.

Brooklyn Botanic Garden

1000 Washington Ave. April–Sept Tues–Fri 8am–6pm, Sat & Sun 10am–6pm, Oct–March Tues–Fri 8am–4.30pm, Sat & Sun 10am–4.30pm; $5, students and seniors $3, free all day Tues, Sat before noon, and weekdays mid Nov–end Feb; ☎718/623-7200, Ⓦwww .bbg.org. #1 or #2 to Eastern Parkway/Brooklyn Museum.

One of the most enticing park spaces in the city, the **Brooklyn Botanic Garden**, just south of the Brooklyn Museum, is smaller and more immediately likeable than its more celebrated rival in the Bronx (see p.176), and makes for a relaxing place to unwind after a couple of hours in the museum next door. Some 12,000 plants from around the world occupy 52 acres of manicured terrain. Sumptuous, but not overplanted, there is a Rose Garden, a Japanese Garden, a Shakespeare Garden (laid out with plants mentioned in the Bard's plays), the Celebrity Path (a winding walkway studded with leaf-shaped plaques that honor Brooklyn's famous), and some delightful lawns draped with weeping willows and beds of flowering shrubs. A conservatory houses, among other things, the country's largest collection of bonsai trees, and a gift shop stocks a wide array of exotic plants, bulbs, and seeds.

Coney Island

Accessible to anyone for the price of a subway ride, the beachfront amusement spot of **Coney Island** has long given working-class New Yorkers the kind of holiday they just couldn't get otherwise. It brings to mind old black-and-white photos from the earlier part of the nineteenth century; find out for yourself by taking the subway to Stillwell Avenue (last stop on the #F, #M, #Q, or #W train). These days, the music blares louder than it once did, the language of choice on the boardwalk is Spanish or Russian as often as English, and the rides look a bit worse for the wear.

The beach can be overwhelmingly crowded on hot days, and it's never the cleanest place in or out of the water. But show up for the annual **Mermaid Parade** on the first Saturday of summer and you'll get caught up in the fun of what's got to be one of the oddest small-town festivals in the country, where paraders dress in (often provocative) King Neptune and mermaid attire.

Coney Island's **amusement area** comprises several parks, none of which offers a deal that makes a lot of sense – unless you have kids (nearly all the children's rides are in Deno's Wonder Wheel Park) or plan on riding one ride more than four times. Still, the 85-year-old **Wonder Wheel** ($4, plus a free children's ticket to the New York Aquarium; see below) is a must. After nearly a century, it's still one of the tallest Ferris wheels in the world, and the *only* one on which two-thirds of the cars slide on serpentine tracks, shifting position as the wheel makes its slow circle twice around. The rickety **Cyclone** rollercoaster ($5, $4 for a repeat ride) is another landmark, but if you're used to slick, modern loop-coaster rides, be forewarned: this low-tech wooden coaster is not for the faint of heart, though it is great, frantic, whiplashing fun.

Further down the boardwalk, halfway to Brighton Beach is the seashell-shaped **New York Aquarium** (April–Oct Mon–Fri 10am–5pm, Sat & Sun 10am–6pm; Nov–April 10am–4.30pm daily; $11, seniors and children 2–12 $7; ☎718/265-FISH, ⊛www.nyaquarium.com). Walruses, sea otters, California sea lions, penguins, and seals, as well as an extensive collection of seahorses, abound at the Sea Cliffs exhibit, which re-creates the coast of the Pacific Northwest, while the "Alien Stingers" exhibit provides an intriguing glimpse into the weird and wonderful world of jellyfish. Try to schedule your visit with a free animal-enrichment session, where zookeepers work on games and challenges to keep the animals alert, both physically and mentally, or the daily feeding hours – call for information of that day's times.

Brighton Beach

East along the boardwalk from Coney Island, at Brooklyn's southernmost point, lies **Brighton Beach**, once an affluent seaside resort complete with a racetrack, casino, and major hotel. Today, the largely residential neighborhood is often referred to as "Little Odessa" (the film of the same name was set here), and is home to the country's largest community of Russian émigrés, who arrived here in the 1970s following a relaxation of Soviet emigration restrictions.

The main attractions of Brighton Beach are the **restaurants**, which really heat up each evening, becoming a near-parody of a rowdy Russian night out with lots of food, loud live music, lots of glass-clinking, and free-flowing chilled vodka. Guests dress to the nines, and the dancing girls will have you feeling like you've landed in a foreign Vegas. The most popular and accessible spots are *National*, *Ocean*, and *Odessa*, all on Brighton Beach Avenue, at nos. 273, 1029, and 1113, respectively.

Williamsburg

Williamsburg, easily accessed by the Bedford Street stop on the #L train, is a self-consciously hip pocket in north Brooklyn largely populated by artists and various scenesters. Many dilapidated buildings along North 6th Street have been put to creative use and the face of the neighborhood changes daily. Indeed, with easy access to Manhattan and excellent waterfront views, it's not hard to see why this area has exploded.

Williamsburg also boasts more than a dozen **contemporary art galleries**, ranging in ambience from ultra-professional to makeshift, and run by an international coterie of artists; the most sophisticated is Pierogi 2000, 177 N 9th St (Thurs–Mon noon–6pm; ☎718/599-2144, ⓦwww.pierogi2000.com).

You can tour the **Brooklyn Brewery**, 79 N 11th St (☎718/486-7422, ⓦwww.brooklynbrewery.com), on Saturdays at 1, 2, 3, and 4pm, or hang out in their tasting room for live music at happy hour (Fri 6–11pm). Around 1900 there were nearly fifty breweries in Brooklyn, and this is the last successful one in the borough since Schaefer and Rheingold closed in 1976. The beer's not bad, either.

For other things to do in Williamsburg, look west toward the water and let the old Pfizer smokestack lead you to **Grand Ferry Park**, one of the few waterfront parks left in Brooklyn; here you'll find a great view of the Williamsburg Bridge, which, if you so choose, you can walk across into the Lower East Side.

Queens

Of New York City's four outer boroughs, its largest, **Queens**, is, apart from Staten Island, probably the least-visited by outsiders – not counting their arrival in the city via Queens' airports, LaGuardia and JFK. Unlike Brooklyn or the Bronx, Queens has no hyped drawing card to pull visitors in. However, the individuality of its neighborhoods, a leftover from it having never been its own city before New York City was tied together in 1898 – Queens was just a county of separate towns and villages – is reason enough to warrant exploration.

While here, you can travel from industrial **Long Island City** and Greek **Astoria** through Irish **Woodside** to Indian and South American **Jackson Heights** and finally Asian **Flushing**, which can feel as suburban as Long Island on some days and as exotic as Hong Kong on others. You'll find a few underrated museums and no shortage of delicious ethnic foods – just follow the #7 train, which chugs through most of the borough: Turkish breads, Romanian sausage, Indonesian noodles, Tibetan pork, Argentinean steak, vegetarian Indian, and Cantonese dim sum await.

Long Island City

Long Island City provides the first view of Queens for most visitors. Here, the #7 train cuts above ground after crossing from Manhattan; look west for a majestic view of Midtown, particularly when Queens is clear and Manhattan is shrouded in fog. Crisscrossed by elevated trains and highways, Long Island City is not particularly pretty or even pleasant-looking, but it's nevertheless a major artery of New York's contemporary arts scene, and home to some innovative museums. Chief among these are the **P.S.1 Contemporary Art Center** and the **Noguchi Museum**.

P.S.1 Contemporary Art Center

22–25 Jackson Ave, at 46th. Thurs–Mon noon–6pm; suggested donation $5, students and seniors $2; ☎718/784-2084, 🌐www.ps1.org.
#7 to 45th Road/Courthouse Square.

P.S.1, a venerable outpost of MoMA (see p.100), is one of
the city's best-loved contemporary art exhibition spaces,
focusing on work that might be considered too innovative or
contemporary for its big sister downtown. Summer Saturday
afternoons and evenings are spent dancing in the courtyard or
chilling to the sounds of world-famous DJs spinning live, for
free, in a specially commissioned architectural installation.

The Noguchi Museum

901 33rd Rd, at Jackson. Wed–Fri 11am–6pm, Sat & Sun 10am–
6pm; $5, students and seniors $2.50; 🌐www.noguchi.org. #N or #W
to Broadway.

The **Noguchi Museum** brings together an impressive
selection of the late artist's sculpture, drawings, stage and furniture designs along with substantial correspondence, manuscripts, and photographs. Famous for his Miami memorial to
the astronauts who died in the *Challenger* explosion, as well
as for his ideas and renderings of public sculpture – such
as the infamous cube at Astor Place (see p.66) – Noguchi's
talent receives optimal attention here. On the downside, getting to the museum can be something of a chore: check the
museum's website for detailed walking and driving instruc-
tions from various transit hubs, as well as for info about the
occasional direct bus service from downtown Manhattan.

Astoria

Astoria is known for two things: filmmaking and the largest
single concentration of Greeks outside of Greece itself (or
so they claim). Until the movie industry moved to the West
Coast in the early 1930s, Astoria was the cinematic capital
of the world, and Paramount had its studios here until the
lure of Hollywood's reliable weather left Astoria empty

and disused. That's how it remained until recently, when Hollywood's stranglehold on the industry weakened and interest – in New York in general and Astoria in particular – was renewed, along with the likes of the **Kaufman-Astoria Studios**, at 34–12 36th St (closed to the public).

Apart from movie history, **Greek Astoria** stretches from Ditmars Boulevard in the north down to Broadway, and from 31st Street across to Steinway. Between 80,000 and 100,000 Greeks live here (together with a smaller community of Italians and an influx of Eastern Europeans, Bangladeshis, and Latin Americans), evidenced by the large number of restaurants and patisseries. *Elias Corner* is one of the best Greek seafood spots around here; see p.237 for a review.

The American Museum of the Moving Image

35th Ave, at 36th. Wed & Thurs 11am–5pm, Fri 11am–8pm, Sat & Sun 11am–6.30pm; $10, students and seniors $7.50, under-18s $5, Fri free from 4 to 8pm; ☎718/784-0077, ⓦwww.ammi.org.

More film history can be found in the old Paramount complex, where the **American Museum of the Moving Image** houses a stellar collection of over 1000 objects, from posters and stills to sets and equipment both from Astoria's golden age and more recent times. On Friday, Saturday, and Sunday, the AMMI has evening showings (plus matinees on Sat & Sun) of classic and occasionally cult **films** (included with admission except for Fri). An expansion planned to begin in late 2005 will double the size of the museum, adding a garden for outdoor screenings, an extensive digital library, new exhibition galleries, and an additional 74-seat theater.

Shea Stadium and Flushing Meadows Corona Park

Take the #7 train to Willets Point for **Shea Stadium** (Roosevelt Ave, off Grand Central Parkway; ☎718/507-8499), home of the New York Mets. The Beatles famously played here in 1965 as did the Rolling Stones in 1989; but concerts out here are very rare these days. Baseball games, on the other hand, are frequent between April and October, and the Mets have a solid and loyal fan base. See Chapter 29, "Sports and outdoor activities," for ticket activities.

From Shea, you'll easily find your way to **Flushing Meadows Corona Park**, a lovely expanse of green centered on the large Meadow Lake where, among other things, the beautiful Dragon Boat Festival can be witnessed in mid-August every year. The **New York Hall of Science**, 46th Avenue, at 111th (call ahead as hours vary; $7.50, under-17s $5; ☎718/699-0005, ⊛www.nyhallsci.org), is a concrete and stained-glass structure retained from the 1964 World's Fair (you'll see the best remaining structures deeper within the park). Kids will love this interactive science museum, though it can be exhausting for adults. The adjacent **Wildlife Center** (once the zoo) features exclusively North American animals. But the main reason to come here is to see the **Unisphere** and the **Queens Museum of Art.**

The **Unisphere** is a 140-foot-high, stainless-steel globe that weighs 380 tons – probably the main reason why it never left its place in the park following the World's Fair. It was finally declared a landmark, to the delight of the borough, and it's now lit at night; you may have seen it when you came in from the airport. Carefully designed pathways connect lawns, small pools, and two lakes. On a summer day, the park is swarming with kids on bikes and rollerblades; you can rent a bike yourself, or even a boat.

Queens Museum of Art

In Flushing Meadows Corona Park. Tues–Fri 10am–5pm, Sat & Sun noon–5pm; suggested donation $5; ☎718/592-9700, ⊛www.queens-museum.org. #7 to 111th Street.

Housed in a 1939 World's Fair building which served briefly as the first home of the United Nations, the **Queens Museum** features a vast World's Fair archive (viewable by appointment only), an impressive Tiffany glass collection, and both permanent and visiting collections that concentrate on art in relation to New York. The must-see here, though – and what mostly draws tourists from Manhattan – is the **Panorama of the City of New York**, which was also built for the 1964 World's Fair. With a one-inch model equal to one hundred feet of city, the Panorama (and its 835,000 buildings, plus bridges, piers, rivers, and airports) is the world's largest architectural model.

The Bronx

The city's northernmost borough, **the Bronx** was for a long time believed to be New York's toughest and most notoriously crime-ridden district – and presented as such in films like *Fort Apache, the Bronx* and books like *Bonfire of the Vanities*, even after urban renewal was under way. Indeed, there was no other part of the city about which people were so ready to roll out their most gruesome horror stories. Nowadays its poorer reaches still suffer from severe urban deprivation, but almost all the borough has undergone a successful transformation. The rough-and-tumble South Bronx has even earned the realtor-approved neighborhood sobriquet of "SoBro."

The South Bronx and Yankee Stadium

A trip to the borough on the elevated #4 train affords a good general view of the **South Bronx**, if you haven't got time to go visiting individual neighborhoods – and there's not much reason to do so in any case. The area consists of the segment of the Bronx south of Fordham Road, yet most visitors come here to visit **Yankee Stadium** (first stop on the #B and #D subways after leaving Manhattan, and the third such stop on the #4), home to the New York Yankees baseball team. Baseball fanatics can go on the Babe Ruth Tour, starting at the press gate, which lasts around one hour. The tour includes a historical film, Monument Park, the clubhouse, the press box, and dugout (Mon–Fri 10am–4pm, Sat 10am–noon, Sun noon only; $10, seniors and children $5; ☏718/579-4531, ⓦwww.yankees.com). If you'd rather just see a game, there are plenty throughout the spring, summer, and early fall; see Chapter 29 for ticket info.

Central Bronx and Belmont

It's a shame that few tourists make it up this way, because where real Italian flavor is concerned, **Belmont** makes Little Italy look like Disneyland. **Arthur Avenue** is the neighborhood's main thoroughfare, a mixture of tenements and clapboard houses that is home to one of the largest, and definitely the most authentic, segments of New York's Italian community. There has been a small influx of other ethnic groups – most notably Haitians, Mexicans, and Albanian Yugoslavs – but the staunch Italian community, where everyone knows everyone else (and asks about their mother), is still the dominant force.

There's no better part of the Bronx if you want to **eat**, particularly if you're on your way to the zoo. Manhattanites have even been known to schlep up here for the cooking, the bakeries, and the old-country delicatessens. Choose restaurants on Arthur Avenue with care: swanky *Mario's* at no. 2342 (supposedly where the scene in *The Godfather* in which Al Pacino shot the crooked cop was filmed) is popular but more pricey than others around. Recommended spots include *Pasquale Rigoletto* and *Emilia's*, at nos. 2311 and 2331, respectively.

The Bronx Zoo

End March to end Oct Mon–Fri 10am–5pm, Sat, Sun & holidays 10am–5.30pm; winter daily 10am–4.30pm; summer $12, seniors and children $9, winter $8/$6, suggested donation year-round on Wed, rides and some exhibits additional; ☎718/367-1010, ⓦwww.bronxzoo.com. #2 or #5 to Pelham Parkway.

Accessible either by its main gate on Fordham Road or by a second entrance on Bronx Park South, the **Bronx Zoo** is probably the only reason many New Yorkers from outside the borough ever visit the Bronx – but it's a good one. Opened in 1899 and centered around a cluster of original buildings, this is arguably America's greatest zoo, certainly its largest urban one, and also one of the first to realize that animals both looked and felt better out in the open. This humane environment has been artfully achieved through a variety of simulated natural **habitats**, including the Congo Gorilla Forest ($3) and the spectacular Tiger Mountain, where Siberian tigers thrive in a great re-creation of their natural environment. Camel rides are available in summer ($5), as are trips on the Bronx Zoo Bug Carousel ($2); zoo shuttle transports are also on hand to whisk tired feet around the massive complex. Visit in **summer** to appreciate the zoo at its best; in **winter**, many of the animals, for their own warmth and well-being, are kept in indoor enclosures without viewing areas.

New York Botanical Gardens

April–Oct Tues–Sun 10am–6pm, Nov–March 10am–5pm; combo ticket $13, seniors and students $11, children ages 2–12 $5, free all day Wed and Sat 10am–noon; ☎718/817-8700, ⓦwww.nybg.org. #B or #D to Bedford Park Boulevard.

Across the road from the zoo's main entrance is the rear turnstile of the **New York Botanical Gardens**, incorporated in 1891, which in their southernmost reaches are as wild as anything you're likely to see upstate. Its scientific facilities include a museum, library, herbarium, and a research laboratory. Further north near the main entrance are more cultivated stretches. The **Enid A. Haupt Conservatory**, a landmark turn-of-the-nineteenth-century crystal palace, showcases jungle and desert ecosystems, a palm court, and a fern forest, among other seasonal displays.

The North Bronx

The **North Bronx** is the topmost fringe of New York City, and if anyone actually makes it up here it's to see the luminary-filled **Woodlawn Cemetery**. Accessible from Jerome Avenue at Bainbridge (last stop, Woodlawn, on the #4), this is a prime example of how New Yorkers in the 1850s took in the air. For many years, Woodlawn has been a celebrity cemetery, and boasts a number of tombs and mausolea that are memorable mainly for their garishness. It's a huge place, but there are some monuments that stand out: F.W. Woolworth has himself an Egyptian palace guarded by sphinxes; while Jay Gould, not most people's favorite businessman when he was alive, takes it easy in a Greek-style temple. Pick up a **guide** from the office at the entrance to locate the many larger-than-life individuals buried here, including Herman Melville, Irving Berlin, George M. Cohan, Fiorello LaGuardia, Robert Moses, Miles Davis, and Duke Ellington.

Listings

Listings

20

Accommodation

Accommodation in New York definitely eats up the lion's share of a traveler's budget. Many hotels in the city charge somewhere in the neighborhood of $150–200 a night, not to mention the **taxes** tacked on to that, and some go well beyond that price. With some planning, it is possible to get a decent-sized clean room for $150 or less, but in truth it's far easier to hunt splurges than bargains. Make your **reservations** as far ahead as possible; most hotels cite "supply and demand" as the main influence on their room rate. Don't even think of calling a day before during Christmas and summer when you're likely to find everything (and we mean this) full.

Bear in mind all-included flight and hotel package vacations. Booking services – see box, p.187 – reserve rooms at discount prices and usually for no extra charge. Also, you might try booking through hotel websites for the occasional special deal.

The best advice regarding **discounts** is simply to ask – discounts may also be available in the form of promotional specials or corporate rates. The Internet is worth a try: ⓦwww.nycvisit.com has listed specials (which come with a list of restrictions, and require that you pay with an American Express card). Furthermore, several consolidator-type sites are available (try ⓦwww.hotres.com, ⓦwww.travelscape .com, or ⓦwww.hoteldiscounts.com).

For full hotel listings and prices, consult the New York Convention and Visitors' Bureau **leaflet**, *Hotels in New York City*, available from any of their offices.

Hostels and YMCAs

Hostels and **YMCAs** are just about the only option for cash-strapped backpackers in New York, with dorm beds going for as little as $25 a night. YMCAs are better if you want privacy because they have private single and double rooms, though they tend to have a more institutional feel than the more relaxed hostels. For a comprehensive listing of hostels in New York and across North America, purchase *The Hostel Handbook* (US and Canada $6, international $10; both prices include shipping) online at ⓦwww.hostel-handbook.com or by writing to Jim Williams, *The Hostel Handbook*, 730 St Nicholas Ave, New York, NY 10031. The following, meanwhile, is a small selection of the best hostels and YMCAs in the city.

Bowery's Whitehouse Hotel of New York Map 5, H5. 340 Bowery, btw Great Jones and 2nd ☏212/477-5623, ⓦwww.whitehousehotelofny.com. Basic, very small single ($33) and double rooms ($64) with latticework roofing make this place a little too public for those seeking total privacy, but perfect for shoestring travelers looking for a bed in a great location and better-than-average security.

Central Park Hostel Map 8, E3. 19 W 103rd St, near Central Park West ☏212/678-0491, ⓦwww.centralparkhostel.com. This Upper West Side hostel has dorm beds for four, six, or eight people ($29–36), some private two-bed rooms and lovely studio apartments ($99–129), some with kitchenettes, in a five-story renovated walk-up. All rooms share clean bathrooms, and lockers are available (bring a padlock). Payment in cash or travelers' checks only; you must have a foreign passport or international student ID to stay here.

Chelsea Center Hostel & Chelsea Center Hostel Eastside Map 6, E5. 313 W 29th St, near 8th Ave ☏212/643-0214, Ⓕ473-3945, ⓦwww.chelseacenterhostel.com.

Reputable, clean, safe, and friendly, the *Chelsea Center Hostel* has dorm beds for $30–33 with breakfast and clean sheets and blankets included. Well situated for Midtown West, Chelsea, and the West Village (the hostel also has a second location in the East Village, on East 12th St near 1st Ave; the exact address is given out only upon booking). Make reservations well in advance in high season. Office hours 8.30am to 11pm, no curfew; cash only.

Chelsea International Hostel Map 6, F7. 251 W 20th St, btw 7th and 8th ☏212/647-0010, ⓕ727-7289, ⓦwww.chelseahostel.com. Situated in the heart of Chelsea, this is the closest hostel to Downtown. Beds (130 in all) are $28 a night, including tax, and the rooms, which sleep four or six, are small with bathrooms in the hall (though larger rooms for six at the back of the hostel have their own bathrooms). Private rooms for two are $70 a night. Accommodation is rudimentary, but the location is the hostel's main attraction. Desk open 8am–9pm. There are security guards and sign-in at night. Passport required.

Hosteling International – New York Map 8, C3. 891 Amsterdam Ave, at 103rd ☏212/932-2300, ⓦwww.hinewyork.org. This historic Upper West Side building has 480 dormitory-style beds in rooms of four to twelve beds each, costing $30–36 for IYHA members (on-the-spot membership is $28 for US citizens or $18 for foreigners), and private rooms that sleep four, with one double and one bunk bed, for $135 a night with bath or $120 without; it's $3 extra for nonmembers per night. Though the place is large, it may be heavily booked; reserve at least a day in advance (at least a week in the summer). Open 24 hours.

Jazz on the Park Map 8, E2. 36 W 106th St, at Central Park West ☏212/932-1600, ⓕ932-1700, ⓦwww.jazzhostel.com. This groovy bunkhouse, just a stone's throw from the park, boasts a TV/game room, rooftop barbecues, and the *Java Joint Café*. The rooms, sleeping between two and fourteen, are clean, bright, and air-conditioned. Beds cost between $32 and $38 a night (including tax, linen, and a light breakfast); a two-bed room is $88–154. Reservations essential June–Oct and over Christmas and New Year's (when rates are a little higher).

Jazz on the Town Map 6, L9. 307 E 14th St, at 2nd ☏212/228-2780, ⓦwww.jazzonthepark.com. Great location for travelers wanting to spend time below 14th Street, with beds in clean, modern four-, six-, or eight-bed dorms with a/c and lockers costing from $38 to $43 a night, including linen and towels. No curfew, a TV/game room, and rooftop terrace/bar make this a good spot for party people wanting to live New York life on the cheap.

Sugar Hill International House Map 9, C5. 722 St Nicholas Ave, at 146th ☎212/283-1490, ⓦwww .sugarhillhostel.com. This Harlem hostel charges $25 a night for dorm beds ($20 if you stay for a week), with a limited number of double rooms, available only on a first-come, first-served basis, for $30 per person per night ($25 if you stay a week), maybe the cheapest doubles in the city. Has kitchens and Internet, and bed linens are included in the price.

Vanderbilt YMCA Map 7, J8. 224 E 47th St, btw 2nd and 3rd ☎212/756-9600, ⓦwww.ymcanyc .org. Smaller and quieter than most of the hostels listed above, and neatly placed in Midtown, just five minutes' walk from Grand Central. Inexpensive restaurant, swimming pool, gym, and laundromat. Singles start at $75, doubles at $88–126 (shared bath).

Westside YMCA Map 7, E4. 5 W 63rd St, at Central Park West ☎212/875-4173 or 875-4273, ⓦwww .ymcanyc.org. A wonderfully situated Y next to Central Park and Lincoln Center with air-conditioned singles and doubles from $72 to $140 per night, with or without bath. Free use of two pools, saunas, gym, and sports facilities.

Bed-and-breakfasts

Choosing a **B&B** can be a good way of staying right in the heart of Manhattan at a reasonably affordable price. All rooms – except for a few which we've found off the beaten path (see p.186) – are rented via the following official agencies; they all recommend making your reservations as far in advance as possible, especially for the most inexpensive rooms. In cases where landlords–ladies prefer that visitors reserve in advance rather than show up on their doorsteps, we have omitted addresses.

B&Bs agencies

Affordable New York City Map 5, F2. 21 E 10th St, at University ☏212/533-4001, ⊛www.affordablenewyorkcity.com. Established network of 120 properties (B&Bs and apartments) around the city, with detailed descriptions. B&B accommodations from $95 to $120 (shared bath) and $125 to $145 (private), unhosted studios $150–175, and one-bedrooms $175–230. Cash or travelers' checks only; three-night minimum, four for an apartment. Very customer-oriented and personable.

Bed and Breakfast Network of New York Map 5, B4. 130 Barrow St, near Washington ☏1-800/900-8134 or 212/645-8134, ⊛www.bedandbreakfastnetny.com. Growing network with hosted singles for $75–100, doubles $110–150; prices for unhosted accommodation run from $130 to luxury multi-bed apartments for $400. All prices do not include tax. Weekly and monthly rates also available. For an assured booking write at least a month in advance; make short-notice reservations by phone. Offices open Mon–Fri 8am–6pm.

City Lights Bed & Breakfast PO Box 20355, Cherokee Station, NY 10021 ☏212/737-7049, ⊛citylightsbandb.com. More than 400 carefully screened B&Bs (and short-term apartment rentals) on its books, with many of the hosts involved in theater and the arts. Hosted singles and doubles (without kitchen) run from $80 to $130 a night; unhosted accommodation costs $135 to $300 and up per night depending on size and duration of stay – all prices exclude tax. Weekly and monthly deals. Minimum stay two nights; reserve well in advance.

CitySonnet.com Village Station, PO Box 347, NY 10014 ☏212/614-3034, ⊕425/920-2384, ⊛www.citysonnet.com. Small, personalized B&B/short-term apartment rental agency with accommodations all over the city, but specializing in Downtown and the West Village. Singles from $80 to $125; doubles $110–155; entire apartments and lofts with kitchen start at $135. All prices include tax.

Gamut Realty Group Map 7, L1. 301 E 78th St, at 2nd ☏212/879-4229, ⊛www.gamutnyc.com. Fully automated agency that can fax or email sample listings of available rooms and apartments for nightly or longer-term stays. Unhosted studio apartments for $100–175, and one-bedroom apartments for $140–200. Has accommodation all over Manhattan, some in luxury buildings or artists' lofts.

B&B properties

Bed & Breakfast on the Park
☏718/499-6115, ⊜499-1385,
⊛www.bbnyc.com. A quiet and
secluded 1892 Park Slope
limestone townhouse with lavish
antique furnishings and views
over Prospect Park. Eight double
rooms from $155 to $300 a night
(two-night minimum).

East Village Bed and Coffee Map
5, M3. 110 Ave C, btw 7th and 8th
☏212/533-4175, ⊛www
.bedandcoffee.com. Lovely, tastefully themed single-, twin-, and
queen-bedded rooms with a/c
and CD players which, along
with the wooden floors, open
brick walls, garden, and communal kitchen and living areas,
make this the best-kept secret
in a very happening area of the
East Village/Lower East Side. All
rooms share bathrooms; singles
start at $80 a night, doubles at
$90, including all taxes.

The Harlem Flophouse Map 9, D8.
242 W 123rd St, btw Powell and

Douglass ☏212/662-0678, ⊛www
.harlemflophouse.com. There's an
atmosphere steeped in history
in this lovely old Harlem brownstone, just steps from the Apollo
Theater and boasting large
rooms with fixtures dating from
the Harlem Renaissance. Two
cats preside over great Uptown
spot. Singles $100, doubles
$125.

Inn at Irving Place Map 6, K8. 56
Irving Place, btw 17th and 18th
☏1-800/685-1447 or 212/533-
4600, ⊛www.innatirving.com. It
costs $325–495 a night for one
of the lavishly decorated twelve
rooms – each named after a
famous architect, designer, or
actor – in this handsome pair of
1834 brownstones, which must
rank as one of the most exclusive guesthouses in the city. The
Inn offers five-course high teas
at *Lady Mendl's*, cocktails at the
refined *Cibar Lounge*, wireless
Internet, a/c, and workspaces,
along with free access to a local
gym.

Hotels

Most of New York's **hotels** tend to be in midtown Manhattan, which is fine if you want to be close to the Broadway
theaters and main tourist sights (and large clusters of tourists),
but it's hardly the makings of a restful vacation. If you're going
to be spending a lot of time in the West Village or SoHo,
you might want to try one of the handful of Downtown

or Chelsea hotels. Consider the Upper West or East Side if you're more interested in Central Park, the museums, or Lincoln Center.

Taxes will add 13.25 percent to your bill, and there is also a $2 per night "occupancy tax." This will add about $15 a night to a $100 room. Hotel prices given in the following pages are all before tax unless otherwise noted.

At the more upmarket hotels, **tipping** is expected: unless you firmly refuse, a bellhop will grab your bags when you check in and expect up to $5 to carry them to your room. For housekeeping, figure $2 minimum per day for cheaper hotels, more for the nicer establishments.

Hotel booking services

Should you be uncertain about what you're looking for in an NYC hotel, or if you just don't trust the hotel PR machines, consider using a **hotel booking service**. The various companies listed below offer a selection of rooms at discount prices, tailored to your own criteria.

Central Reservation Service (CRS) ☎407/740-6442 or 1-800/555-7555, ⓦwww.reservation-services.com.

Express Reservations ☎1-800/407-3351 or 303/440-8481, ⓦwww.express-res.com. Weekdays only.

Hotel Reservations Network ☎1-800/715-7666 or 214/369-1264, ⓦwww.hoteldiscount.com.

The Room Exchange 450 7th Ave, at 35th ☎1-800/846-7000, ⓕ212/760-1013.

Below 14th Street

60 Thompson Map 5, E7. 60 Thompson St, btw Spring and Broome ☎212/431-0400 or 1-877/431-0400, ⓦwww.60thompson.com.
With excellent proximity to SoHo's hip restaurants and chic shopping, the handsome 60

Thompson offers 100 modern guestrooms and suites. It further indulges visitors with a rooftop garden/bar and an in-house DVD library. Upstairs rooms look out over SoHo's rooftops. Rooms $375–715.

Hotel Gansevoort Map 6, D9. 18 9th Ave, at 13th ☎212/206-06700 or

1-877/426-7386, ⓦwww
.hotelgansevoort.com. Hugely
popular fashionista hangout in
the happening Meatpacking
District, with a glass-surrounded,
heated rooftop pool with under-
water music, garden, and bar.
Rooms are lushly appointed
and some proffer views of the
Hudson River. Fancy chic with
attitude to match. Rooms from
$435, suites from $675.

Hotel on Rivington Map 5, K6. 107
Rivington St, btw Essex and Ludlow
ⓣ1-800/915-1537 or 212/475-
2600, ⓦwww.hotelonrivington.com.
This controversial monument to
modernity is the first real high-
rise building to be built in the
Lower East Side. Every room
has floor-to-ceiling windows
and steam showers, and most
boast balconies and Japanese-
style soaking tubs. Doubles
$295–490.

Larchmont Map 5, E2. 27 W 11th
St, btw 5th and 6th ⓣ212/989-
9333, ⓦwww.larchmonthotel.com.
Budget hotel in the heart of the
West Village, on a beautiful tree-
lined street. Hotels are a rarity
in this residential area, so this is
a real find. Rooms are small but
nicely decorated and clean, and
all have TV, a/c, phones, and
sinks. Small kitchens and bathrooms with showers are on each
corridor. Prices include continental breakfast. Very small singles

$75–105, doubles $99–135.

The Mercer Map 5, F6. 147 Mercer
St, at Prince ⓣ1-888/918-6060 or
212/966-6060, ⓦwww.mercerhotel
.com. The epitome of SoHo discreet "boutique" chic. Rooms are
stylish with simple furnishings,
high ceilings, walk-in closets,
and oversized bathrooms. The
occasional celebrity will share
your sofa in the smart lobby, and
trendy *Mercer Kitchen* provides
room service 24hrs a day. Doubles $410–650.

Ritz-Carlton Battery Park Map 4,
D8. 2 Little West St, below 1st Place
ⓣ212/344-0800, ⓦwww
.ritzcarlton.com/hotels/new_york
_battery_park/. Incredible views
of Lady Liberty, Ellis Island, and
the harbor around them can be
had from the upper floors of this
highly reputable luxury hotel.
The folk at *Ritz-Carlton* spared
nothing in the design of large
bedrooms that whisper rest and
relaxation, while the 14th-floor
bar with scenic outdoor terrace,
three dining options, and a fitness center with spa services
ensure that your every need is
catered for. Doubles $260–715.

Soho Grand Map 5, E8. 310 W
Broadway, at Grand ⓣ1-800/965-
3000 or 212/965-3000, ⓦwww
.sohogrand.com. Great location
at the edge of SoHo, and many
guests exude the attitude that
comes with the territory: rock

stars, models, actors, and the like. Still, the staff is surprisingly helpful, the rooms are stylishly appointed, if a bit small, with classic New York photographs from a local gallery and an optional goldfish (ask and ye shall receive). The hotel also boasts an elegant bar, restaurant, and fitness center. Doubles $270–650.

Tribeca Grand Map 4, D2. 2 6th Ave, btw White and Walker ☎1-877/519-6600 or 212/519-6600, Ⓦwww.tribecagrand.com. Unlabeled, and hidden by a brick facade like a brand-new train station, the *Tribeca Grand* is close to its sister the *Soho Grand* in location and spirit. Once inside, the *Church Lounge*, one of the more striking hotel public spaces, beckons with a warm orange glow. The rooms are stylish yet understated, though each bathroom boasts a phone and built-in TV. Doubles $450–550.

Washington Square Map 5, D3. 103 Waverly Place, at MacDougal ☎212/777-9515 or 1-800/222-0418, Ⓦwww.washingtonsquarehotel.com. An ideal location: bang in the heart of the West Village, just off Washington Square Park, and a stone's throw from NYU. This atmospheric, lovely old brownstone boasts welcoming, perfectly adequate rooms, some with views over the park.

Continental breakfast included; there's also a fitness room and a lobby bar. Book two months in advance for the summer. Singles from $149, doubles from $190.

Chelsea and the West Side: West 14th to 34th streets

Chelsea Hotel Map 6, F7. 222 W 23rd St, btw 7th and 8th ☎212/243-3700, Ⓦwww.hotelchelsea.com. One of New York's most noted landmarks, both for its aging neo-Gothic building and, more importantly, its long list of former guests, from Dylan Thomas to Bob Dylan (see p.76 for a fuller cast). If you check into the *Chelsea* you may find yourself staying in somebody's apartment, surrounded by their belongings. Ask instead for a renovated room with polished wood floors, log-burning fireplaces, and plenty of space to cram a few extra friends into. Singles from $175, doubles from $210, suites from $350.

Herald Square Map 6, H4. 19 W 31st St, btw 5th and Broadway ☎1-800/727-1888 or 212/279-4017, Ⓦwww.heraldsquarehotel.com. The original home of *Life* magazine, *Herald Square* still features Philip Martiny's golden sculptured cherub *Winged Life* over the doorway of this Beaux-Arts building. Inside it's meticulously clean, but without much in the way of extras, and somewhat soulless. Very small singles (with shared bathrooms) go for as low as $69 a night, with doubles from $139 and triples and quads from $169. Students with ISIC cards get ten percent off.

Hotel Pennsylvania Map 6, F4. 401 7th Ave, at 32nd ☎1-800/223-8585 or 212/736-5000, ⓦwww .hotelpenn.com. Standing right across from Madison Square Garden, this hotel offers every possible convenience in its 1705 rooms, though you can't help thinking it once looked better. Decent-sized doubles for $220, dropping to around $170 in summer. Pet-friendly.

Stanford Map 6, H4. 43 W 32nd St, btw Broadway and 5th ☎1-800/365-1114 or 212/563-1500, ⓦwww.hotelstanford.com. Rooms here are a tad small, but attractive and very quiet, and the hallways are well-lit, if a little narrow. The *Stanford* offers free continental breakfast and valet laundry, a cocktail lounge and good Korean cuisine (in the very relaxing surroundings of the *Gam Mee Ok* restaurant), and the efficient and friendly staff would be welcome in hotels twice this price. Doubles and twins from $139, suites from $199.

Wolcott Map 6, H4. 4 W 31st St, btw 5th and Broadway ☎212/268-2900, ⓦwww.wolcott.com. A surprisingly relaxing budget hotel, with a gilded, ornate Louis XVI–style lobby full of mirrors and lion reliefs (even the ceiling is lavish). The rooms, while much more staid, are more than adequate, all with (somewhat old-fashioned) bathrooms. Doubles and twins from $180, triples from $200.

Union Square to Murray Hill: East 14th to 42nd streets

70 Park Avenue Hotel Map 6, J2. 70 Park Ave, at 38th ☎1-877/707-2752 or 212/973-2400, ⓦwww.70parkave.com. Right in the middle of Midtown, this classy boutique hotel boasts re-creations of classical friezes and frescoes, and original lighting and furnishing design. Rooms are of "American classicism" pedigree, all rich woods and muted earth tones. Pet- and WiFi-friendly, with excellent service. Doubles from $425.

Carlton Arms Map 6, K6. 160 E 25th St, btw 3rd and Lexington ☎212/679-0680, ⓦwww .carltonarms.com. One of the city's latest bohemian hangouts, with eclectic interior decor by would-be artists, few mod cons, and a clientele made up of Europeans, down-at-the-heel artists, and long-staying guests. Discount rates available for students and foreign travelers, with an extra ten-percent discount if you pay for seven nights in advance. Singles with shared bath from $70, doubles from $99, triples from $120, and quads from $140. Add $10–15 per night for private bath. Reserve well in advance for summer.

Gershwin Hotel Map 6, I5. 7 E 27th St, btw 5th and Madison ☎212/545-8000, ⊛www.gershwinhotel.com. A twenty-something's hotel just off Fifth Ave in the Flatiron District that also functions as a hostel. The 110 private double rooms with bathrooms cost about $169 a night; weekends are $15 extra. Imaginatively decorated with a Pop Art theme, the Gershwin has an astroturfed rooftop (where parties are held on the weekend), a small bar, a well-priced restaurant, and a friendly staff. Try to book well in advance.

Library Map 6, I1. 299 Madison Ave, at 41st ☎1-877/793-READ or 212/983-4500, ⊛www.libraryhotel .com. In this whimsical hotel, each floor is devoted to one of the ten major categories of the Dewey Decimal System, and each room's artwork and books reflect a different pursuit within that group. Only those with a serious sense of purpose could design sixty unique rooms and handpick more than 6000 books for the place, and the dedication

shows in other ways, notably in the lovely Poet's Garden on the roof. Doubles from $325, with various offers available via the hotel's website.

The Metro Map 6, H3. 45 W 35th St, btw 5th and 6th ☎1-800/356-3870 or 212/947-2500, ⊛www .hotelmetronyc.com. This very stylish, Art Deco–sensible hotel has old Hollywood posters on the walls, a delightful rooftop terrace, spacious communal areas, clean rooms, and free continental breakfast. A few more extras (like a fitness room, and the highly recommended *Metro Grill* restaurant on the first floor) than normally expected in this category. Doubles $195–275, quads $275–375.

Murray Hill Inn Map 6, K5. 143 E 30th St, btw Lexington and 3rd ☎1-888/996-6376 or 212/683-6900, ⊛www.murrayhillinn.com. It's easy to see why young travelers and backpackers line the *Inn's* narrow halls. Although the rooms are smallish, they all have a/c, telephone, cable TV, and sink; some also have private bathrooms. Also, the staff is friendly and the residential locale offers a breather from the bustle. Singles $79 (shared bath), doubles $89 (shared bath) or $129 (private); additional costs if more than two in a room. Inquire about weekly rates for single rooms.

Hotel Roger Williams Map 6, I4. 131 Madison Ave, at 31st ☎1-888/448-7788 or 212/448-7000, ⓦwww.rogerwilliamshotel.com. At some point during its $2 million "boutique" renovation, this hotel made a turn onto Madison and its prices shot up exponentially. Still, the mellow, Scandinavian/Japanese fusion rooms with Aveda bath gels, fluted zinc pillars in the lobby, European breakfast, and the 24hr espresso/cappuccino bar go some way to justifying the extra greenbacks. Doubles from $210; triples from $215; prices double Sept–Dec.

Seventeen Map 6, L8. 225 E 17th St, btw 2nd and 3rd ☎212/475-2845, ⓦwww.hotel17ny.com. As recently renovated budget accommodation, *Seventeen* is clean and friendly, and it can't be beaten either for location – it's on a pleasant, tree-lined street and very handy if you want to spend your time in the East Village, only a few blocks away. Singles, doubles, and triples with shared bath from $79, $89, and $120, respectively; doubles with private bath from $120.

Thirty Thirty Map 6, J5. 30 E 30th St, at Madison ☎1-800/804-4480 or 212/689-1900, ⓦwww.thirtythirty-nyc.com. Small, welcoming budget hotel with well-appointed, clean, and functional rooms. The smaller, standard accommodations can feel a little cramped (singles are from $119, doubles and twins from $149), so if you can spare the cash, consider upgrading to a much swankier executive double ($199–279).

W Union Square Map 6, J8. 201 Park Ave, at Union Square North ☎1-877/W-HOTELS or 212/253-9119, ⓦwww.whotels.com. Located in the former Guardian Life Building, this is really the only upscale hotel in the area, and boasts Todd English's *Olives* restaurant as well as a bar scene that lasts from after work to after hours. The artificial green grass and corkscrewing bamboo in the lobby are just a prelude to the modern rooms decorated with velvet and featuring plush, really comfortable feather beds. Doubles $369–619.

Midtown West: West 34th to 59th streets

Algonquin Map 7, G9. 59 W 44th St, btw 5th and 6th ☎1-800/555-8000 or 212/840-6800, ⓦwww.camberleyhotels.com. New York's classic literary hangout for the past century, as created by Dorothy Parker and her associates and perpetuated by the likes of Noël Coward, George Bernard Shaw, and Irving Berlin.

The cabaret in the *Oak Room* perpetuates the air of hushed sophistication, while the rooms, bathrooms, and lobby were handsomely refurbished in 1998 and the rest of the hotel in July 2004. From $259–519.

Broadway Inn Map 7, E8. 264 W 46th St, btw Broadway and 8th ⊤1-800/826-6300 or 212/997-9200, ⊛www.broadwayinn.com. Cozy, reasonably priced bed-and-breakfast hotel in the heart of the Theater District on the corner of charmless Eighth Ave, but just a skip away from Times Square and Restaurant Row. Guests get a twenty-percent discount at the restaurant downstairs and an excellent staff makes up for the lack of an elevator. Singles from $109 (summer) to $225, doubles $150–299.

Casablanca Map 7, F9. 147 W 43rd St, btw 6th and 7th ⊤1-888/922-7225 or 212/869-1212, ⊛www.casablancahotel.com. Moorish tiles, ceiling fans, and, of course, *Rick's Café* are all here in this unusual, thoughtful, and under-stated theme hotel. While the feeling is 1940s Morocco, the amenities (Internet access, cable television, work spaces) are more up-to-date, with wine, cheese, and cookies served in the after-noon, and bottled water and Belgian chocolates at turndown. Doubles from $239.

Essex House Map 7, F5. 160 Central Park South, btw 6th and 7th ⊤212/247-0300, ⊛www.essexhouse.com. A beautiful hotel for a special occasion, *Essex House* was restored by its previous Japanese owners to its original Art Deco splendor. The best rooms have spectacular Central Park views. Despite the excellent service and marble lobby, the atmosphere is not at all formal or hushed. Doubles $379–649, or as low as $259 in summer.

Le Parker Meridien Map 7, F6. 118 W 57th St, btw 6th and 7th ⊤212/245-5000, ⊛www.parkermeridien.com. Five years of work and $60 million transformed the famous *Parker Meridien*, which now boasts a huge fitness center, a rare rooftop pool, and 24hr room service, as well as gimmicky pluses like cartoon-playing elevators and glowing room numbers. The acclaimed breakfast-only *Norma's* restaurant has fun with its many inventive options: Foie Gras Brioche French Toast, Flat-As-A-Pancake Crabcake, or Zillion Dollar Lobster Frittata with Seruga caviar ($100–1000). From $355 ($275 in the summer).

Mandarin Oriental New York Map 7, E5. 80 Columbus Circle, at 60th ⊤1-866/801-8880 or 212/805-8800, ⊛www.mandarinoriental.com. Situated on floors 35 to 54

ACCOMMODATION

of the Time Warner Center on Columbus Circle, with some of the best views in the city, lies this brand-new luxury hotel. Rooms are a testament to opulence, featuring cherrywood floors and original artwork, deep marble baths, and LCD flat-screen TVs, with floor-to-ceiling views of Central Park, the Hudson River, or the Manhattan skyline. Doubles from $655–995 (from $479 in the summer).

Mansfield Map 7, H9. 12 W 44th St, at 5th ℡1-800/255-5167 or 212/227-8700, Ⓦwww .mansfieldhotel.com. One of the loveliest hotels in the city, with its recessed floor spotlighting, copper-domed salon, clubby library, and nightly jazz welcoming guests from behind the front desk. There's a charming, slightly quirky feel about the place – an echo, perhaps, of its turn-of-the-nineteenth-century role as a pad for New York's most eligible bachelors. With the European breakfast and all-day cappuccino, a great deal at $249–339 for a double.

Mayfair Map 7, E8. 242 W 49th St, btw Broadway and 8th ℡1-800/556-2932 or 212/586-0300, Ⓦwww.mayfairnewyork.com. This nonsmoking boutique hotel, across the street from the St Malachay Actors' Chapel, has beautifully decorated rooms, its

own restaurant, and a charming, old-world feel, emphasized by the historic photographs on loan from the Museum of the City of New York. Doubles $204–280, with summer rates from $188.

Paramount Map 7, E8. 235 W 46th St, btw Broadway and 8th ℡212/764-5500, Ⓦwww .nycparamount.com. Popular with a pop and media crowd that comes to enjoy the theatrical public space (blue-lit staircase strewn with tea candles, gift shop as concession stand) designed by Philippe Starck. Rooms feature silk-screened headboards and fresh flowers, while the *Paramount Bar*, the *Library Bar*, and the *Mezzanine* restaurant are all busy and fun. Rates as low as $285 (or $189 in summer).

Royalton Map 7, G9. 44 W 44th St, btw 5th and 6th ℡1-800/606-6090 or 212/869-4400, Ⓦwww .royalton.com. Despite its midtown location, the *Royalton* attempts to capture the market for the discerning style-conscious, with white-draped chairs and candle-filled interiors designed by Philippe Starck. It has tried to become the new *Algonquin*, but is really as much a power-lunch venue for NYC's media and publishing set as a place to stay. Rooms are luxuriously minimalist, all white and stainless steel, although many boast working fireplaces to warm things up. Doubles $395–575 (summer $295–415).

Warwick Hotel New York Map 7, G7. 65 W 54th St, at 6th ☎212/247-2700, ⓦwww.warwickhotelny .com. Stars of the 1950s and 1960s – including Cary Grant, the Beatles, Elvis Presley, and JFK – stayed here as a matter of course. Although the hotel has lost its showbiz cachet, it's still a pleasant place, from the elegant lobby to the old-fashioned Italian-style *Ciao Europa* restaurant. Doubles $305–475, summer Web specials from $240.

Midtown East and the Upper East Side: East 42nd to 96th streets

The Drake Map 7, I6. 440 Park Ave, at 56th ☎212/421-0900, ⓦwww .newyork.swissotel.com. A first-class Swissôtel hotel with a bustling cocktail bar and superb seafood restaurant (*Quantum 56*), a spa, and gym. This was once an apartment building, so the rooms are large (the suites are super-large and expensive) and a bit more stylish than most others of the same level. Doubles $469–559, or $239–319 in summer.

Mark Map 7, I1. 25 E 77th St, at Madison ☎212/744-4300, ⓦwww .themarkhotel.com. A hotel that really lives up to its claims of sophistication and elegance. A redesign has kitted the lobby out with Biedermeier furniture and sleek Italian lighting. In the guestrooms, restaurant, and invitingly dark *Mark's Bar*, there's a similar emphasis on the best of everything. Doubles $540–660, or $435–525 in summer.

Pickwick Arms Map 7, J6. 230 E 51st St, btw 2nd and 3rd ☎212/355-0300, ⓦwww.pickwick arms.com. A pleasant budget hotel and, for the price, one of the best deals you'll get on the East Side. All 400 rooms are air-conditioned, with cable TV, direct-dial phones, and room service. The open-air roof deck with stunning views and café are added attractions. Single room with shared bathroom from $79 or private bathroom from $109, twins with bunk beds from $99, and doubles with private bathroom from $139.

Roger Smith Map 7, J8. 501 Lexington Ave, at 47th ☎1-800/445-0277 or 212/755-1400, ⓦwww .rogersmith.com. One of the best midtown hotels with very helpful service, individually decorated rooms, a great restaurant, and artworks and sculpture on display. Breakfast is included in the price, along with VCRs in most rooms and 2000 videos available from the hotel's library. Popular with bands and guests who like the artsy ambience. Doubles from $265; summer rates drop to $229.

San Carlos Map 7, J8. 150 E 50th St, btw Lexington and 3rd ☎1-800/722-2012 or 212/755-1800, ⓦwww.sancarloshotel.com. Well-situated near plenty of bars and restaurants, this is a useful standby when everything else is booked. Most of the large rooms have fully equipped kitchenettes. Doubles $330–390; in summer rates can drop to $270–310.

W Map 7, J8. 541 Lexington Ave, btw 49th and 50th ☎212/755-1200, ⓦwww.whotels.com. If the crowd hanging out in the *Whiskey Blue* bar, dining at *Heartbeat*, or just posing in the *Living Room* (that's the feel of the lobby, and its name, too) are anything to go by, the *W* might well be the hippest hotel in town. Clean, stylish rooms and other perks: Egyptian cotton on the feather beds, business services, gym, and spa. Doubles $369–449, summer weekends $209–269, summer weekdays $279–369.

Waldorf-Astoria Map 7, I8. 301 Park Ave, btw 49th and 50th ☎1-800/WALDORF or 212/355-3000, ⓦwww.waldorf.com. One of the great names in New York hotels, and restored to its 1930s glory, making it a wonderful place to stay if you can afford it – or

someone else is paying. Doubles $479–529; promotional summer rates can drop to $229.

The Upper West Side: Above West 59th Street

Lucerne Map 8, C9. 201 W 79th St, at Amsterdam ☎1-800/492-8122 or 212/875-1000, ⓦwww.thelucernehotel.com. This beautifully restored 1904 brownstone, with its extravagantly Baroque, red terracotta entrance, charming rooms, and friendly, helpful staff is a block from the American Museum of Natural History and close to the liveliest restaurant stretch of Columbus Ave. Doubles from $255, with summer rates from $195.

Malibu Studios Map 8, B3. 2688 Broadway, at 103rd ☎212/222-2954, ⓦwww.malibuhotelnyc .com. Excellent-value budget accommodation within walking distance of plenty of restaurants and nightlife. Prices range from $69 for clean, decent singles with shared facilities to $149 for a double with private bathroom. Credit cards not accepted.

Riverside Tower Map 8, B9. 80 Riverside Drive, at 80th ☎1-800/724-3136 or 212/877-5200, ⓦwww .riversidetowerhotel.com. Although the hallways are plain as can be and rooms – all with small refrigerators – are ultra-basic, it's the location in this exclusive and safe neighborhood, flanked by one of the city's most beautiful parks and with (on the upper floors) stunning views of the Hudson River, that sets this budget hotel apart from the others. Singles from $84 with private bathroom, while quads work out to around $30 per person per night. For a few dollars more than the double ($89), get the two-room suite for two people ($99).

Cafés, snacks, and light meals

N ew York's **cafés** and **bakeries** run the gamut of its population's ethnic and cultural influences. They can be found in every neighborhood, with the usual French, Italian, and American favorites probably most visible. The city also has a number of **coffeehouses** and **tearooms**, which outside of the obvious also might offer fruit juices, pastries, light snacks, and, on occasion, full meals. Most places more suitable for sit-down dinners we've listed in Chapter 22, "Restaurants"; what follows is a neighborhood by neighborhood guide to where to get a bite fast, usually quite cheap, and always delicious.

Chinatown, Little Italy, and the Lower East Side

Café Gitane Map 5, H6. 242 Mott St, at Prince ☎212/334-9552. Sunny little café that's extremely popular, serving coffee and creative, light lunch fare with a Moroccan slant.

Caffè Roma Map 5, H7. 385 Broome St, btw Mulberry and Mott

☎ 212/226-8413. Old Little Italy *pasticceria*, ideal for a drawn-out coffee and pastry. Try the homemade Italian cookies, exceptionally good cannoli (plain or dipped), or *gelato* at the counter in back.

Ceci-Cela Map 5, H7. 55 Spring St, at Mulberry ☎ 212/274-9179. Tiny French patisserie with a stand-up counter and bench out front for coffee and delectable baked goods. The croissants and palmiers are divine.

Chinatown Ice Cream Factory Map 4, G2. 65 Bayard St, btw Mott and Elizabeth ☎ 212/608-4170. An essential stop after sampling one of the restaurants nearby, but the wondrously unusual flavors make it good anytime. Specialties include green tea, ginger, almond cookies, and lychee ice cream.

Ferrara's Map 4, G1. 195 Grand St, btw Mott and Mulberry ☎ 212/226-6150. The best-known and most traditional of the Little Italy coffeehouses, this landmark has been around since 1892. Try the cheesecake, cannoli, or *granite* (Italian ices) in summer.

Grilled Cheese NYC Map 5, K6. 168 Ludlow St, btw Houston and Stanton ☎ 212/982-6600. Great grilled-cheese sandwiches and tomato soup, made with gourmet ingredients; very tiny dining space.

Kossar's Map 4, I1. 367 Grand St, at Essex ☎ 212/473-4810. Jewish baker whose bialys may be the best in New York.

Kwong Wah Cake Company Map 4, F2. 242 Canal St, at Lafayette ☎ 212/925-3614. You can't get more authentically Chinese than this cake establishment on teeming Canal Street.

Saint's Alp Teahouse Map 4, G2. 20 Elizabeth St, at Canal ☎ 212/227-2880. Great stop-off in Chinatown's heart if you don't want the full restaurant experience, with hot green tea, Chinese fruit drinks and shakes (many with tapioca pearls at the bottom of the cup), and a good choice of snacks – try the vegetable dumplings or preserved eggs.

Yonah Schimmel's Map 5, J5. 137 E Houston St, btw Forsyth and Eldridge ☎ 212/477-2858. Knishes, baked fresh on the premises, and wonderful bagels. Unpretentious and patronized by a mixture of wrinkled old men wisecracking in Yiddish and young uptowners slumming it while they wade through the Sunday papers.

CAFÉS, SNACKS, AND LIGHT MEALS

SoHo and TriBeCa

Balthazar Bakery Map 5, G7. 80 Spring St, btw Crosby and Broadway ☎212/965-1414. Next door to the celebrated *Balthazar* brasserie, this bakery has wonderful breads and pastries both simple and ornate, without the attitude.

Bouley Bakery Cafe Map 4, D3. 120 W Broadway, btw Duane and Reade ☎212/964-2525. Wunder-kind David Bouley's latest, a tiny bakery-restaurant with truly great breads and baked goods, as well as reasonably priced light food. Make sure to turn right once through the door, or you'll end up in the *très* expensive restaurant.

Hampton Chutney Map 5, G6. 68 Prince St, at Crosby ☎212/226-9996. The American sandwich takes a detour through Indian breads and ingredients. Out of the ordinary, and quite good.

Snack Map 5, E6. 105 Thompson St, btw Prince and Spring ☎212/925-1040. Some fresh Greek food and *mezzes* will only set you back about $10 at lunch. Be prepared to wait for a table at this thimble-sized space.

Teany Map 5, K6. 90 Rivington St, btw Orchard and Ludlow ☎212/475-9190. Nice Lower East Side stop-off for a wide selection of teas and tea sandwiches, baked beans on toast, and Welsh rarebit.

Yaffa Tea Room Map 4, C3. 353 Greenwich St, at Harrison ☎212/274-9403. Hidden in an unassuming corner of TriBeCa next to the *Yaffa Bar*, this res-taurant serves Mediterranean-style dinners, good brunch, and a cozy high tea (reservations required).

The West Village

A Salt and Battery Map 5, C2. 112 Greenwich Ave, at West 13th ☎212/691-2713. Run by the Brits from *Tea and Sympathy* next door, and an authentic enough affair, with decent battered cod and plaice, great chips, and mushy peas. However, it may be the most expensive chippie in the world, with a fish supper costing

you a good twenty bucks.

Café Le Figaro Map 5, D5. 184 Bleecker St, at MacDougal ☎212/677-1100. Former Beat hangout during the 1950s and now sporting a somewhat forced "Left Bank" sidewalk-café vibe, though with good cappuccino and pastries. If you want to watch weekend tourists flooding

West Village streets, this is the place to do it.

Caffè Dante Map 5, D5. 79 MacDougal St, btw Bleecker and Houston ☎212/982-5275. A morning stop-off for many locals since 1915. Good cappuccino, double espresso, and caffè alfredo with ice cream. Often jammed with NYU students and teachers.

Caffè Reggio Map 5, D4. 119 MacDougal St, btw Bleecker and 3rd ☎212/475-9557. One of the first Village coffeehouses, dating back to the 1920s, always crowded and with tables outside in warm weather for people-watching.

Elixir Map 5, A3. 523 Hudson St, btw 10th and Charles ☎212/352-9952. Casual, friendly joint where you can order juices, smoothies, and seasonal elixirs, or just park yourself and think healthy. There's another branch in TriBeCa at 95 W Broadway, btw Reade and Chambers (☎212/233-6171).

Magnolia Bakery Map 5, A3. 401 Bleecker St, at 11th ☎212/462-2572. Like you've died and gone to sweets heaven: huge slabs of moist crumbly dessert, that homemade smell in the air, and staff frosting cakes while you watch. In addition to chocolate, vanilla, hummingbird (a mix of carrots, pineapple, coconut, and nuts), and red velvet, there's banana pudding with wafer cookies and cupcakes.

Peanut Butter and Company Map 5, E4. 240 Sullivan St, at West 3rd ☎212/677-3995. This establishment serves up peanut butter, on sandwiches and otherwise, in ways you never imagined.

Tea and Sympathy Map 5, C2. 108 Greenwich Ave, btw 12th and 13th ☎212/807-8329. Self-consciously British tearoom, serving an afternoon high tea full of traditional British staples like jam roly-poly and treacle pudding, along with shepherd's pie and scones. Perfect for British tourists feeling homesick.

Village Delight Map 5, B4. 323 Bleecker St, btw Christopher and Grove ☎212/633-9275. Healthy-sized sandwiches of whole turkey or roast beef (made daily), with an assortment of Middle Eastern side dishes.

The East Village

B & H Dairy Map 5, I3. 127 2nd Ave, btw 7th and St Mark's ☎212/505-8065. This tiny luncheonette serves homemade soup, challah, and latkes. You can also create your own juice combination, and they've got a good veggie choice.

Café Pick Me Up Map 5, K3. 145 Ave A, at 9th ☎212/673-7231. This softly-lit East Village charmer hosts locals both young and old, with tiny wooden tables designed for close conversations or a quiet read. Choose from quiche or cake, coffee or wine, and enjoy the owner's varied collection of international music. Snag the sidewalk seating and you can pick up WiFi from Tompkins Square Park, just across the way.

Damask Falafel Map 5, K4. 89 Ave A, btw 5th and 6th ☎212/673-5016. One of the better Middle Eastern snack providers in the area. The usual falafel and hummus are supplemented by exquisite baklavas and similarly rich Mediterranean dessert pastries.

De Robertis Map 5, J2. 176 1st Ave, btw 9th and 10th ☎212/674-7137. Traditional Italian bakery/café that's been here since 1904 and has since been featured in multiple Woody Allen flicks for its Old New York vibe. Wonderful ricotta cheesecake and espresso.

Liquiteria Map 5, I2. 170 2nd Ave, at 11th ☎212/358-0300. The best smoothies in Manhattan (try the Orangasm) plus delicious, healthy lunches like oatmeal with fresh fruit and organic PB&Js.

Moishe's Map 5, I3. 115 2nd Ave, btw 7th and St Mark's ☎212/505-8555. Good prune danishes, excellent hamantashen (three-cornered cookies stuffed with chocolate or jam), seeded rye, and other kosher treats at this take-out bakery.

Pomme Frites Map 5, I3. 123 2nd Ave, btw 7th and 8th ☎212/674-1234. Arguably the best fries in the city, with plenty of creative, Belgian-style dipping sauces available.

Via Della Pace Map 5, I3. 48 E 7th St, at 2nd ☎212/253-5803. Dark and cozy East Village café with good Argentine pastas and sandwiches, plus a great selection of coffees and desserts; the tiramisu is especially delicious.

Chelsea

Amy's Bread Map 6, D9. 75 9th Ave, btw 15th and 16th ☎212/462-4338. You can find Amy's Bread in fine stores citywide – but it's freshest here; they make great cakes, too.

Big Cup Map 6, E7. 228 8th Ave, btw 21st and 22nd ☎212/206-0059. Popular coffee shop with fresh muffins and big, hot cups of joe. Comfortable couches and chairs make it the perfect place to read the paper and relax into your day.

Bagels

Theories abound as to the origin of the modern **bagel**. Most likely, it is a derivative of the pretzel, with the word bagel coming from the German *beigen*, "to bend," and the famous hole made them easy to carry on a long stick to hawk on street corners. Whatever their birthplace, bagels are a New York institution. They are most traditionally enjoyed with cream cheese and lox (smoked salmon), though of course you can top them with anything you like. A list of some of the better bagel purveyors is below. (If you prefer bialys, a drier, flatter bagel-type bread without a hole, head straight to *Kossar's*; see p.199.)

Bagel Buffet Map 5, D3. 406 6th Ave, btw 8th and 9th ☏212/477-0448.

Bagels on the Square Map 5, D4. 7 Carmine St, btw Bleecker and 6th ☏212/691-3041.

David's Bagels Map 5, J1. 228 1st Ave, btw 13th and 14th ☏212/533-8766.

Ess-A-Bagel Map 6, M7. 359 1st Ave, at East 21st ☏212/260-2252.

H & H Bagels Map 7, C1. 2239 Broadway, at West 78th ☏212/595-8000.

Hot & Crusty Bagel Café Map 8, B7. 2387 Broadway, btw 87th and 88th ☏212/496-0632.

Yonah Schimmel's Map 5, J5. 137 E Houston St, btw Forsyth and Eldridge ☏212/477-2858.

F&B Güdtfood Map 6, F7. 269 W 23rd St, btw 7th and 8th ☏646/486-4441. Unusual premise and a chic (for a slender storefront) execution: all manner of franks (vegetarian, too) and beignets (awesome with apricot dip), with fries of course. Humorous menu, and classy cheap joint.

Eat-in or take-out.

News Bar Map 6, H8. 2 W 19th St, btw 5th and 6th ☏212/255-3996. Tiny minimalist café with equally great selections of pastries and periodicals. Draws photographer and model types as well as regular people, making it good for people-watching.

Union Square, Gramercy Park, and Murray Hill

Chez Laurence Map 6, I2. 245 Madison Ave, at 38th ☎ 212/683-0284. Well-placed, friendly little patisserie that makes cheap breakfasts and decent, inexpensive lunches – and good coffee at any time of the day. Closed Sun.

City Bakery Map 6, I8. 22 E 17th St, btw Broadway and 5th ☎ 212/366-1045. Local bakery with a small, no-frills seating area. They use fresh greenmarket ingredients from around the corner at Union Square, and serve reasonable soups and light lunch fare, but above all masterfully delicate tartlets, creamy hot chocolate, and crème brûlée. Closed Sun.

Eisenberg's Sandwich Shop Map 6, I7. 174 5th Ave, btw 22nd and 23rd ☎ 212/675-5096. This narrow little restaurant is a Flatiron institution. A tuna sandwich and some matzoh-ball soup will cure what ails you.

Midtown West

Brasserie Centrale Map 7, F7. 1700 Broadway, at West 53rd St ☎ 212/757-2233. A rare midtown place where you can linger over coffee, freshly baked treats, or a full meal. The menu offers a range of burgers, soups, salads, pastas, and average French-tinged brasserie standards (stick with the simpler items on the menu). Large outdoor seating area. Open 24hrs.

Cupcake Café Map 6, D2. 522 9th Ave, at West 39th ☎ 212/465-1530. A delightful little joint, offering decent soups and sandwiches at bargain prices, as well as great cakes, cupcakes, and pies. Anything with fruit is a must.

Poseidon Bakery Map 7, D9. 629 9th Ave, btw 44th and 45th ☎ 212/757-6173. Decadent baklava and other sweet Greek pastries, strudels, and cookies, as well as spinach and meat pies. Known for the hand-rolled phyllo dough they make on the premises and supply to many restaurants in the city. Closed Sun and Mon.

Soup Kitchen International Map 7, E6. 259A W 55th St, at 8th ☎ 212/757-7730. The real-life counterpart of Jerry Seinfeld's friend the Soup Nazi, with rich soups highly priced but worth it. Closed in summer.

Midtown East

Little Pie Company Map 6, J1.
Grand Central Station, lower food concourse ☎212/736-4780. True to its name, the *Little Pie Company* serves three-berry pies that are to die for, while the peach-raspberry, available in summer, has been known to provoke rioting. If it's just you, pick up a five-inch personal pie.

Grand Central bites

Midtown East is largely a culinary wasteland for those seeking a good café or a quick nosh, but **Grand Central Station**, at 42nd St and Lexington Ave (**Map 6, J1**), has a host of small spots on its dining concourse level that are of surprisingly high quality, plus a sprawling market on the main concourse that holds a number of specialty grocery shops and a nice bakery. Here you'll find everything from Southern BBQ, gourmet pizza, a kosher deli counter, and even exotic spices for cooking at home. It's the best spot for a quick bite in the entire neighborhood.

Brother Jimmy's BBQ dining concourse ☎212/661-4022. Don't miss the Carolina-style yellow barbecue pulled-pork sandwiches here. All BBQ is cooked for 5–12 hours over an open flame before serving. They also deliver locally.

Café Spice dining concourse ☎646/227-1300. Quickie high-quality curries. The lamb vindaloo is tasty and very hot.

Ciao Bella Gelateria dining concourse ☎212/867-5311. Exceptional Italian treats including an out-of-this-world blood-orange sorbet and a fine pistachio *gelato*.

Corrado main concourse ☎212/599-4332. Fresh-baked breads, a yummy chocolate-mousse cake, and a small sit-down area in which to enjoy a brief respite from Midtown.

Jacques-Imo's To Geaux dining concourse ☎212/661-4023. Yummy Cajun take-out treats include fried green tomatoes, spicy crawfish, and sweet-potato pie.

21

CAFÉS, SNACKS, AND LIGHT MEALS

Upper West Side and Morningside Heights

Café Lalo Map 8, C8. 201 W 83rd St, btw Amsterdam and Broadway ☎212/496-6031. The spirit of Paris, complete with cramped tables and inconsistent service. Try the "shirred" eggs (made fluffy with a cappuccino machine) with all sorts of herbs and add-ins, or the wonderful Belgian waffles. Great desserts.

Café Mozart Map 7, E3. 154 W 70th St, btw Central Park West and Columbus ☎212/595-9797. This faded old Viennese coffeehouse is the place to go after a night at the opera. Double up on dessert and get the apple crumb cake and the iced espresso with chocolate ice cream.

Caffè la Fortuna Map 7, E2. 69 W 71st St, btw Central Park West and Columbus ☎212/724-5846. The atmosphere here is dark, comfy, and inviting. You can sip a coffee all day long in the shade of their peaceful garden, and their Italian pastries are heavenly.

Edgar's Café Map 8, B8. 255 W 84th St, btw West End Ave and Broadway ☎212/496-6126. A pleasant coffeehouse with good (though expensive) desserts and light snacks, great hot cider in the winter, and well-brewed coffees and teas all the time.

Gray's Papaya Map 7, C2. 2090 Broadway, at West 72nd ☎212/799-0243. Order two all-beef franks and a papaya juice for a true New York experience. No ambience, no seats, just good, cheap grub.

Hungarian Pastry Shop Map 8, C1. 1030 Amsterdam Ave, btw 110th and 111th ☎212/866-4230. This simple, no-frills coffeehouse is a favorite with Columbia University students and faculty alike. You can sip your espresso and read all day if you like; the only problem is choosing amongst the pastries, cookies, and cakes on offer, all of which are made on the premises.

Upper East Side

Payard Patisserie & Bistro Map 7, J2. 1032 Lexington Ave, btw 72nd and 73rd sts ☎212/717-5252. This is real Parisian pastry – buttery, creamy, and over-the-top. Cookies, cakes, and crème brûlée made to the exacting standards of the kitchen staffs of local millionaires.

Serendipity 3 Map 7, J5. 225 E 60th St, btw 2nd and 3rd ☎212/838-3531. Long-established eatery and ice-cream parlor adorned with Tiffany lamps. The frozen hot chocolate, a trademarked and copyrighted recipe, is out of this world, and the wealth of ice-cream offerings are a real treat too.

Wildgreen Café Map 8, J7. 1555 3rd Ave, at East 88th ☎212/828-7656. A small-town feel adds to the draw of this shop "where natural foods become gourmet." It's justly known for its muffins, salads, wraps, and juices.

Harlem and the outer boroughs

Athens 32–01 30th Ave, at Newtown, Astoria, Queens ☎718/626-2164. The Greekest of cafés, with spinach pies and specialty desserts.

Bedouin Tent 405 Atlantic Ave, at Bond, Brooklyn ☎718/852-5555. Fresh, delicious Middle Eastern pita sandwiches, salads, and pitzas; convenient to Brooklyn Heights and Cobble Hill.

Nathan's Famous Surf and Stillwell aves, Coney Island, Brooklyn ☎718/266-3161. The original hotdog stand – crowded, greasy, and totally irresistible.

Settepani Bakery 602 Lorimer St, btw Skillman and Conselyea, Williamsburg, Brooklyn ☎718/349-6524. Relaxing little Italian bakery that's been here for decades, with perfectly prepared cappuccinos and excellent chocolate croissants, marzipan, and other goodies.

Strictly Roots Map 9, C4. 2058 Adam Clayton Powell Blvd, btw 122nd and 123rd ☎212/864-8699. Harlem health-food café with protein shakes, smoothies, and apple-cider-sweetened sweetpotato pie.

22

Restaurants

New York is a rich port city that can get the best foodstuffs from anywhere in the world, and, as a major immigration gateway, it attracts chefs who know how to cook the world's cuisines properly, even exceptionally. As you stroll through the streets of New York, heavenly odors seem to emanate from every corner; it's not hard to work up an appetite.

Outside of **American** and **Continental cuisines** (more or less including New American, which can either dazzle with its inventive fusions or fail miserably and pretentiously), be prepared to confront a startling variety of **ethnic food**. In New York, none has had so dominant an effect as **Jewish food**, to the extent that many Jewish specialties – bagels, pastrami, cream cheese, and lox – are now considered archetypal New York. Others retain more specific identities. **Chinese** food includes the familiar Cantonese, as well as spicier Szechuan and Hunan dishes; most restaurants specialize in one or the other. **Japanese** food is widely available and very good; other Asian cuisines include **Indian** and a broad sprinkling of **Thai**, **Korean**, **Vietnamese**, and **Indonesian** restaurants.

Italian cooking is widespread and not terribly expensive, and typically a fairly safe bet. **French** restaurants tend to be pricier, although there are an increasing number of bistros and brasseries turning out authentic and reliable French nosh for attractive prices.

There is also a whole range of **Eastern European** restaurants – Russian, Ukrainian, Polish, and Hungarian – that serve well-priced, filling fare. **Caribbean**, **Central American**, and **South American** restaurants are on the rise in New York, and often offer a good deal and a large, satisfying, and often spicy meal. Other places include weird hybrids like Chinese-Peruvian, Japanese-Brazilian, and any number of **vegetarian** and **wholefood** eateries to cater to any taste or fad.

As for where you'll be going for these foods, we've divided our selections below by **neighborhood** (and then cuisine), and have given very brief descriptions for what you might expect to find in those areas. For the most part you won't have to walk very far to find a good place in almost any district, but many of the ones listed here are worth a trip on the subway or in a cab.

Financial District and City Hall

Financial District restaurants vary between lunchtime take-out feeding troughs and overpriced power-lunch spots for the Wall Street crowd. There are, though, a couple of excellent options should you find yourself in the neighborhood. The area revolves around trading hours, so many restaurants close early, and are closed or have reduced hours on weekends.

American and Continental

Bridge Café Map 4, G5. 279 Water St, at Dover ☎212/227-3344. They say there's been a bar here since 1794, but this place looks very up-to-the-minute. The good crab cakes come fresh out of Long Island Sound, and there are plenty of upscale beers with

which to wash them down. The rare eighteenth-century frame house, painted red with black trim, is well worth a look. Entrees are priced between $20–28.

Italian

Carmine's Bar and Grill Map 4, G5. 140 Beekman St, at Front

☎212/962-8606. In business since 1903, this place specializes in Northern Italian–style seafood and exudes a comfortable if run-down old New York ambience.

Try a glass of the house wine and a bowl of linguini in clam sauce for lunch. Reasonably priced at $15–20 for an entree.

Chinatown and Little Italy

If authentic Chinese, Thai, and Vietnamese food is what you're after, best head for the busy streets of **Chinatown**. Mulberry Street is **Little Italy**'s main drag, and though often crowded with tourists, the carnival atmosphere can make dinner and coffee a worthwhile excursion.

Asian

Canton Map 4, H2. 45 Division St, btw Bowery and Market ☎212/226-4441. Fairly upscale compared to other Chinatown restaurants in terms of decor, style, and service, but only marginally more expensive. Seafood is the specialty here; bring your own booze. Closed Mon and Tues.

Joe's Shanghai Map 4, G3. 9 Pell St, btw Bowery and Mott ☎212/233-8888. Probably Chinatown's most famous restaurant, this place is always packed, with good reason. Start with the soup dumplings and work through some seafood dishes for the main course; communal tables.

New York Noodletown Map 4, G2. 28 Bowery, at Bayard ☎212/349-0923. Despite the name, noodles aren't the real draw at this down-to-earth eatery – the soft-shell crabs are crisp, salty, and delicious. Good roast meats (try the baby pig) and soups too.

Sun Hop Shing Map 4, G3. 21 Mott St, at Mosco ☎212/267-2729. Not much to look at (really a diner) but this dim sum spot has some of the best seafood in China-town. Order from the menu but watch out for the chef's unwritten, rotating specials.

Thailand Restaurant Map 4, G2. 106 Bayard St, at Baxter ☎212/349-3132. The well-priced Thai food is eaten at long communal tables here; whole-fish dishes, crispy and spicy, are standouts.

Italian

La Luna Map 5, H9. 112 Mulberry St, btw Canal and Hester ☎212/226-8657. One of Little Italy's longest-

established and best-value choices. The attitude of the waiters is gruff, and the food only middling, but the atmosphere is fun and it's a popular joint, packing in a crowd.
Lombardi's Map 5, H7. 32 Spring St, btw Mott and Mulberry ☎212/941-7994. Arguably some of the best pizza in town, including an amazing clam pie; no slices though. Ask for roasted garlic on the side.
Vincent's Clam Bar Map 5, H8. 119 Mott St, at Hester ☎212/226-8133. A Little Italy mainstay that serves fresh, cheap, and spicy seafood dishes – clams, mussels, and squid.

The Lower East Side

In spots, the **Lower East Side** seems like a throwback to early immigrant sweatshop days; at others it's a place where the city's hipsters hang out. Either way, it's still the best place to get a pickle.

American and Continental

71 Clinton Fresh Food Map 5, L6. 71 Clinton St, at Rivington ☎212/614-6960. Popular with foodies and hipsters alike, this cozy spot serves some of the best food in the city. Either the beer-braised short ribs or sea bass crusted with edamame will send you for a loop; start with the potato torte or salmon-avocado tartare.
Schiller's Liquor Bar Map 5, K6. 131 Rivington St, at Norfolk ☎212/260-4555. Fairly high-end foodie restaurant made up to look like a prohibition-era speakeasy. Menu offerings are eclectic and self-consciously "Americana", including pan-fried trout and pork chops with sautéed onions.

WD-50 Map 5, L6. 50 Clinton St, btw Rivington and Stanton ☎212/477-2900. The emperor's new clothes or the future of gourmet food? Decide for yourself at this experimental *haute cuisine* spot crammed into a retrofitted corner bodega, where the *71 Clinton Fresh Food* chef gets to "go diva" with unconventional entrees like venison tartar with edamame ice cream and pork belly with black soy beans and turnips.

Italian

Petrosino Map 5, K5. 190 Norfolk, at Houston ☎212/673-3773. The cool interiors make for a romantic environment within which to enjoy *nouveau* Sicilian dishes, including roast branzino, rigatoni with sausage and peas, and a flourless chocolate cake. Also has an outstanding and fairly priced southern Italian wine list.

Jewish and Eastern European

Katz's Deli Map 5, K5. 205 E Houston St, btw Essex and Ludlow ☎212/254-2246. Cafeteria-style or sit down and be served. The overstuffed pastrami or corned beef sandwiches, doused with mustard and with a side pile of pickles, should keep you going for about a week. Also famous for their egg creams; open seven days a week. Don't lose your meal ticket or they'll charge you an arm and a leg.

TriBeCa

Still one of New York's trendiest neighborhoods, **TriBeCa** is the place to come for high-end New York dining, though you often pay for the vista as much as the victuals. That said, there are divine meals to be had in TriBeCa – and the people-watching is not bad either.

American and Continental

Bubby's Map 4, C2. 120 Hudson St, btw Franklin and North Moore ☎212/219-0666. A relaxed TriBeCa restaurant serving homely, health-conscious American food. Great scones, mashed potatoes, rosemary chicken, and soups. A good, moderately priced brunch spot, too – the trout and eggs is killer.
Odeon Map 4, D3. 145 W Broadway, at Thomas ☎212/233-0507. *Odeon* has shown surprising staying power, perhaps because the eclectic food choices are actually pretty good and the people-watching still can't be beat. Entrees go for around $15–20 and, on the whole, are worth it.
Tribeca Grill Map 4, C2. 375 Greenwich St, at Franklin ☎212/941-3900. Some people come for a glimpse of owner Robert De Niro, when they should really be concentrating on the fine American cooking with Asian and Italian accents at around $30 a main course. The setting is nice, too: an airy, brick-walled eating area around a central Tiffany bar. Worth the money as a treat, despite the trendy scene and gawking tourists.

Asian

66 Map 4, E3. 241 Church St, at Leonard ☎212/925-0202. Located in the historic Textile Building and designed by Richard Meier, this Vongerichten hot spot is all Chinese, serving inspired dishes from a variety of provinces. Communal tables make the atmosphere lively.

Nobu Map 4, C2. 105 Hudson St, at Franklin ☎212/219-0500. Robert De Niro's best-known New York restaurant, whose lavish woodland decor complements superlative Japanese cuisine, especially sushi, at the ultra-high prices you would expect. If you can't get a reservation, try *Next Door Nobu*, located – wait for it – just next door.

Austrian and Hungarian

Danube Map 4, D3. 30 Hudson St, at Duane ☎212/791-3771 Opulent puff pastry of a restaurant that evokes old-world Viennese dining rooms, with Gustav Klimt–inspired murals, and service so efficient it can make you feel inadequate. Try the port-glazed venison and top it off with a Middle-European white wine.

French and Belgian

Bouley Map 4, E3. 120 W Broadway, btw Duane and Reade ☎212/964-2525. Modern French food made from the freshest ingredients. Popular with city celebrities, but costs for the magnificent meals can be softened by opting for the prix-fixe lunch and dinner options.

Chanterelle Map 4, C3. 2 Harrison St, at Hudson ☎212/966-6960. Some say while in New York you should live on stale bread all week and spend all your money on the *haute* French cuisine here – like roast asparagus with black truffles or crêpinette of guinea hen – which is of the finest order.

SoHo and NoLita

Though **SoHo** is slowly losing cachet to TriBeCa and other trendy neighborhoods, a number of the city's top restaurants still make their home here. The **NoLita** strip at the east end of SoHo is notable for its wildly popular budget restaurants, while in the district's heart you should expect to pay top dollar for the more venerable hot spots.

Asian

Blue Ribbon Sushi Map 5, D6. 119 Sullivan St, btw Prince and Spring ☎212/343-0404. The focus here is actually more on the outstanding raw bar, but they have excellent sushi as well. The lines for a table can be long and they don't take reservations. Our advice: have a couple of cocktails and relax – the kitchen is open until 2am.

Lovely Day Map 5, H7. 196 Elizabeth St, btw Prince and Spring ☎212/925-3310. Budget restaurant frequented by the SoHo/Lower East Side hipster set. The homely interior decor belies the place's jam-packed, lively atmosphere at all hours. Asian-leaning menu with nicely priced pad Thai, satay, and curry.

Omen Map 5, E6. 113 Thompson St, at Prince ☎212/925-8923. Traditional Kyoto restaurant with a soothing atmosphere and nice touches like beautiful crockery and menus made from bamboo and rice paper, with traditional Japanese calligraphy. Named for a noodle shop but with the best sushi in the area by far (try the bluefin sashimi platter, formed in the shape of a rose), with a rotating seasonal menu and extensive sake list. If you go to one Japanese restaurant in New York, make it this one.

Caribbean, Central, and South American

Café Habana Map 5, H6. 17 Prince St, at Elizabeth ☎212/625-2002. Small and always crowded, this Cuban/South American eatery features some of the best skirt steak and fried plantains this side of Havana. They also have a take-out window next door with great *café con leche*.

French

Balthazar Map 5, G7. 80 Spring St, btw Crosby and Broadway ☎212/965-1414. The tastefully ornate Parisian decor and non-stop beautiful people keep your eyes busy until the food arrives; then all you can do is savor the fresh oysters and mussels, the exquisite pastries, and everything in between. Great for late dinners as the kitchen is open until 2am.

Raoul's Map 5, E6. 180 Prince St, btw Sullivan and Thompson ☎212/966-3518. French bistro seemingly lifted from Paris. The food, especially the steak *au poivre* and crayfish risotto, plus service are wonderful – as you'd expect at prices as high as these. Reservations recommended. Closed Aug.

Italian

Bianca Map 5, H5. 5 Bleecker St, btw Bowery and Elizabeth ☎212/260-4666. Great little Italian spot with an array of excellent pastas, though people come here for the delicious Mediterranean whitefish and the fried artichokes – a house specialty. Great hangout for those who want an intimate dinner without a lot of the ambient noise found in other area eateries.

The West Village

The **West Village** offers a decent array of discreet, upscale spots in its angled streets, and is probably the most popular neighborhood of all for langorous weekend brunches.

American and Continental

Blue Hill Map 5, D3. 75 Washington Place, btw MacDougal and 6th ☎212/539-1776. One of the better spots in the West Village, crowded but with elbow room between tables, serving rustic American fare like parsnip soup and braised cod. Don't miss the rich chocolate bread pudding.

Corner Bistro Map 5, A2. 331 W 4th St, at Jane ☎212/242-9502. Down-home pub with cavernous cubicles, a great jukebox, and maybe the best burger and fries ($6.50) in town. Long-standing haunt of West Village literary types and jazz aficionados, a mix of locals and die-hard fans line up nightly until 4am, but don't be discouraged – the line moves faster than it looks.

Grange Hall Map 5, B4. 50 Commerce St, at Barrow ☎212/924-5246. Tucked away in one of the most beautiful West Village corners, this Depression era–designed eatery is a hit for dinner, brunch, and drinks. Cranberry pork chops and potato pancakes are recommended. Entrees $11–17.

Mary's Fish Camp Map 5, B3. 64 Charles St, at 4th ☎646/486-2185. Lobster rolls, bouillabaisse, and seasonal veggies adorn the menu at this intimate West Village spot, where you can almost smell the salty air. Go early, as the reservation line lasts into the night – and bring a healthy wallet.

The Pink Teacup Map 5, B4. 42 Grove St, btw Bleecker and Bedford ☎212/807-6755. Long-standing

Southern soul-food-institution in the heart of the Village, with good smothered pork chops, exceedingly tender fried catfish, and heaping pulled-pork sandwiches. Brunch too, but no credit cards.

Asian

Prem-on Thai Map 5, D5. 138 W Houston, btw MacDougal and Sullivan ℡212/353-2338. Friendly Thai outpost with a lovely garden dining area. Pad Thai is a good bet, but they also have delicious Southeast Asian curries and fish dishes.

Tomoe Sushi Map 5, E5. 172 Thompson St, btw Bleecker and Houston ℡212/777-9346. While the nightly lines might look daunting, the wait is worth it for the fresh, melt-in-your-mouth sashimi in this back-to-basics space. If they have soft-shell crabs, get 'em rolled.

Mexican

Mi Cocina Map 5, A1. 57 Jane St, at 8th ℡212/627-8273. Authentic Mexican food such as spiced, meat-stuffed *poblano* chillies in an upscale setting. Often crowded, so be prepared to wait.

French and Belgian

Café de Bruxelles Map 6, E9. 118 Greenwich Ave, at 13th ℡212/206-1830. Very authentic and popular Belgian restaurant in the West Village. Try the *waterzooi*, a rich and creamy chicken stew, or mussels served any way you like.

Chez Brigitte Map 5, B2. 77 Greenwich Ave, btw Bank and 7th ℡212/929-6736. Only a dozen people fit into this tiny restaurant, which serves stews, all-day roast meat dinners for under $10, and other bargains from a simple menu.

Jarnac Just west of Map 5, A2. 328 W 12th St, at Greenwich ℡212/924-3413. Cozy little West Village restaurant whose hearty and authentic southwestern French food makes a great low-key excuse for avoiding the trendy masses at nearby *Pastis*. The menu changes regularly, but *Jarnac* is principally a rustic French restaurant, with an occasional New York twist. Moderate prices, too – the prix-fixe menu is $34 and most main courses run around $20–25.

Markt Map 6, D9. 401 W 14th St, at 9th ℡212/727-3314. Very large and very noisy brasserie, serving decent Belgian standards – mussels, *waterzooi*, and of course *frites* – along with one of the city's best choice of Belgian ales. Not the place for a quiet tête-à-tête, though.

Paris Commune Map 5, A3. 99 Bank St, at Greenwich ℡212/929-0509.

Romantic West Village bistro with reliable French home cooking and a fireplace. Memorable French toast and wild-mushroom ravioli at moderate prices. Long lines for brunch.

Italian

Arturo's Pizza Map 5, E5. 106 W Houston St, at Thompson ☎212/677-3820. Coal-oven pizzas (no slices) that rival some of the best pies in town. While-you-eat entertainment often includes live jazz, and there are a couple of outdoor tables on busy Houston Street.

Babbo Map 5, D3. 110 Waverly Place, btw 6th and MacDougal ☎212/777-0303. This Mario Batali eatery offers delicious, creative Italian dishes – beef-cheek ravioli and various takes on scrapple garner much of the praise – attentive service, and an interesting selection of wine; it's quite popular, so reserve well in advance (two weeks is best). Expect to pay at least $50–70 per head.

John's of Bleecker Street Map 5, C4. 278 Bleecker St, btw 6th and 7th ☎212/243-1680. A full-service restaurant that serves some of the city's best and most popular pizza, with a crust that is thin and coal-charred. Be prepared to wait in line. No slices, no takeaways. Uptown branches at

408 E 64th St, btw 1st and York (☎212/935-2895) and 48 W 65th St, btw Columbus and Central Park West (☎212/721-7001).

Lupa Map 5, E5. 170 Thompson St, btw Bleecker and Houston ☎212/982-5089. Another Mario Batali restaurant, this fine, moderately priced trattoria serves hearty, rustic Italian specialties such as osso buco, saltimbocca, and gnocchi with fennel sausage. Hint: go before 6.30pm and you'll have no problem getting a table.

Spanish

Sevilla Map 5, B3. 62 Charles St, at 4th ☎212/929-3189. Wonderful Village old-timer that is still a favorite neighborhood haunt. Dark, fragrant (from garlic) restaurant with good, moderately priced food. Terrific paella and large pitchers of strong sangría.

Spain Map 5, B1. 113 W 13th St, btw 7th and 8th ☎212/929-9580. Modest prices (entrees are $10–18) and large portions are the prime attractions of this cozy Spanish restaurant. Casual atmosphere and tacky decor in the larger back dining room – this neighborhood place has been here forever. Order the paella and split it with a friend.

The East Village

It seems a new Italian restaurant, sushi bar, or chic café opens every day in the **East Village**, and the prices here are typically significantly lower than what you'll find for high-quality meals in the rest of the city. Even more inexpensive are the homely Indian restaurants on East 6th Street and the filling Ukrainian eateries a bit north.

American and Continental

Gotham Bar & Grill Map 5, F2. 12 E 12th St, btw 5th and University ☎212/620-4020. This restaurant serves marvelous American fare in an airy, trendy setting. Generally reckoned to be one of the city's best restaurants, and it's worth a drink at the bar to see the beautiful people walk in.

Jack's Luxury Oyster Bar Map 5, I4. 246 E 5th St, btw 2nd and 3rd ☎212/673-0338. Great seafood joint, but eye-poppingly pricey. Their raw bar is among the best, and they also do a $75 tasting menu that's worth every penny. You can choose to sit in the downstairs "brasserie" or the more intimate and homely upstairs space, which has a fireplace.

Prune Map 5, I5. 54 E 1st St, btw 1st and 2nd ☎212/677-6221. Cramped yet adventurous and full of surprises, this Mediterranean restaurant delivers one of the city's most exciting dining experiences, serving dishes such as sweetbreads wrapped in bacon, seared sea bass with Berber spices, and buttermilk ice cream with pistachio puff pastry. Pricey, but not as expensive as you might think.

The Tasting Room Map 5, J5. 72 E 1st St, btw 1st and 2nd ☎212/358-7831. A longtime favorite for its casual fine dining, the ostensible purpose of the food here is to accompany the enviable wine list (hence the name). But the grub itself is worth going out of your way for: braised pork tongue, poached trout, sautéed blowfish, and a good cheese course.

Asian

Cyclo Map 5, J1. 203 1st Ave, btw 12th and 13th ☎212/673-3957. A wide range of well-prepared Vietnamese dishes, reasonably priced in an attractive setting. The crispy whole red snapper with spicy lime sauce is especially good, as are the desserts.

Dok Suni Map 5, J3. 119 1st Ave, btw 7th and St Mark's ☏ 212/477-9506. This dimly lit, somewhat small but stylish East Village restaurant has fast become a favorite for Korean home cooking like bibimbop (stir-fried vegetables, rice, and beef in a spicy red-pepper sauce), seafood pancakes, or *kim chee* rice. Moderately priced.

Hasaki Map 5, H3. 210 E 9th St, at 3rd ☏ 212/473-3327. Some of the best sushi around at this popular but mellow downstairs Japanese cubby hole. Sit at the sushi bar and the chefs will regale you with a variety of impromptu dishes that you won't find on the menu.

Jewel Bako Map 5, I4. 239 E 5th St, btw 2nd and 3rd ☏ 212/979-1012. Expensive Japanese delicacies, including a lot of sushi/sashimi offerings that you can't get elsewhere in New York and some exotic delicacies like live raw lobster (not for the faint of heart). A memorable dining experience, though very expensive.

Shabu Tatsu Map 5, I2. 216 E 10th St, btw 1st and 2nd ☏ 212/477-2972. This place offers great and moderately priced Korean barbecue. Choose a combination of meat or seafood platters, and have them cooked right at your table.

South American

Boca Chica Map 5, J5. 13 1st Ave, at 1st ☏ 212/473-0108. This is real South American stuff, piled high and washed down with black beer and fancy, fruity drinks. It gets crowded, especially late and on weekends, and the music is loud, so come in a party mood and bring your dancing shoes.

Flor's Kitchen Map 5, J2. 149 1st Ave, btw 9th and 10th ☏ 212/387-8949. Four-table Venezuelan *comedor* with delicious shredded beef and grilled chicken with saffron rice and beans. Don't miss the fruit shakes. Inexpensive.

Middle Eastern

Khyber Pass Map 5, I3. 34 St Mark's Pl, btw 2nd and 3rd ☏ 212/473-0989. Afghan food, which, if you're unfamiliar, is filling and has plenty to offer vegetarians (pulses, rice, and eggplant are frequent ingredients). The lamb dishes are tasty. Excellent value for around $15 per person.

Indian

Gandhi Map 5, J3. 345 E 6th St, btw 1st and 2nd ☏ 212/614-9718. One of the best and least expensive of the East 6th Street Indian restaurants – also one of the more spacious, with two open dining areas. Try the lamb *muglai* and the light, fluffy *poori* bread.

Italian

Frank Map 5, I4. 88 2nd Ave, btw 5th and 6th ☎212/420-0202. This tiny, neighborhood favorite serves basic, traditional Italian dishes at communal tables. It's packed every night with hungry locals looking for the closest thing to a home-cooked meal at a very reasonable price.

Supper Map 5, K5. 156 E 2nd St, btw A and B ☎212/477-7600. Great little Italian restaurant with over-sized, medieval-looking tables and benches, and some of the best Italian around. Try the "priest stranglers" with marinara and fresh ricotta. No reservations.

Jewish and Eastern European

Second Avenue Deli Map 5, I2. 156 2nd Ave, btw 9th and 10th ☎212/677-0606. An East Village institution, serving up marvelous burgers, hearty pastrami sandwiches, matzoh ball soup, and other deli goodies in ebulliently, snap-happy style – and not nearly as cheap as you'd think. The star plaques in the sidewalk

out front commemorate this area's Yiddish theater days. **Veselka Map 5, I3. 144 2nd Ave, at 9th** ☎212/228-9682. Great, always bustling late-night standby that offers fine homemade hot borscht (and cold in summer), latkes, *pierogies*, and great burgers and fries. Open 24hrs.

Spanish

Xunta Map 5, J2. 174 1st Ave, btw 10th and 11th ☎212/614-0620. This electric East Village gem buzzes with hordes of young faces perched on rum barrels downing pitchers of sangría and choosing from the dizzying tapas menu – try the mussels in fresh tomato sauce, shrimp with garlic, and the mushrooms in brandy. You can eat (and drink) very well for around $20.

Vegetarian

Angelica Kitchen Map 5, I2. 300 E 12th St, btw 1st and 2nd ☎212/228-2909. Vegetarian macrobiotic restaurant with various daily specials for a decent price. Patronized by a colorful downtown crowd and considered by many to be the best veggie food in NYC.

22

RESTAURANTS

Chelsea

Retro diners serving traditional American, Cuban–Chinese greasy spoons along Eighth Avenue, increasingly trendy restaurants, and cute brunch spots characterize **Chelsea**. Perhaps the best and most reasonably priced offerings are to be had in the area's Central American joints, though there is also a mosaic of international cuisines: Thai, Austrian, Mexican, and Italian.

American and Continental

Cafeteria Map 6, F8. 119 7th Ave, at 17th ☏212/414-1717. Don't let the name fool you: while *Cafeteria* is open 24hrs and has great chicken-fried steak, meatloaf, and macaroni and cheese, this place is anything but a trucker's dream: modern, plastic-designed, and always packed with beautiful diners.

Empire Diner Map 6, C7. 210 10th Ave, btw 22nd and 23rd ☏212/243-2736. With its gleaming chrome-ribbed Art Deco interior, this is one of Manhattan's original diners, still open 24hrs and still serving up plates of simple (if not much better than average) American diner food. A bit pricey for what you get.

The Old Homestead Map 6, D9. 56 9th Ave, btw 14th and 15th ☏212/242-9040. Steak. Period. But really gorgeous steak, served in an almost comically old-fashioned walnut dining room by waiters in black vests. Huge portions and high quality, but very expensive.

Asian

Wild Lily Tea Room Map 6, B7. 511 W 22nd St, at 10th ☏212/691-2258. A serene little spot that boasts over 200 kinds of tea, though it's equally worth visiting for the delicious and healthy pan-Asian cuisine. Request the elevated window table beside the goldfish pond.

Caribbean

Cuba Libre Map 6, E7. 165 8th Ave, btw 18th and 19th ☏212/206-0038. Tapas, *mojitos*, and hip-swinging music make this airy, reasonably priced eatery a Chelsea favorite with the predominantly gay crowd.

Negril Map 6, D7. 362 W 23rd St, btw 8th and 9th ☏212/807-6411. An enormous aquarium and colorful decor add to the pleasure of eating at this Jamaican restaurant. Spicy jerk chicken or goat, stews, and other dishes keep 'em coming, as do the reasonable prices (around $12–15 for an entree).

French

La Lunchonette Map 6, C8. 130 10th Ave, at 18th ☏ 212/675-0342. Tucked away in a remote corner of Chelsea but perpetually crowded with loyal patrons, this understated little restaurant features the best of French country cooking, including steak *au poivre*, rabbit stew, and lamb sausages with sautéed apples.

Italian

Bottino Map 6, C6. 246 10th Ave, btw 25th and 26th ☏ 212/206-6766. One of Chelsea's most popular restaurants, *Bottino* attracts the in-crowd looking for some honest Italian food served in a very downtown atmosphere. The homemade leek *tortelloni* (winter months only) is truly tantalizing.

Union Square

The area around **Union Square**, known variously as the Flatiron District, Silicon Alley, and Park Avenue South, is not considered an especially trendy neighborhood, but it does have a surprising number of high-end restaurants frequented by business types.

American and Continental

Blue Water Grill Map 6, I8. 31 Union Square West, at 16th ☏ 212/675-9500. High-quality all-around seafood restaurant with commensurate high prices. Hard to go wrong here, though, whether it's grilled fish, caviar, or raw bar. **Chat 'n' Chew** Map 6, I9. 10 E 16th St, btw 5th and Union Square West ☏ 212/243-1616. Cozy comfort food in a colorful diner setting,

serving large portions of standard American classics like macaroni and cheese, and fried chicken. Good budget option and great sweet-potato fries.
Gramercy Tavern Map 6, J7. 42 E 20th St, btw Park and Broadway ☏ 212/477-0777. Widely regarded one of New York's finest, featuring gourmet dining and great service without any of the usual stuffiness. Among the many fine items on the menu are ricotta

ravioli with asparagus and wild mushrooms, and baby lobster with artichoke and pearl onions. Try the seasonal tasting menu, which changes every three months. Pricey but memorable. **Union Square Café** Map 6, H8. 21 E 16th St, btw 5th and Union Square West ☎212/243-4020. Choice California-style dining with a classy but comfortable downtown atmosphere. No one does salmon like they do. Not at all cheap – prices average $120 for two – but the creative menu is a real treat.

South American

Coffee Shop Map 6, J7. 29 Union Square West, at 16th ☎212/243-7969. Reasonably priced Brazilian food and great turkey burgers. A solid lunch spot and also a good late-night hangout; the kitchen's open until 5:30am from Wed to Sat and they serve great *caipirinha* drinks.

Gramercy Park, Murray Hill, and the Garment District

While not the best neighborhoods for dining in NYC, **Gramercy Park**, **Murray Hill**, and the **Garment District** are picking up the pace. The area around Lexington Avenue in the upper 20s is a good place to sample cheap and filling Indian fare. It's also a fantastic place to find a number of crowded sushi bars and small French bistros.

American and Continental

Craft Map 6, J8. 43 E 19th St, btw Broadway and Park ☎212/780-0880. Highly popular but with an eminently relaxed atmosphere, this kitchen serves up some of New York's best food. Among the most popular dishes are roast foie gras, dayboat scallops, and tasty sides of sautéed wild mushrooms.

El Rio Grande Map 6, K2. 160 E 38th St, btw Lexington and 3rd ☎212/867-0922. Long-established Murray Hill Tex-Mex place with a gimmick: you can eat Mexican or, if you prefer, Texan, by simply crossing the "border" and walking through the kitchen. Personable and fun – and the margaritas are earth-shattering.

Asian

Hangawi Map 6, I4. 12 E 32nd St, btw 5th and Madison ☎212/213-0077. An elegant vegetarian and vegan-safe Korean restaurant. The autumn rolls are a great starter. A little pricey, but quite good.

French

Les Halles Map 6, J5. 411 Park Ave South, btw 28th and 29th ☎212/679-4111. *Kitchen Confidential* author Anthony Bourdain's noisy, bustling bistro with carcasses dangling in a butcher's shop in the front. Very pseudo–Rive Gauche, serving rabbit, steak *frites*, and other

staples. Entrees range $15–25. Not recommended for veggies.

Indian

Curry in a Hurry Map 6, K5. 119 Lexington Ave, at 28th ☎212/683-0900. No-frills curry trough popular with local cab drivers (with good reason). Excellent and filling Indian dishes for around $10.

Tabla Map 6, J6. 11 Madison Ave, at 25th ☎212/889-0667. Swank *nouveau* Indian fare in an elegant, glassed-in second-floor dining room, a bit overrun by young banker types but with memorable food. Start off with the duck samosas and move on to the pan-seared skate with baby artichokes and chickpeas.

Midtown West

While the majority of Manhattan's best dining occurs Downtown, some manifold good meals await you in **Midtown West**, a neighborhood whose restaurants encompass Greek, South American, Japanese, African, French, and everything in between. Restaurant Row (West 46th St between Eighth and Ninth aves), is a frequent stopover for theatergoers seeking a pre-show or late-night meal, though Ninth Avenue offers cheaper and generally better alternatives.

American and Continental

Aquavit Map 7, H7. 65 E 55th St, btw Madison and Park ☎212/307-7311. Superb Scandinavian food

– pickled herring, salmon, even reindeer – in a lovely atrium restaurant with a mock waterfall cascading down one of the walls. A real treat, and priced accordingly; reserve well in advance.

Joe Allen's Map 7, E8. 326 W 46th St, btw 8th and 9th ☎212/581-6464. Tried and true formula of checkered tablecloths, old-fashioned barroom feel, and reliable American food at moderate prices. The calf's liver with spinach and potatoes has been on the menu for years. Popular pre-theater spot, so reserve well in advance unless you can arrive after 8pm.

Stage Deli Map 7, F7. 834 7th Ave, btw 53rd and 54th sts ☎212/245-7850. Another reliable all-night standby, and longtime rival to the *Carnegie Deli* (see p.227). More genuine New York attitude and big overstuffed sandwiches, but it's not at all cheap.

West Bank Café Map 7, D9. 407 W 42nd St, at 9th ☎212/695-6909. Some French, some American, all delicious and not as expensive as you'd think – pastas and entrees range from $11 to $20. Very popular with theater people before, and especially after, a performance.

Asian

Ruby Foo's Map 7, F8. 1626 Broadway, at 49th ☎212/489-5600. Best dining option in Times Square, with a wide-ranging Asian menu that runs from sushi platters to dim sum to Thai noodle dishes, all done surprisingly well. There's another branch at 2182 Broadway, at 77th (☎212/724-6700).

Ollie's Noodle Shop Map 7, E9. 190 W 44th St, btw Broadway and 8th ☎212/921-5988 Good Chinese restaurant that serves noodle soups, barbecued meats, and spare ribs. Not, however, a place to linger. Very cheap, very crowded, and very noisy. Also very popular pre-theater place, so don't be alarmed if there are long lines – but due to the rushed service, they move fast. There are two other branches on Broadway, one at no. 2315, at 84th (☎212/362-3111), and the other at no. 2957, at 116th (☎212/932-3300).

Shun Lee

Map 7, D4. 43 W 65th St, at Columbus ☎212/371-8844. The service and table settings here are strictly formal, but you should feel free to dress casually. This venerable local institution – conveniently across the street from Lincoln Center – has top-notch Chinese food. Steer yourself toward the menu's many seafood delicacies.

Central and South American

Churrascaria Plataforma Map 7, D8. 316 W 49th St, btw 8th and 9th ☎212/245-0505. Housed in a vast, festive hall packed to the gills with beautiful people, this eminent Brazilian institution features a $50 prix fixe for all the various grilled meats you can manage to keep down. Don't miss the addictive *caipirinhas* (Brazil's national drink).

Hell's Kitchen Map 7, D8. 679 9th Ave, btw 46th and 47th t212/977-1588. Lively party atmosphere – aided and abetted by six different kinds of frozen margarita – and sophisticated renderings of Mexican cuisine. Reserve first unless you're arriving early.

Rice 'n' Beans Map 7, D7. 744 9th Ave, btw 50th and 51th t212/265-4444. Narrow, no-frills space serving up affordable and delicious Brazilian fare. In addition to the namesake dish, there are grilled steaks, hearty soups, and some tasty seafood offerings.

Rosa Mexicano Map 7, D4. 61 Columbus Ave, btw 62nd and 63rd ☎212/977-7700. Right across from Lincoln Center, so the perfect location for a post-opera meal. Don't miss the guacamole, which is mashed at your table, or their signature pomegranate margaritas.

French

Chez Napoleon Map 7, E8. 365 W 50th St, btw 8th and 9th ☎212/265-6980. Owing to this neighborhood's proximity to the docks, it became a hangout for French soldiers during World War II, leading to the creation of several highly authentic Gallic eateries here in the 1940s and 1950s. This is one of them, and it lives up to its reputation. A friendly, family-run bistro; bring a wad to enjoy the tradition, though.

Hourglass Tavern Map 7, E8. 373 W 46th St, btw 8th and 9th ☎212/265-2060. Tiny French restaurant, which serves an excellent-value, two-course prix-fixe menu for between $20 and $30. The gimmick is the hourglass above each table, the emptying of which means you're supposed to leave and make way for someone else. In reality they seem to last more than an hour, and they only enforce it if there's a line. Cash only.

Le Bernardin Map 7, H7. 155 W 51st St, btw 6th and 7th ☎212/554-1515. The most storied seafood restaurant in the United States, and priced to match, serving incomparable new angles on traditional Brittany fish dishes in elegant surroundings. This is one dinner you'll never forget, though you may cry when the bill arrives.

Middle Eastern

Afghanistan Kebab House Map 7, F8. 155 W 46th St, btw 6th and

7th ☎212/768-3875. Inexpensive lamb, chicken, and seafood kebabs, served with a variety of side dishes. Complete dinners for under $15. Another branch at 1345 2nd Ave, btw 70th and 71st (☎212/517-2776).

Italian

Julian's Map 7, D7. 802 9th Ave, btw 53rd and 54th ☎212/262-4800. Light and inventive Mediterranean fare in a bright, pleasing room and clever dining garden tucked away in an alley. Whether you want sandwiches or scaioppini, this is a safe bet in the Hell's Kitchen area.

Trattoria dell'Arte Map 7, F6. 900 7th Ave, btw 56th and 57th ☎212/245-9800. Unusually nice restaurant for this rather tame stretch of Midtown, with a lovely, airy interior, excellent service, and good food. Great, wafer-thin crispy pizzas, decent and imaginative pasta dishes for around $20, and a mouth-watering antipasto bar – all eagerly patronized by an elegant out-to-be-seen crowd.

Jewish

Carnegie Deli Map 7, F6. 854 7th Ave, btw 54th and 55th ☎212/757-2245. This place is known for the size of its sandwiches – by popular consent the most generously stuffed in the city, and a full meal in themselves. The chicken noodle soup is good, too. Not cheap, however, and the waiters are among New York's rudest.

Midtown East

Catering mostly to lunchtime office-going crowds that swarm the sidewalks on weekdays, **Midtown East** overflows with restaurants, most of them on the pricey side. You probably won't want to make it the focal point of too many culinary excursions but, that said, there are a few timeworn favorites in the neighborhood.

American and Continental

Four Seasons Map 7, I7. 99 E 52nd St, btw Park and Lexington ☎212/754-9494. Housed in Mies van der Rohe's Seagram Building, this is one of the city's most noted restaurants, not least for the decor, which includes murals by Picasso, sculptures by

Richard Lippold, and interior design by Philip Johnson. The food isn't at all bad either, and there's a relatively inexpensive pre-theater menu for $55. Somewhat stuffier than the other top restaurants.

Keen's Steakhouse Map 6, H3. 72 W 36th St, btw 5th and 6th ⏀212/947-3636. *Keen's* has been around since 1885, and it feels like it as you walk into the inviting lobby and the fustily comfortable restaurant festooned with the clay pipes they've been collecting here since the turn of the century. You can just drink and snack on the pub menu in the bar on the right, or have the full works in the restaurant. *Keen's* is known for its steak and lamb chops, and although not cheap – reckon on $30–40 a main course – they're mightily good. A handy place for visiting after shopping at Macy's – in a neighborhood rather devoid of good restaurants.

Oyster Bar Map 7, I9. Lower level, Grand Central Terminal, 42nd St and Park Ave ⏀212/490-6650. Atmospheric turn-of-the-nineteenth-century place located down in the vaulted dungeons of Grand Central Station, where midtown execs and others break for lunch. The oyster appetizers are particularly good, while seafood entrees go for a minimum of $25 per dish. If you're hard up, just saddle up to the bar for a bowl of excellent clam chowder, or great creamy bowls of pan-roasted oysters or clams.

Rosen's Delicatessen Map 7, H7. 23 E 51st St, btw 5th and Madison ⏀212/371-7676. Enormous Art-Deco restaurant, renowned for its pastrami and corned beef, and handily situated for those suffering from midtown shopping fatigue. Good breakfasts, too.

Smith and Wollensky Map 7, J8. 797 3rd Ave, at 49th ⏀212/753-1530. Clubby atmosphere in a grand setting, where waiters – many of whom have worked here for twenty years or more – serve you the primest cuts of beef imaginable. Quite pricey (you'll pay at least $33 a steak) but worth the splurge. Go basic with the sides and wines.

Asian

Hatsuhana Map 7, H8. 17 E 48th St, btw 5th and Madison ⏀212/355-3345. Every sushi-lover's favorite sushi restaurant now has two branches. Not at all cheap, so try to get there for the prix-fixe lunch. Second restaurant at 237 Park Ave, at 46th (⏀212/661-3400).

Vong Map 7, J7. 200 E 54th St, at 3rd ⏀212/486-8664. Best Southeast Asian food in Midtown, housed in a trendy dining room in the bowels of the appropriately named Lipstick Building (as it's shaped like a lipstick cylinder). Great early-evening prix-fixe meals; don't miss the crab cakes.

French

Lutèce Map 7, J8. 249 E 50th St, btw 2nd and 3rd ☏212/752-2225. A favorite of many well-to-do New Yorkers, the classic French food here is top-notch, while the service is elegant and under-stated. What's surprising is how low-key and totally unpretentious *Lutèce* is, though you do need big bucks and reservations in advance. Worth every penny.

Italian

Luna Piena Map 7, J7. 243 E 53rd St, btw 2nd and 3rd ☏212/308-8882. One of the better local Italians in a neighborhood of many mediocre restaurants. The food is good, the service is friendly, and there's a nice enclosed garden for warm sum-mer evenings.

The Upper West Side

The **Upper West Side** encompasses a large chunk of real estate, and thus offers a wide array of ethnic and price choices. There are lots of generous burger joints, Chinese restaurants, friendly diners, and delectable, if a bit pricey, brunch spots, so you'll never be at a loss for good meals.

American and Continental

Big Nick's Map 7, C1. 70 W 71st St, at Columbus ☏212/799-4444. If you want a hamburger or pizza on the Upper West Side, this is a fun, New York kind of place. In his crowded, chaotic little wooden-table restaurant, Big Nick has been serving them up all night long to locals for twenty-plus years.

Boat Basin Café Map 7, A1. W 79th St, at the Hudson River (access through Riverside Park) ☏212/496-5542. An outdoor restaurant, open May–Sept, with informal tables covered in red-and-white checked cloths, some under a sheltering overhang. The food is standard, but inexpensive considering the prime location – burgers with fries ($7.75), hot dogs, sandwiches, and some more serious entrees like grilled salmon ($14.50).

Boathouse Café Map 7, G2. Central Park Lake, East 72nd St entrance ☎212/517-2233. A peaceful retreat from a hard day exploring the Fifth Avenue museums. You get great views of the famous Central Park skyline and decent American/Continental cuisine, but at very steep prices. Closed from Oct to March.

Dock's Oyster Bar Map 8, B6. 2427 Broadway, btw 89th and 90th ☎212/724-5588. Popular uptown seafood emporium with a raw bar, great mussels, and a wide variety of high-quality fresh fish. The Upper West Side location (see below for the other) is the original and tends to have the homlier atmosphere – though both can be noisy and service slow. Reservations recommended on weekends. There's another branch at 633 3rd Ave, at 40th St (☎212/986-8080).

Tom's Restaurant Map 8, B1. 2880 Broadway, at 112th St ☎212/864-6137. Cheap, greasy-spoon fare. This is the *Tom's* of *Seinfeld* fame (it was known as *Monk's* on the show), usually filled with students from Columbia. Great breakfast deals – you can get a large meal for under $6.

Asian

Hunan Park Map 7, D3. 235 Columbus Ave, btw 70th and 71st ☎212/724-4411. Some of the best Chinese food on the Upper West Side is served here, in a large, crowded room, with typically quick service and moderate prices. Try the spicy noodles in sesame sauce and the dumplings. A good, less-expensive option within a few blocks of Lincoln Center.

Haru Map 8, C8. 433 Amsterdam Ave, btw 80th and 81st ☎212/579-5655. A solid standby in this part of town if you're craving sushi – extremely popular so you should expect to wait a half-hour for a table, but the quality is good once you finally take your seat.

Caribbean

Café con Leche Map 8, C9. 424 Amsterdam Ave, at 80th ☎212/595-7000. Great neighborhood Dominican joint that serves roast pork, rice and beans, and some of the hottest chilli sauce you've ever tasted. Cheap and very cheerful. There's another location further north on Amsterdam and 96th.

Calle Ocho Map 8, D8. 446 Columbus Ave, btw 81st and 82nd ☎212/873-5025. Very tasty Latino fare, such as *ceviches* and *chimchuri* steak with yucca fries, is served in an immaculately designed dining room or a hopping couch lounge, with *mojitos*

RESTAURANTS

as tasty and potent as any in the city.

La Caridad Map 7, C1. 2199 Broadway, at 78th ☎212/874-2780. This is something of an Upper West Side institution, a tacky, no-frills eatery that doles out plentiful and cheap Cuban-Chinese – ie, the cuisine of Cuba's large Chinese community – food to hungry diners (the Cuban-slanted dishes are better than the Chinese). Bring your own beer, and expect to wait in line.

French and Belgian

Café Luxembourg Map 7, C3. 200 W 70th St, btw Amsterdam and West End ☎212/873-7411. Trendy Lincoln Center–area bistro that packs in (literally) a self-consciously hip crowd to enjoy its first-rate contemporary French food. Not too pricey – two people can eat for $60 or so.

Jean Georges Map 7, E5. Trump International Hotel, 1 Central Park West, btw 60th and 61st sts ☎212/299-3900. This is French at its finest, crafted by star chef Jean-Georges Vongerichten. Definitely the place for a special occasion when you don't mind dropping a pretty penny (up to $250 per person). For the more money-conscious, the front-room *Nougatine* has a prix-fixe summer brunch for $20. But

whatever you do, don't miss the rhubarb tart for dessert.

Indian

Mughlai Map 7, D3. 320 Columbus Ave, at 75th ☎212/724-6363. Uptown, upscale Indian with prices about the going rate for this strip: $11–16 an entree. The food is surprisingly good.

Italian

Gennaro Map 8, C6. 665 Amsterdam Ave, btw 92nd and 93rd ☎212/665-5348. A tiny outpost of truly great Italian food, with room for only about fifty people (and thus perpetual lines to get in). Standouts include a warm potato, mushroom, and goat cheese tart (incredible), and braised lamb shank in red wine. The desserts are also worth the wait. Moderate prices, open for dinner only.

Jewish

Barney Greengrass Map 8, C7. 541 Amsterdam Ave, btw 86th and 87th ☎212/724-4707. A West Side deli and restaurant that's been around since time began. The smoked salmon and sturgeon section is a particular treat. Cheese blintzes are tasty, too.

Fine & Schapiro Map 7, D2. 138 W 72nd St, btw Broadway and Columbus ☎212/877-2721.

22

RESTAURANTS

Longstanding Jewish deli that's open for lunch and dinner, serving delicious old-fashioned kosher fare. Great chicken soup.

The Upper East Side

Upper East Side restaurants cater mostly to a discriminating mixture of Park Avenue matrons and the young upwardly mobile; many of the city's best Japanese and French restaurants are here. For a change of pace, try a wurst and some strudel at *Heidelberg*, the last remaining of Yorkville's old-world German luncheonettes.

American and Continental

E.A.T. Map 8, I9. 1064 Madison Ave, btw 80th and 81st ☎212/772-0022. Expensive and crowded but with excellent food (celebrated restaurateur and gourmet grocer Eli Zabar is the owner, so that's no surprise), especially the soups and breads, and the ficelles and Parmesan toast.

Lenox Room Map 7, J2. 1278 3rd Ave, btw 73rd and 74th t212/772-0404. Fairly swank seafood spot centered on an expansive raw bar (over a dozen varieties of oyster), delicious tuna tartar, and other *fruits de mer*.

Post House Map 7, H4. 26 E 63rd St, at Madison ☎212/935-2888. Classic American food in an elegant, comfortable, typically Upper East Side setting. It's reasonably unpretentious for the area, and does very good steaks and chops, though not all that cheaply.

Rathbones Map 8, K7. 1702 2nd Ave, btw 88th and 89th ☎212/369-7361. Take a window seat to watch the stars arrive at overpriced celeb hot-spot *Elaine's* (across the street) and eat here for a fraction of the price. Steaks and fish for around $15 – and a wide choice of beers.

Asian

Donguri Map 8, K8. 309 E 83rd St, btw 1st and 2nd ☎212/737-5656. This little five-table room is something special, a family-run shop where dad does the cooking and mom waits the tables with ruthless efficiency. The bluefin tuna is tops in town, plus don't miss the *kumamoto* oysters, special mushroom tempura, or broiled whitefish. There are only two seatings (7 & 9pm) and they tend to hustle out the early shift ASAP, so don't plan on lingering.

Pig Heaven Map 8, K9. 1540 2nd Ave, btw 80th and 81st ℡212/744-4333. Good-value Chinese restaurant decorated with images of pigs, and serving lean and meaty spare ribs, among other things. In case you hadn't guessed, the accent is on pork.

Sushi of Gari Map 8, L9. 402 E 78th St, btw 1st and York ℡212/517-5340. Amiable neighborhood sushi shop with top-quality fish. Try the tasting menu and you're in for a host of unusual sushi offerings – from *toro* and pickled radish to salmon and a droplet of cream cheese – that will make it a memorable evening.

French and Belgian

Café Boulud Map 7, H1. 20 E 76th St, btw Madison and 5th ℡212/772-2600. As the less expensive (but not lesser) of celebrity chef Daniel Boulud's two Manhattan eateries, the muted but elegant interiors make this an exceedingly pleasant place to savor the sublime concoctions coming out of the kitchen. By all means save room for dessert: lime-grapefruit soup with lemon-vodka sorbet or coffee profiteroles with chocolate sauce.

Le Refuge Map 8, J8. 166 E 82nd St, btw Lexington and 3rd ℡212/861-4505. Quiet, intimate, and deliberately romantic old-style French restaurant situated in an old city brownstone. The bouillabaisse and other seafood dishes are delectable. Expensive but worth it; save for special occasions. Closed Sun during the summer.

Payard Patisserie & Bistro Map 7, J2. 1032 Lexington Ave, btw 72nd and 73rd ℡212/717-5252. This is real Parisian pastry – buttery, creamy, and over-the-top. Cookies, cakes, and crème brûlée made to the exacting standards of the kitchen staffs of local millionaires.

Middle Eastern

Rectangles Map 7, K2. 1431 1st Ave, btw 74th and 75th ℡212/744-7470. Probably the best Middle Eastern food in the city, this newly relocated Yemeni–Israeli restaurant features knockout standards like hummus, *baba ganoush*, and a spicy chicken soup that can instantly cure the common cold. Closed Sat.

Indian

Dawat Map 7, J6. 210 E 58th St, btw 2nd and 3rd ℡212/355-7555. One of the most elegant gourmet Indian restaurants in the city. Try the Cornish game hen with green chilli, or the leg of lamb. A bit pricey – entrees average about $17. For an extra charge, the owner, Beverly, will give you a tarot-card reading.

Italian

Caffé Buon Gusto Map 7, J1. 243 E 77th St, btw 2nd and 3rd ☎212/535-6884. This stretch of the Upper East Side has plenty of cool Italian joints: what *Buon Gusto* lacks in style it makes up for in taste and low prices. The vodka sauce is excellent.

German and Eastern European

Heidelburg Map 8, K7. 1648 2nd Ave, btw 85th and 86th ☎212/628- 2332. The atmosphere here is mittel-European kitsch, with gingerbread trim and waitresses in Alpine goatherd costumes. But the food is the real deal, featuring excellent liver dumpling soup, *Bauernfrühstück* omelets, and pancakes (both sweet and potato). And they serve *weiss-bier* the right way, too – in giant, boot-shaped glasses.

Mocca Hungarian Map 8, K8. 1588 2nd Ave, btw 82nd and 83rd ☎212/734-6470. Yorkville restaurant serving hearty portions of Hungarian comfort food – schnitzel, cherry soup, goulash, and chicken paprikash, among others. Moderately priced, and be sure to come hungry – the portions are more than generous.

Upper Manhattan: Morningside Heights, Harlem, and above

Cheap Cuban, African, Caribbean, and the best soul-food restaurants in the city abound in and around **Harlem**; even institutions like *Sylvia's*, touristy and crowded as it may be, remain reasonably priced.

American

Amy Ruth's Map 9, D9. 113 W 116th St, btw Lenox and 7th ☎212/ 280-8779. Surprisingly cheap considering the enormous por- tions, this new soul-food spot draws Harlemites and visitors with its outstanding fried chicken and ribs. The desserts are excellent, too.

Sylvia's Restaurant Map 9, D8.

328 Lenox Ave, btw 126th and 127th ⊕**212/996-0660**. The most well-known Southern soul-food restaurant in Harlem – so famous that Sylvia herself even has her own package food line. While some find the barbecue sauce too tangy, the fried chicken is exceptional at $16.95 and the garlic-mashed potatoes and candied yams are justly celebrated. Also famous for the Sunday Gospel brunch – though be prepared for a thirty-minute wait.

Caribbean

Sisters Map 9, F8. 47 E 124th St, btw Madison and Park ⊕**212/410-3000**. Spicey, inexpensive Caribbean classics like jerk chicken, goat curry, callaloo, and oxtail stew in an unassuming diner. Best for lunch or an early dinner, as the best dishes start selling out as the evening wears on.

Brooklyn

In **Brooklyn**, lower Atlantic Avenue offers some of the city's best Middle Eastern food; Brighton Beach features the most authentic Russian food in NYC; and Park Slope, Carroll Gardens, Cobble Hill, and Fort Greene all have burgeoning restaurant rows.

American and Continental

Diner 85 Broadway, at Berry, Williamsburg ⊕**718/486-3077**. Located in a refurbished dining car under the Williamsburg Bridge, this local favorite dishes out a superb array of food that includes fantastic burgers, French standards, and a wealth of daily specials. Kitchen open nightly until 2am.
Peter Luger Steak House 178 Broadway, at Driggs, Williamsburg ⊕**718/387-7400**. Catering to carnivores since 1873, *Peter Luger* may just be the city's finest steakhouse. The service is surly and the decor plain, but the porterhouse steak – the only cut served – is divine. Cash only; expect to pay at least $60 per head.

Italian

Al Di Là 248 5th Ave, at Carroll, Park Slope ⊕**718/783-4565**. Venetian country cooking at its finest at this husband-and-wife-run eatery. Standouts include beet ravioli, grilled sardines, *saltimbocca*, and salt-baked striped bass. Invariably crowded. **Di Fara** 1424 Ave J, at 15th, Midwood ☎718/258-1367. This unassuming local pizza joint has been popular with Brooklynites for decades but is just now gaining its due across the city as one of the finest pizzerias in town. Super-thin-crust masterpieces far more subtle and delicious than anything you'll find in Manhattan.

French

Banania 241 Smith St, at Douglass, Cobble Hill ☎718/237-9100. French bistro serving brunch and dinner for quite reasonable prices; steaks and fish dishes, like pan-roasted cod, stand out. Average price for entrees is $14; cash only.

Russian

Primorski 282 Brighton Beach Ave, btw 2nd and 3rd, Brighton Beach ☎718/891-3111. Perhaps the best of Brighton Beach's Russian hangouts, serving up a

huge menu of authentic Russian dishes, including blintzes and stuffed cabbage, at absurdly cheap prices. Live music in the evening.

American

Heights Café Map 4, L8. 84 Montague St, at Hicks, Brooklyn Heights ☎718/625-5555. Near the Esplanade overlooking the East River and the Manhattan skyline, this mainstay offers a great environment for a drink and appetizers at the bar or a decent-priced American eclectic meal at one of the sidewalk tables.
River Café Map 4, K6. 1 Water St, at Old Fulton, DUMBO ☎718/522-5200. There's no more romantic spot in all of New York than this riverfront eatery with spectacular glassed-in views of the East River and the Financial District skyline. The seafood preparations here are quite good as well – including excellent crab cakes and a remarkably tender halibut filet – though perhaps an afterthought for most lovestruck patrons.

Queens

The most ethnically diverse of all the boroughs, **Queens** holds the city's largest Greek, South American, Slavic, and Asian communities, thus some of the best examples of these cuisines. Notable in particular are Astoria – an old Greek neighborhood – and Flushing, which boasts the best Chinese restaurants in New York.

Greek

Elias Corner 24–02 31st St, at 24th, Astoria ☎718/932-1510.
Pay close attention to the seafood on display as you enter, for *Elias Corner* does not have menus and the staff is not always forthcoming. This informal Astoria institution, with open-air seating when weather permits, serves some of the best and freshest fish as well as a myriad of salads.

Uncle George's 33–19 Broadway, at 34th, Astoria ☎718/626-0593.
This well-known 24hr joint serves excellent and ultracheap authentic Greek food, including some of the top *souvlaki* and *spanakopita* in the city.

Chinese

East Lake 42–33 Main St, at Franklin, Flushing ☎718/539-8532.
Fantastic and very inexpensive dim sum, plus a selection of over fifty teas. The *har gow* (shrimp dumplings) and *taro* cakes are a great place to start, and there are also sautéed frog's legs and sizzling grilled calamari, perfectly spiced.

Indian

Jackson Diner 37–47 74th St, btw Roosevelt and 37th, Jackson Heights ☎718/672-1232. Manhattan foodies make regular pilgrimages to this distant but locally famous Indian restaurant, with outstanding versions of classics like tandoori chicken, goat curry, and shrimp *biryani*. If you love spicy food, don't miss the *vindaloo*. Cash only.

American

Waterfront Crab House 203 Borden Ave, at 2nd, Long Island City ☎718/729-4862. Don't let the corny carnival decor put you off this place, as this is the best place in Queens for low-priced, super-fresh seafood, including delicious local rock crabs, *escargot*, and a classic Marseille bouillabaisse. Also offers a majestic view of the Manhattan skyline.

The Bronx

In the **Bronx**, Belmont is one of the best places in the city to eat authentic Italian cuisine – much better than Little Italy in Manhattan. There's also quite a lot of cheap Latin food on offer, as well as some affordable seafood shacks along the beach at City Island.

American

The Crab Shanty 361 City Island Ave, at Tier, City Island ☎718/885-1810. While the decor is cheesy to say the least, the fried clams and Cajun fried fish specials at this City Island favorite are worth the trip.

Italian

Dominick's 2335 Arthur Ave, at 187th St, Belmont ☎718/733-2807. All you could hope for in a neighborhood Italian: great, rowdy atmosphere, communal family-style seating, wonderful food, and low(ish) prices. As there are no menus, pay close attention to your waiter. Stuffed baby squid, veal *parmigiana*,

and chicken *scarpariello* are standouts.

Mexican

Mister Taco 2255 White Plains Rd, at Astor, Central Bronx ☎718/882-3821. Makes for a great snack or meal after walking around the nearby Bronx Botanical Garden. The *tamales* are the call here. No English spoken.

Caribbean

Sam's 596–598 Grand Concourse, at 151st, South Bronx ☎718/665-5341. Located just a hop away from Yankee Stadium, *Sam's* makes for a tasty and inexpensive pre-game meal. Go for the chicken, jerked or fried.

23

Drinking

Y ou can't walk a block along most Manhattan avenues (and many of the side streets) without passing one or two bars. The **bar scene** in New York City is a varied one, with a broader range of places to drink than in most American cities, and prices to suit most pockets. Bars generally open from mid-morning (around 10am) to the early hours – 4am at the latest, when they have to close by law. Bar kitchens usually stop operating around midnight or a little before.

The best spots are below 14th Street, where the **West Village** takes in a wide range of taste, budget, and purpose, and equally good hunting grounds can be found in the **East Village**, **NoLita**, **SoHo**, and the **Lower East Side**. There's a decent choice of **Midtown** bars, though these tend to be geared to an after-hours office crowd and (with a few notable exceptions) can consequently be pricey and rather dull. The **Upper West Side** has a small array of bars, some interesting, although most tend to cater to more of a clean-cut yuppie crowd; across the park, **Upper East Side** bars can be very loud and frat-boy- and sorority-girl-oriented. In northern Manhattan, the bars of **Harlem**, while not numerous, offer some of the city's most affordable jazz in a relaxed environment.

While most visitors to New York may not have time or occasion to check out the bar scenes in the outer boroughs, those that venture to **Williamsburg**, **Park Slope**, **Brooklyn Heights**, and **Fort Greene** in Brooklyn or to **Astoria** in Queens will find both some of the hippest and also most neighborly spots around. Also, if you're looking for predominantly gay and lesbian bars, these are gathered together and reviewed in Chapter 26.

Whether you wind up sipping a martini in a swank lounge or downing a pint in a seedy dive, you'll be expected to **tip**; figure about a buck a drink. Remember too that **smoking** in bars is technically illegal, and that the legal **drinking age** is 21; if you look young, be prepared to show ID.

23 The Financial District and South Street Seaport

The Full Shilling Map 4, F7. 160 Pearl St, btw Wall and Pine ☎212/422-3855. The wooden bar here was shipped in from Belfast, and recently celebrated its centenary. Think excellent pub grub and copious pints of Guinness, with a clientele consisting of younger Wall Street types, and you get the general idea.

Jeremy's Alehouse Map 4, G5. 228 Front St, btw Peck Slip and Beekman ☎212/964-3537. An earthy sports bar near South Street Seaport, *Jeremy's* serves up cheap pints and machismo – as well as some of the city's best calamari and clams.

TriBeCa

Grace Map 4, D2. 114 Franklin St, btw Church and West Broadway ☎212/343-4200. An excellent cocktail-and-olives spot teeming with old-school class – there's a 40ft-long mahogany bar and a huge selection of malts. Top-notch drink selection for a thirty-something clientele.

Knitting Factory Tap Bar Map 4, E3. 74 Leonard St, btw Church and Broadway ☎212/219-3006. Street-level bar and rather cozy downstairs taproom with eighteen draft microbrews and free live music – usually some revolutionary form of jazz – from 11pm. (For details on the jazz venue upstairs, see p.256.)

Mehanata 416 B.C. Map 5, F9. 416 Broadway, at Canal ☎212/625-0981. This is one strange and crazy joint. Open only on the weekend, *Mehanata* – more commonly known as just "the Bulgarian Bar" – starts to heat up around 10 or 11 and turns into an international electro-punk-pop dance party in the wee hours. Homemade mixed drinks help patrons lose their inhibitions and join in the fun.

SoHo and NoLita

Ear Inn Map 5, B7. 326 Spring St, btw Washington and Greenwich ☎212/226-9060. This cozy pub, a stone's throw from the Hudson River, has a good mix of beers on tap, serves basic, reasonably priced American food, and claims to be the second-oldest bar in the city.

Fanelli Map 5, F7. 94 Prince St, at Mercer ☎212/226-9412. Established in 1872, *Fanelli* is one of the city's oldest bars, relaxed and informal and a favorite of the not-too-hip after-work crowd. The food is simple American fare: burgers, salads, and such.

Pravda Map 5, G6. 281 Lafayette St, btw Houston and Prince ☎212/334-5015. Very tasteful, pseudo-exclusive bar with nothing Communist about the place but its name – instead, think caviar and cocktails, all washed down with Champagne.

Sweet and Vicious Map 5, I7. 5 Spring St, btw Bowery and Elizabeth ☎212/334-7915. A neighborhood favorite, it's the epitome of rustic chic with exposed brick and wood, replete with antique chandeliers. The atmosphere makes it seem all cozy, as does the back garden.

Toad Hall Map 5, E8. 57 Grand St, btw Wooster and West Broadway ☎212/431-8145. Great, tiny, atmospheric bar with none of the pretension or attitude of nearby establishments. Pool table and good jukebox. There's no food, but you can order in or bring your own dinner.

The Lower East Side

Belly Map 5, F6. 155 Rivington St, btw Clinton and Suffolk ☎212/533-1810. Just round the corner from the newly swanky LES restaurant row on Clinton, *Belly* proffers good wines and cocktails in an eclectically low-key, convivial lounge atmosphere.

The Delancey Map 5, L7. 168 Delancey St, btw Clinton and Attorney ☎212/254-9920. A kind of twenty-something hipster super-bar, this triple-level layer cake features a lounge, a basement bar, and stage for up-and-coming acts, plus a much-coveted rooftop bar with great views over the East River and the Williamsburg Bridge.

King Size Map 5, K9. 21 Essex St, btw Hester and Canal ☎212/995-5464. No sign and a shady doorway lead to this great late-night DJ bar that despite its newness speaks of cooler, shabbier times on the LES. Cheap drinks and friendly staff are added bonuses.

Kush Map 5, I6. 191 Chrystie St, btw Rivington and Stanton ☎212/677-7328. The newly refurbished and relocated *Kush* is one of New York's more popular hookah bars. A successful Moroccan theme with good, strong drinks and great music make it a solid neighborhood choice. Indoor smoking allowed.

Orchard Bar Map 5, J6. 200 Orchard St, btw Houston and Stanton ☎212/673-5350. A Lower East Side stalwart that features walls lined with glass display cases filled with nature and neon lights; there are cozy recesses to whisper in and some of the nicest barstaff in town.

The West Village

Blind Tiger Ale House Map 5, A4. 518 Hudson St, at 10th ☎212/675-3848. You could easily leave here with things looking a bit foggy after you choose from the 26 excellent beers on tap and eclectic bottled selection. Come on Wednesday evenings for new beer tastings – with free cheese thrown in for good measure.

Cedar Tavern Map 5, F2. 82 University Place, btw 11th and 12th ☎212/741-9754. The original *Cedar Tavern*, situated just a block away, was a legendary Beat and artists' meeting point in the 1950s. The new version, a homely bar with food, reasonably

23

DRINKING

priced drinks, and occasional poetry readings, retains the bohemian feel. All year round you can eat under the stars in their covered roof garden.

Chumley's Map 5, B4. 86 Bedford St, btw Grove and Barrow ☎212/675-4449. It's not easy to find this former speakeasy, owing to its unmarked entrance, but it's worth the effort, especially in winter when the good choice of beers and food lures in many a cold, hungry soul. Best arrive early if you want a seat.

Hogs & Heifers Map 6, C9. 859 Washington St, at 13th ☎212/929-0655. Hogs as in the burly motorcycles parked outside; heifers as in, well, ladies. Though officially there's no more bar dancing (Julia Roberts was famously photographed doing so here), those bold enough to venture into this rough-and-tumble monument to the Meatpacking District's gory days can still drink to excess.

Where to smoke

Yes, a few bars in the city are still legally allowed to let you **light up**. Anywhere else, you'll have to go outside (not fun in the winter months) or wait until the wee hours when the barstaff occasionally get a little lax with the law.

Manhattan

Carnegie Bar & Books Map 7, F6. 156 W 56th St, btw 6th and 7th.

Circa Tabac Map 5, E7. 32 Watts St, at Thompson.

Hudson Bar & Books Map 5, A2. 636 Hudson St, btw Horatio and Jane.

Karma Map 5, J4. 51 1st Ave, btw 3rd and 4th.

Kush Map 5, I6. 191 Chrystie St, btw Stanton and Rivington.

Lexington Bar & Books Map 7, J2. 1020 Lexington Ave, btw 72nd and 73rd.

Shebeen Map 5, H7. 202 Mott St, btw Prince and Spring.

Brooklyn

Capone's 221 N 9th St, btw Roebling and Driggs, Williamsburg

Larry Lawrence 295 Grand St, btw Roebling and Havemeyer, Williamsburg.

**Employees Only Map 5, B4.
510 Hudson St, at Christopher**
T212/242-3021. Very refined and
richly decorated cocktail lounge
and dinner joint, featuring mixed
drinks made with fresh ingredients and an in-house fortune-tell-
er for a thirty-something crowd.
**White Horse Tavern Map 5, A3. 567
Hudson St, at 11th** T212/243-9260.

Greenwich Village institution
where Dylan Thomas drank his
last before being carted off to
the hospital where he died from
alcoholic poisoning. The beer
and food are cheap and palat-
able, and outside seating is available in the summer – if you can
battle your way past the crowds,
that is.

The East Village

DRINKING

7B Map 5, L3. 108 Ave B, at 7th
T212/473-8840. Quintessential
East Village hangout with an
extremely mixed crowd that has
often been used as a sleazy
set in films and commercials
– recall the bar brawl in *Crocodile
Dundee*. It features deliberately
mental bartenders, strong, cheap
booze, and one of the best punk
jukeboxes in the Village.
**Bowery Bar Map 5, H4. 40 E 4th St,
at Bowery** T212/475-2220. Once
the place to see and be seen,
the *Bowery Bar* still pulls in a
high volume of beautiful people
and wannabe celebrities – as
well as commoners – who come
to sip pricey cocktails or share a
bottle of wine in the serene, fairy-
lit garden.
**Decibel Map 5, I3. 240 E 9th, btw
2nd and 3rd** T212/982-2733.
Great, eclectically decorated

underground sake bar with
good tunes and a rocking
atmosphere. The inevitable wait
for a table will be worth it, guaranteed.
**Eleventh Street Bar Map 5, K2. 510
E 11th, btw A and B** T212/982-
3929. Friendly pub with a house
cat, filled with locals, and,
occasionally, their beer-drinking
pooches. Big round tables in the
back make this place great for
bigger groups, while subdued
lighting lends itself to intimate
tête-à-têtes.
**Holiday Cocktail Lounge Map 5, J3.
75 St Mark's Place, btw 1st and 2nd**
T212/777-9637. An East Village
classic, this Christmas-lights-
bedecked dive has been around
since the area was a haven for
punk rockers and drug addicts.
It's banged up and dilapidated,
and you'll be drinking beer,

whiskey, or the most basic cocktails. The real thing.

KGB Map 5, H4. 85 E 4th St, btw 2nd and Bowery ☎212/505-3360. A lovely dark bar on the second floor, which claims to have been the HQ of the Ukrainian Communist party. The Eastern European edge remains, making it popular with Off-Off-Broadway theater crowds and wannabe Beats.

Lakeside Lounge Map 5, L2. 162 Ave B, btw 10th and 11th ☎212/529-8463. Owned by a local DJ and a record producer who have stocked the jukebox with old rock, country, and R&B. A down-home hangout, with live music four nights a week.

Union Square, Gramercy Park, Murray Hill, and Midtown East

Cibar Map 6, K8. 56 Irving Place, btw 17th and 18th ☎212/460-5656. Innovative cocktails, elegant decor, and a sweet garden make this cozy hotel bar a local hot-spot for a slightly older crowd.

No Idea Map 6, J7. 30 E 20th St, btw Broadway and Park Ave South ☎212/777-0100. Bizarre palace of inebriation has something for most barflies – from $4.50 pints of mixed drinks, to a pool room, TV sports, and even a drink-for-free-if-your-name's-on-the-wall night.

Old Town Bar and Restaurant Map 6, J8. 45 E 18th St, btw Broadway and Park Ave South ☎212/529-6732. One of the oldest and still one of the very best bars in the city, although it can get packed, especially when the suits from the Flatiron District get off work to enjoy its excellent, if standard, menu of chili, burgers, and the like. It was regularly featured on the old *David Letterman Show*.

P.J. Clarke's Map 7, J6. 915 3rd Ave, btw 55th and 56th ☎212/759-1650. One of the city's most famous watering holes, a spit-and-sawdust alehouse with a not-so-cheap restaurant out the back. You may recognize it as the setting of the film *The Lost Weekend*.

Pete's Tavern Map 6, K8. 129 E 18th St, at Irving Place ☎212/473-7676. Opened in 1864, this former speakeasy claims to be the oldest bar in New York, but in fact was beaten by a decade by *McSorley's* on East 7th St. These days the place trades on its history, which included such illustrious patrons as JFK Jr. and O'Henry, who allegedly wrote

The *Gift of the Magi* in his regular booth here.

Chelsea, the Garment District, and Midtown West

The Collins Bar Map 7, E8. 735 8th Ave, btw 46th and 47th ☎212/541-4206. Sleek, stylish bar has choice sports photos along one side, original art works along the other – not to mention perhaps the most eclectic jukebox in the city.

Half King Map 6, B7. 505 W 23rd St, btw 10th and 11th ☎212/462-4300. Media bar on the far West Side, run by *Perfect Storm* author Sebastian Junger and some other literary types. A pleasant, warm place, kind of like an antique living room.

Jimmy's Corner Map 7, F9. 140 W 44th St, btw Broadway and 6th ☎212/221-9510. The walls of this long, narrow corridor of a bar, owned by ex-fighter/trainer Jimmy Glenn, are a virtual Boxing Hall of Fame. You'd be hard-pressed to find a more charac-terful dive anywhere in the city – or a better jazz/R&B jukebox.

Park Map 6, C8. 118 10th Ave, btw 17th and 18th ☎212/352-3313. It's easy to get lost in this vast war-ren of rooms filled with fireplaces, geodes, and even a Canadian redwood in the middle of the floor. The garden is a treat, and the servers are some of the best-dressed in New York.

Rudy's Bar and Grill Map 7, D9. 627 9th Ave, btw 44th and 45th ☎212/974-9169. One of New York's cheapest, friendliest, and liveliest dive bars, a favorite with local actors and musicians. *Rudy's* offers free hot dogs and a back-yard that's great in the summer.

Russian Vodka Room Map 7, F7. 265 W 52nd St, btw Broadway and 7th ☎212/307-5835. As you might expect, many different kinds of vodka, as well as excellent borscht and *pierogi*, and a lot of Russian and Eastern European expats.

The Upper West Side

Dead Poet Map 8, C9. 450 Amster-dam Ave, btw 81st and 82nd

☎212/595-5670. You'll be waxing poetical and then dropping down dead if you drink through this sweet little bar's generous happy hour: from 4 to 8pm, you're offered draft beers, bottles, and shots at $3 a pop. There's a backroom with armchairs, books, and even a pool table – a welcome respite from the college

pick-up crowds of several other establishments nearby.
Smoke Map 8, B2. 2751 Broadway, at 105th St ☎212/864-6662. Seductively mellow jazz lounge – a real find in this neighborhood. Live music most nights. $15–20 cover at the weekend.

The Upper East Side

American Trash Map 7, L1. 1471 1st Ave, btw 76th and 77th ☎212/988-9008. Self-styled "professional drinking establishment" has friendly barstaff, a pool table, a sing-a-long-friendly jukebox, and a happy hour dedicated to getting you there.
The Cocktail Room Map 7, K2. 334 E 73rd St, btw 1st and 2nd ☎212/988-6100. Fancy-schmancy bar with couches, dim lighting, and a modish Sixties theme. Popular with singles and groups who go to lounge on the couches in the back, this neighborhood anomaly throbs on weekends.
Metropolitan Museum of Art Map 8, H8. 1000 5th Ave, at 82nd ☎212/535-7710. It's hard to imagine a more romantic spot to sip a glass of wine, whether

it's enjoying one of the very best views in the city up on the Cantor Roof Garden (open only in warm weather; see p.127) or on the Great Hall Balcony listening to live chamber music (Fri and Sat 5–8pm).
Phoenix Park Map 7, J3. 206 E 67th St, btw 2nd and 3rd ☎212/717-8181. Nothing special about this Irish pub, except it's sociable, has decent food, a jukebox, TVs, and a pool table – and there's very little else happening in this part of town. Happy-hour beers (noon–7pm) are only $3.
Subway Inn Map 7, J5. 143 E 60th St, at Lexington ☎212/223-8929. Downscale neighborhood dive bar across the street from Bloomingdale's. A great spot for a late-afternoon beer.

Harlem

Lenox Lounge Map 9, D8. 288 Lenox Ave, btw 124th and 125th ☎212/427-0253. Elegant Art-Deco Harlem landmark, formerly graced by Billie Holiday, is celebrated for its swanky *Zebra Room*, whose ceiling is adorned with zebra skins. Jazz is played on weekends.

John's Recovery Room Map 9, E7. 2535 Lenox Ave, btw 136th and 137th. No phone. Long-established neighborhood bar just across from the Harlem Hospital, with friendly barstaff and an almost geriatric clientele. Buzz to enter.

Brooklyn

Barbes 376 9th St, at 6th, Park Slope ☎718/965-9177. Just like a French village bistro, hipster-style, this local joint proffers pastis, good wines, and an excellent array of live world music, plus spoken-word nights and jam sessions.

Brooklyn Inn 138 Bergen St, at Hoyt, Boerum Hill ☎718/625-9741. Locals – and their dogs – gather at this friendly Boerum Hill favorite with high ceilings and friendly barstaff. Great place for a daytime buzz or shooting pool in the back room.

Enid's 560 Manhattan Ave, at Driggs, Greenpoint ☎718/349-3859 Good Guinness and a not-too-painfully-high hipster quotient rule in this relaxed bar, with tattered couches and a great brunch on Sundays (be prepared for long lines).

Frank's Lounge 660 Fulton St, at South Elliott, Fort Greene ☎718/625-9339. A stone's throw from the Brooklyn Academy of Music, this mellow bar with a classic-to-modern R&B jukebox comes alive at night when DJs spin hip-hop and the party spreads upstairs.

Pete's Candy Store 709 Lorimer St, btw St Cono Strada and Frost, Williamsburg ☎718/302-3770. Once a Mafia joint fronting as a soda parlor, and now a haven of punk rock and seedy, cheap cocktails, *Pete's* retains an underground vibe.

Union Pool 484 Union Ave, at Meeker, Williamsburg ☎718/609-0484. Great fun and a relaxed atmosphere at this long-time hipster hangout, with tasty drinks, good prices, and a lovely garden area out back.

Be sure to get your photo taken with friends in the old black-and- white photo booth; everyone else is doing it.

Queens

Bohemian Beer Garden 29–19 24th Ave, btw 29th and 31st, Astoria ☎718/728-9776. Old-world Czech Bohemians and twenty-something bohemians mingle at New York's largest beer garden, which features a variety of pilsners. Summer bands range in style from polka to rock to hip-hop. Well worth the train ride out to Queens.

Café-Bar 32–90 34th Ave, at 33rd, Astoria ☎718/204-5273. With its plush couches and outdoor seating, the ultra-relaxed *Café-Bar* is the perfect place to kill time before a matinee at the nearby American Museum of the Moving Image (see p.172).

24

Nightlife

New York is undeniably a **nightlife** city: this is a town where bars don't get packed until 11pm, if not later, and clubs look like empty rooms until midnight or 1am. Even confirmed early birds should at least try to stay out late for a few nights, as New York's legendary energy is most obvious late at night when most other cities would be safely home in bed.

New York's **clubs** are currently recovering from a string of closures and police raids in the late 1990s, as well as the infamous "no dancing allowed" cabaret law, that hobbled major venues and sent customers scattering. Recently, though, a handful of new clubs have opened their doors, mostly in the warehouses of West Chelsea and the Meatpacking District, and depending on what party's being thrown that night, you can hear virtually anything, no matter the club: few slavishly devote themselves to one style of music, although specialist venues certainly do exist.

As for **live music**, New York has been enjoying a **rock 'n' roll** revival for the past few years, fueled by residents and bands from the East Village, the Lower East Side, and Williamsburg in Brooklyn – and it's still going strong. On any night of the week you can take your pick from several good, small Lower East Side clubs, as well as more spacious joints in Brooklyn, and be sure to hear something exciting. Downtown clubs such as *Tonic* and the *Knitting Factory* offer a hearty mix of modern and classic **jazz**, **electronica**, and strange things created by laptops, while the likes of *SOBs* offer excellent opportunities to dance to music from all over the world.

Whatever you're planning to do after dark, remember to **carry ID** at all times to prove you're over 21 – you'll likely be asked by every doorman; note that some venues do not even allow under-21s to enter, let alone drink – call to check if you're concerned. For **tickets**, visit Ⓦwww.ticketmaster.com or Ⓦwww.ticketweb.com; between them, the two cover most of the city's venues. They do charge hefty "convenience" fees, though, so if a venue has a pick-up box-office policy (see websites), consider this instead of purchasing online.

The sections that follow provide accounts of the pick of the city's **venues**. Since the music and club scenes are constantly changing, it's a good idea to get current what's-on info once you hit the ground. The listings magazine *Time Out New York* is pretty reliable; you can pick up the current week's issue for a few bucks from virtually any newsstand. Otherwise, grab a freesheet like *The Village Voice* (Ⓦwww.villagevoice.com), *The Onion* (whose cultural listings are excellent), or the monthly club sheet *Flyer*. These can be found on street corners in self-serve newspaper boxes, as well as in many music stores and bars; all contain detailed **listings** for most scenes.

Rock music

New York's **rock music** scene is still built on white-boy guitar bands, with three-chord rock the default setting. That said, many foreign acts – especially British bands – travel to New York's shores first when trying to break into America. Frequently you'll have the opportunity to see these groups play in small venues at low admission prices. In Manhattan, most of the energy is provided by bars and venues located in the **East Village** and the **Lower East Side**. The listings below will point you to the primary spots where you should find something for your ears, no matter what you're looking for.

Large venues

Madison Square Garden Map 6, E4. 7th Ave, at 32nd ☎212/465-6741, ⓦwww.thegarden.com New York's principal large stage, the Garden hosts not only hockey and basketball but also a good proportion of the stadium rock acts that visit the city. Seating 20,000+, the arena is not the most soulful place to see a band, but it may be the only chance you get.

Radio City Music Hall Map 7, G7. 1260 6th Ave, at 50th ☎212/247-4777, ⓦwww.radiocity.com. Not the prime venue it once was; most of the acts that play here now are firmly in the mainstream. The building itself has as great a sense of occasion, though, and Rockette dolls are still sold in the gift shop.

Small to mid-sized venues

Apollo Theatre Map 9, D8. 253 W 125th St, btw 7th and 8th ☎212/531-5301 (show info), ☎212/531-5305 (tickets), ☎212/531-5337 (tours), ⓦwww.apolloshowtime.com. Stars are born and legends are still made at the Apollo, where everyone from Billie Holiday to Aretha Franklin and Duke Ellington had their day. Now this renovated theater features a slate of black music acts, comedy, and weekly amateur nights (Wed). Tickets usually $15–50.

Arlene Grocery Map 5, K6. 95 Stanton St, btw Ludlow and Orchard ☎212/995-1652, ⓦwww.arlenesgrocery.net. Frequented by musicians, some talent scouts, and open-minded rock fans, this intimate former *bodega* hosts nightly gigs by local, reliably good indie bands – and there's no cover on weeknights. Go on Monday nights for the punk and heavy-metal karaoke, where you can "sing" along with a live band – it's great fun, and the crowd really gets into it. Cover on Fri & Sat $3, Sun $5.

Beacon Theater Map 7, C2. 2124 Broadway, btw 74th and 75th ☎212/496-7070. Beautiful old theater with great acoustics, featuring mature, well-established though still exciting artists, from Aimee Mann to Sigur Ros. Tickets $25–100.

Bowery Ballroom Map 5, I7. 6

Delancey St, at Bowery ☎212/533-2111, ⊕www.boweryballroom.com. A minimum of attitude among staff and clientele, great sound, and even better views has earned this venue praise from fans and bands alike. Great bar and solid lineup. Shows $10–30.

CBGB (and OMFUG) Map 5, H5. 315 Bowery, at Bleecker ☎212/982-4052. After 20+ years the black, sticker-covered interior may be the last of its kind in New York, but this legendary punk bastion is not as cutting-edge as it once was: noisy rock bands are the order now, often five or six a night. Tickets run $5–10. Its less scruffy counterpart next door, *CB's 313 Gallery*, hosts folk, acoustic, and experimental music seven days a week ($5). As of press time, *CBGBs* was going through some serious issues with its landlord – even operating without a lease – and whether or not this landmark can survive remains to be seen.

Hammerstein Ballroom Map 6, E4. 311 W 34th St, btw 8th and 9th ☎212/564-4882. Refurbished ballroom that hosts a few shows a month, mostly indie rock and electronic music, in a 3600-seat venue. Tickets $20–60.

Irving Plaza Map 6, K8. 17 Irving Place, btw 15th and 16th ☎212/777-6800, ⊕www.irvingplaza.com. Host to an impressive array of rock and pop acts, though not the best venue qua venue: the balcony hangs way over the ground floor, making for muddled acoustics. Stand on the ground floor in front of the balcony for the best sound mix. Tickets $15–25.

Mercury Lounge Map 5, K5. 217 E Houston St, at Essex ☎212/260-7400, ⊕www.mercuryloungenyc.com. Small, dark Lower East Side mainstay, which hosts a mix of local, national, and international rock acts. It's owned by the same crew as the Bowery Ballroom, but generally features less-established bands. Tickets generally $8–15, though sometimes more.

Roseland Ballroom Map 7, E7. 239 W 52nd St, btw Broadway and 8th ☎212/247-0200, ⊕www.roselandballroom.com. Opened in 1919, this historic ballroom was once frequented by Adele and Fred Astaire, among others. Now a ballroom-dancing school, six times a month it turns into a concert venue, hosting big names and various rock, pop, and jam bands. Take a gander at the shoes and photographs displayed in the entry hall. Tickets $10–50.

Jazz

Manhattan's **jazz** scene is less dead than some might have you think: there are more than forty locations in Manhattan that present jazz regularly. Look mostly to **Greenwich Village**, the **Lower East Side**, or **Harlem** for a good place; midtown jazz clubs tend to be slick dinner–dance joints – expensive and overrun by businesspeople looking for culture.

Venues

55 Map 5, C3. 55 Christopher St, btw 6th and 7th ☏212/929-9883, ⓦwww.55bar.com. Relaxing, unpretentious underground jazz bar; the best of the old guard, with traditional and modern tunes to soothe the soul. Cover varies; no drink minimum.

Arthur's Tavern Map 5, C3. 57 Grove St, between Bleecker and 7th ☏212/675-6879, ⓦwww.arthurstavernnyc.com. Small, amiable piano bar with some inspired performers and no cover or minimum. Drinks are pricey, though.

Birdland Map 7, E9. 315 W 44th St, btw 8th and 9th ☏212/581-3080, ⓦwww.birdlandjazz.com. Not the original place where Charlie Parker played, but an established supper club nonetheless. Hosts some big names, with sets nightly at 9 and 11pm. Music charge $10–40, with a $10 food/drink minimum and a free drink if you sit at the bar.

The Blue Note Map 5, D4. 131 W 3rd St, at 6th ☏212/475-8592,

ⓦwww.bluenote.net. The famous names here aren't really worth the attendant high prices, cattle-herd atmosphere, and minimal legroom. Cover charges vary wildly, from $7 to $65, plus a $5 minimum per person at the tables or a one-drink minimum at the bar. Sets are at 9 and 11.30pm. On Fri and Sat, the jam sessions after 1am are free if you've seen the previous set, or $8 if you haven't.

Café Carlyle Map 7, I1. In the Carlyle Hotel, 35 E 76th St, at Madison ☏212/744-1600. This intimate place is home to both Bobby Short and Woody Allen, who does the jazz thang here on Monday nights. Cover $75–125, no drinks minimum.

Iridium Jazz Club Map 7, F7. 1650 Broadway, btw 51st and 52nd ☏212/582-2121, ⓦwww.iridiumjazzclub.com. Contemporary jazz performed seven nights a week amid Surrealist decor described as "Dolly meets Disney." The godfather of electric guitar Les Paul plays every Monday. Shows at 8 and 10pm, with extra Fri and Sat shows at 11.30pm. Cover $22–38, with $10 food and drink minimum. Sun jazz brunch $22.

Jazz Standard Map 6, J5. 116 E 27th St, btw Park Ave South and Lexington ℡212/576-2232, ⓦwww .jazzstandard.net. A spacious underground room with great sound and even better performers has earned this club high praise and a loyal clientele. Sets Mon–Thurs at 8 & 10pm, Fri and Sat at 8pm, 10.30pm, and midnight, Sun at 7 & 9pm. Mon $15, Tues–Thurs & Sun $20, Fri & Sat $25; all with $10 minimum.

Smoke Map 8, B2. 2751 Broadway, btw 105th and 106th ℡212/864-6662, ⓦwww.smokejazz.com. Voted the best club in the city by *New York* magazine, this Upper West Side joint is a real neighborhood treat. Sets start at 9pm, 11pm, and 12.30am. There's a retro happy-hour with $3 cocktails Mon–Sun 5–8pm. Cover from nothing to $25.

Village Vanguard Map 5, C2. 178 7th Ave, at 11th ℡212/255-4037, ⓦwww.villagevanguard.net. A NYC jazz landmark that celebrated its sixtieth anniversary a few years back, the *Vanguard* supplies a regular diet of big names. Admission is $20, with a $10 minimum. Sets are at 9 and 11pm.

Zinc Bar Map 5, E5. 90 W Houston, at LaGuardia ℡212/477-8337, ⓦwww.zincbar.com. Great jazz/world music venue with strong drinks and a loyal bunch of regulars. The blackboard above the entrance announces the evening's featured band. Cover is $5 with a one-drink minimum. Hosts new talent and established greats such as Max Roach, Grant Green, and Astrud Gilberto. Sets at 9pm, 11pm, and 12.30am Tues–Thurs, also Mon at 2am, and on the weekend at 10pm, 11.30pm, and 1am.

Other types of music

The best of the rest, in **world** music, **avant-garde**, **noise**, spoken-word, **country**, and more. Take a lark and turn up any old night – you're guaranteed to be intrigued, if not downright impressed.

Venues

13 Map 5, F1. 35 E 13th St, at University ℡212/979-6677, ⓦwww .bar13.com. On Monday nights, this cozy bar is home to "louder MONDAYS", a superior evening of open-mic perform-ances and poetry slams. You can dance here, too – outside in summer – a rare treat in the city. **The Knitting Factory Map 4, E3. 74 Leonard St, btw Church and Broad-way** ☎212/219-3055, Ⓦwww .knittingfactory.com. This club boasts two performance spaces, two bars, and a microbrewery with eighteen beers on draft; it also happens to be one of the city's best places to see avant-garde jazz, experimental acts, and big-name indie rock bands in an intimate setting. Tickets $10–20. **NuYorican Poet's Café Map 5, M4. 236 E 3rd St, between B and C** ☎212/505-8183, Ⓦwww.nuyorican .org. This is the godfather of all slam venues, often featuring stars of the poetry world who pop in unannounced. SlamOpen on Wed and the Friday Night Slam both cost $7 and come highly recommended. **Rodeo Bar Map 6, K5. 375 3rd Ave,** at 27th ☎212/683-6500, Ⓦwww .rodeobar.com. Dust off your spurs, grab your partner, and head down to the *Rodeo* for live country tunes seven days a week. No cover. **SOB's (Sounds of Brazil) Map 5, C6. 204 Varick St, at Houston St** ☎212/243-4940, Ⓦwww.sobs.com. Premier place to hear hip-hop, Brazilian, West Indian, Carib-bean, and other world music acts within the confines of Manhattan. Vibrant, with a high quality of music. Two shows nightly, times vary. Admission $7–25 with $10–15 minimum cover at tables. **Tonic Map 5, K6. 107 Norfolk St, btw Rivington and Delancey** ☎212/358-7503, Ⓦwww.tonicnyc .com. Hip Lower East Side avant-garde venue on two levels, with no cover charge to the lower, *subtonic* lounge. Cover varies, but usually around the $10 mark. You can often see some exciting, fresh bands here.

Clubs

New York's – especially Manhattan's – **club life** is a rapidly evolving creature. While many of the name DJs remain the same, venues shift around, opening and closing according to finances and fashion. To ensure that the party is still there, check such **listings** mags as *Time Out New York*, *Paper*, or *Homo Xtra* – or freebies *The Village Voice* and the *New York*

Press. Fliers placed in record and clothing stores in the East Village and SoHo are the best way to find out about the latest clubs and one-off nights. Many fliers also offer substantial discounts.

The **best time to go out** is during the week, when crowds are smaller, prices cheaper, service better, and the clientele more savvy. Style can be important, so make an effort and you'll probably get beyond the velvet rope.

Level V Map 6, D9. 675 Hudson St, btw 13th and 14th ☏212/699-2410. No sign (of course!) to this basement club hidden underneath *Vento*, where well-to-do beautiful people gather to drink Champagne by the bottle and dance to the latest hip-hop, rock, and house. No cover.

Marquee Map 6, C5. 289 10th Ave, at 27th ☏646/473-0202, ⊛www .marqueeny.com. Self-aware and stylish, *Marquee* has a notoriously strict door policy, but once inside you'll be treated to lots of attitude, lavish furnishings, and a glassed-in upper lounge, all topped off with one hell of a chandelier. The music's nothing special... but nobody's here to listen anyway. Cover $20.

Movida Map 5, C5. 28 7th Ave, btw Bedford and Leroy ☏212/206-0900, ⊛www.movidanyc.com. A dream come true for East Village rockers looking for something a little more salubrious than the tattered bars of their home turf,

this tri-level club offers dance, rock, cage dancers, mirrors, and excellent drinks. All is brought together with an incongruous luxury-yacht theme. No cover.

Roxy Map 6, B8. 515 W 18th St, btw 10th and the West Side Hwy ☏212/645-5156, ⊛www.roxynyc .com. Some of the best times in the city to be had on Wednesday nights at this roller disco, where you skate or blade along to your favorite tunes while drinking and getting lethal with your friends. Doors from 8pm, Wed cover $12–15, weekends $20–30.

Sapphire Lounge Map 5, J5. 249 Eldridge St, at Houston ☏212/777-5153, ⊛www.sapphirenyc.com. Pleasantly sleazy lounge, with a black-lit interior and an art gallery out back, frequented by thirty-something hipsters. Music of all kinds, from old-school and classic rock on Thurs to deep house Tues, and Latin-tinged tunes on Mon. Open nightly, free–$5.

24

25

The performing arts and film

rom Broadway glitter to Lower East Side cool, the range and variety of the **performing arts** in New York is exactly what you might expect. Broadway, and even Off-Broadway, **theater** is notoriously expensive, but if you know where to look, there are a variety of ways to get tickets cheaper, and on the Off-Off-Broadway fringe you can see a play for little more than the price of a movie ticket. As for **dance**, **music**, and **opera**, the big mainstream events are extremely expensive, but smaller ones are often equally as interesting and far cheaper. New York (along with LA) gets the first run of most American **films** (and many foreign ones before they reach Europe) and has a very healthy arthouse and revival scene.

Listings for the arts can be found in a number of places. The most useful sources are the clear and comprehensive listings in *Time Out New York*, the free *Village Voice* (especially the pull-out "Voice Choices" section), or the also-free *New York Press*, all especially useful for things downtown and vaguely "alternative." For tonier events try the "Cue" section in the weekly *New York* magazine, the "Goings On About Town" section of *The New Yorker*, or Friday's "Weekend" or Sunday's "Arts and Leisure" sections of the *New York Times*. Specific Broadway listings can be found in the free *Official Broadway Theater Guide*, available at theater and hotel lobbies or at the New York Convention and Visitors' Bureau (see p.19).

Theater

Theater venues are referred to as Broadway, Off-Broadway, or Off-Off-Broadway, classifications that represent a descending order of ticket price, production polish, elegance, and comfort (but don't necessarily have much to do with location) and an ascending order of innovation, experimentation, and theater for the sake of art rather than cash. In the past few years on **Broadway**, David Mamet's *Glengarry Glen Ross*, and *Spamalot*, a musical adaptation of *Monty Python and the Holy Grail*, have taken the city by storm, while lively, imaginative musicals like *The Lion King*, *Avenue Q*, *Hairspray*, and *The Producers* continue to draw crowds and acclaim.

Off-Broadway, while less glitzy, is the best place to discover new talent and adventurous American theater. Here you'll find social and political drama, satire, ethnic plays, and repertory. Lower operating costs also mean that Off-Broadway often serves as a forum to try out what sometimes ends up as a big Broadway production. Recent examples include the musicals *Urinetown* and *Doctor Sex*, a tongue-in-cheek show based on the life of Alfred Kinsey.

Lastly, **Off-Off-Broadway** is New York's fringe: shows range from shoestring productions of the classics to outrageous performance art; likewise, prices (cheap to free) and quality (electrifying to execrable) can vary.

Tickets

Tickets for Broadway shows can cost as much as $75 for orchestra seats (sometimes even $100 for the hottest show in town) and as little as $15 for day-of-performance rush tickets for some of the longer-running shows. Off-Broadway's best seats are cheaper than those on Broadway, averaging $25–55. Off-Off-Broadway tickets should rarely set you back more than $15.

Line up at the **TKTS booth** (☎ 212/768-1818, Ⓦ www.tdf.org), where you can obtain cut-rate tickets on the day of performance (up to half off plus a $2.50 service charge) for many Broadway and Off-Broadway shows (though seldom for the recently opened and very popular shows). The booth, located at Duffy Square, where Broadway and Seventh Avenue meet between 45th and 47th streets, has long lines and is open Monday–Saturday 3–8pm, 10am–2pm for Wednesday and Saturday matinees, and 11am–7pm for all Sunday performances.

Look for **twofer discount coupons** in the New York Convention and Visitors' Bureau and many shops, banks, restaurants, and hotel lobbies. These entitle two people to a hefty discount and, unlike TKTS, it's possible to book ahead – though again, don't expect to find coupons for the latest shows. The Hit Show Club, 630 Ninth Ave, at 44th St (☎ 212/581-4211), also provides discount vouchers for up to fifty percent off that you present at the box office. Same-day standing-room tickets are also available for some sold-out shows for $10–20. Check listings magazines for availability.

If you're prepared to pay full price you can, of course, go directly to the theater, or call one of the following ticket sales agencies. **Tele-Charge** (☎ 212/239-6200 or 1-800/432-7250) and **Ticketmaster** (☎ 212/307-4100 or 1-800/755-4000) sell tickets over the phone to Broadway shows, but note that no show is represented by both these agencies. **Tickets Central** (☎ 212/279-4200) sells tickets to many Off-Broadway theaters 1–8pm daily. You can also buy theater tickets at individual theater websites or at Ⓦ www.ticketmaster.com and Ⓦ www.telecharge.com.

On and Off-Broadway theaters

Astor Place Theater Map 5, H3. 434 Lafayette St, between Astor and 4th ☎212/254-4370. Since 1992, the theater has been the home of the comically absurd but very popular performance artists The Blue Man Group (ⓦwww .blueman.com).

Brooklyn Academy of Music 30 Lafayette Ave, between Ashland and St Felix, Brooklyn ☎718/636-4100, ⓦwww.bam.org. BAM regularly presents theater and modern dance on its three stages. The academy has imported a number of historic productions over the years, including several by Ingmar Bergman, and the world premiere of minimalist opera masterpiece *Einstein on the Beach*, and it still offers the best of cutting-edge performing arts. Every autumn the annual Next Wave festival is the city's most exciting showcase for large-scale performance art by the likes of Philip Glass and Laurie Anderson, among others.

Daryl Roth Theatre Map 6, J9. 20 Union Square East, at 15th ☎212/239-6200. Home to a steady string of interesting, odd-ball productions, including the current *A Woman of Will*, a musical that features several Shakespearean leading ladies offering generally unhelpful advice to a harried modern-day director of *The Merchant of Venice*.

Manhattan Theater Club Map 7, F6. 131 W 55th St, between 6th and 7th ☎212/581-1212, ⓦwww .mtc-nyc.org. Major midtown venue for serious new theater, many of whose productions eventually transfer to Broadway. See them here first.

New Amsterdam Theatre Map 6, F1. 214 West 42nd St, between 7th and 8th ☎212/307-4100. Disney's over-the-top, refurbished Times Square palace – rescued from neglect and overhauled in 2000 – is home to Julie Taymor's Tony Award–winning extravaganza *The Lion King*.

The Public Theater Map 5, H3. 425 Lafayette St, between Astor and 4th ☎212/239-6200, ⓦwww .publictheater.org. This major Off-Broadway venue produces serious and challenging theater from new, mostly American, playwrights, and is the major presenter of Shakespeare in the city. In the summer the Public puts on the free Shakespeare Festival at the open-air Delacorte Theater in Central Park (☎212/539-8500).

St James Theater Map 7, F8. 246 W 44th St, between 7th and 8th ☎212/239-6200. *The Producers*, still NYC's best-selling musical after a several-year run, makes its home at this large Broadway theater.

25

Shubert Theater Map 7, F9. 225 W 44th St, between 7th and 8th ☎212/239-6200. Fred Astaire and Katharine Hepburn are just two of the stars to have graced the Shubert's stage. These days, it's home to the Monty Python musical send-off *Spamalot*.

Studio 54 Map 7, E7. 524 W 54th St, between Broadway and 8th ☎212/239-6200. The legendary 1970s disco has seen new life as home to a series of acclaimed Broadway revivals, starting with *Cabaret* in the 1990s and, more recently, Tennessee Williams' *A Streetcar Named Desire*.

Off-Off-Broadway and performance art spaces

Bouwerie Lane Theater Map 5, H5. 330 Bowery, at Bond ☎212/677-0060, ⓦwww.jeancocteaurep.org. Home of the Jean Cocteau Repertory, which produces plays by Genet, Sophocles, Shaw, Strindberg, Sartre, Wilde, and Williams, among others.

Dixon Place Map 6, M6. 309 E 26th St, between 1st and 2nd ☎212/532-1546, ⓦwww.dixonplace.org. Popular small venue dedicated to experimental theater, dance, readings, and the like. On the first Wed of the month, Dixon Place has an "Open Performance Night," where the first ten people to sign up can present ten minutes of anything they like.

La Mama E.T.C. Map 5, H4. 74A E 4th St, between Bowery and 2nd ☎212/475-7710, ⓦwww.lamama.org. The mother of all Off-Off theaters and venue for some of the most exciting theater, performance, and dance seen in the city for more than thirty years.

Ludlow Ten Map 5, K7. 113 Ludlow St, between Rivington and Delancey ⓦwww.ludlowten.org. LES performance venue that produces the summer-long "Shakespeare in the Park(ing Lot)" series of free performances, held at the Municipal Parking Lot at Broome and Ludlow streets.

New York Theater Workshop Map 5, H4. 79 E 4th St, between Bowery and 2nd ☎212/460-5475, ⓦwww.nytw.org. Innovative and respected space that seems to choose cult hit shows – it was the original host of the hugely successful *Rent*.

Ontological-Hysteric Theatre Map 5, I2. 131 E 10th St, at 2nd ☎212/533-4650, ⓦwww.ontological.com. Produces some of the best radical theater in the city; especially famous for the work of indie theater legend Richard Foreman.

Performing Garage Map 5, E8. 33 Wooster St, between Broome and Grand ☎212/966-3651, ⓦwww.thewoostergroup.org. The well-respected experimental Wooster

Group (whose most famous member is Willem Dafoe) perform regularly in this SoHo space. Tickets are gold dust but worth every effort.

P.S. 122 Map 5, J3. 150 1st Ave, at 9th ☎212/477-5288, ⓦwww .ps122.org. This converted school in the East Village is a perennially popular venue for a jam-packed schedule of radical performance art, dance, and one-person shows.

Theater for the New City Map 5, J2. 155 1st Ave, at 10th ☎212/254-1109. Known for following the development of new playwrights and integrating dance, music, and poetry with drama. TNC also performs outdoors in summer for free at a variety of venues and hosts the Lower East Side Festi-val of the Arts at the end of May.

Literary events and readings

92nd Street Y Unterberg Poetry Center Map 8, J6. 1395 Lexington Ave, at 92nd ☎212/415-5500, ⓦwww.92ndsty.org. Quite simply, the definitive place to hear all your Booker, Pulitzer, and Nobel Prize–winning favorites, as well as many other exciting new talents.

Symphony Space Map 8, B5. 2537 Broadway, at 95th ☎212/864-5400, ⓦwww.symphonyspace.org. The highly acclaimed Selected Shorts series, in which actors read the short fiction of a variety of authors, packs the Symphony Space theater and can be heard across the country on the radio.

Dance

As with theater, the range of **dance** offered in the city is vast. New York has five major ballet companies, dozens of modern troupes, and untold thousands of soloists – you would have to be very particular indeed in your tastes not to find something of interest. Events are listed in broadly the same periodicals and websites as music and theater – though you might also want to pick up *Dance Magazine* (ⓦwww.dance magazine.com). The following is a list of some of the major dance venues in the city, though a lot of the smaller, more esoteric companies and solo artists also perform at spaces like the Kitchen and P.S.122, which are listed opposite under "Off-Off-Broadway and performance art spaces."

Brooklyn Academy of Music 30 Lafayette St, between Ashland and St Felix, Brooklyn ☎718/636-4100, ⓦwww.bam.org. One of the busiest and most daring dance producers in New York. In the autumn, BAM's Next Wave festival showcases the hottest international attractions in avant-garde dance and music; in winter visiting artists appear, and each spring BAM hosts the annual DanceAfrica Festival, America's largest showcase for African and African-American dance and culture.

City Center Map 7, F6. 131 W 55th St, between 6th and 7th ☎212/581-1212, ⓦwww.city-center.org. This large Midtown venue hosts some of the most important troupes in modern dance, such as Merce Cunningham, Paul Taylor, the Alvin Ailey American Dance Theater, the Joffrey Ballet, and the Dance Theater of Harlem.

Cunningham Studio West of Map 5, A2. 55 Bethune St, at Washington ☎212/255-8240, ⓦwww.merce.org. In the far west reaches of the Village, performances by emerging modern choreographers are held once a week at this, the home of the Merce Cunningham Dance Company.

Dance Theater Workshop's Bessie Schönberg Theater Map 5, F8. 219 W 19th St, between 7th and 8th ☎212/924-0077, ⓦwww.dtw.org. DTW boasts more than 175 performances from nearly 70 artists and companies each season. On the second floor of a former warehouse, the theater has an unintimidating, relaxed atmosphere and ticket prices are very reasonable.

Danspace Project Map 5, I2. St Mark's Church, 131 E 10th St, at 2nd ☎212/674-8194, ⓦwww.danspaceproject.org. Experimental contemporary dance, with a season running from Sept to June in one of the more beautiful performance spaces.

The Joyce Theater Map 6, E8. 175 8th Ave, at 19th ☎212/242-0800, ⓦwww.joyce.org. The Joyce hosts short seasons by a wide variety of acclaimed dance troupes such as Pilobolus, the Parsons Dance Company, and Donald Byrd/The Group. In a space in SoHo at 155 Mercer St, between Prince and Houston (☎212/431-9233), the Joyce puts on a three-week concert series of collaborating choreographers each spring.

Juilliard Dance Workshop Map 7, D4. Juilliard Theater, 155 W 65th St, at Broadway ☎212/799-5000. Juilliard School's dance division often gives free workshop performances, and each spring six students work with six composers to present a "Composers and Choreographers" concert.

Lincoln Center's Fountain Plaza Map 7, D4. At Lincoln Center, 65th and Columbus ☏212/875-5766, ⓦwww .lincolncenter.org. Open-air summer venue for the enormously popular "Midsummer Night Swing," where you can learn a different dance en masse each night (everything from polka to rockabilly) and watch a performance, all for $12. Tickets go on sale at 5.45pm the night of.

Metropolitan Opera House Map 7, D4. At Lincoln Center, 65th and Columbus ☏212/362-6000, ⓦwww.metopera .org. Home of the renowned American Ballet Theater, which performs at the Opera House from early May into July. Prices for ballet at the Met range from $275 for the best seats at special performances to $12–16 for standing-room tickets, which go on sale the morning of the performance.

New York State Theater Map 7, D4. At Lincoln Center, 65th and Columbus ☏212/870-5570, ⓦwww .lincolncenter.org. Lincoln Center's major ballet venue is home to the revered New York City Ballet, which performs for a nine-week season each spring.

Classical music and opera

New Yorkers take **serious music** seriously. Long lines form for anything popular, many concerts sell out, and summer evenings can see a quarter of a million people turning up in Central Park for free performances by the New York Philharmonic. The range of what's available is wide – but it's big names at big venues that pull in the crowds.

Opera venues

Amato Opera Theater Map 5, H5. 319 Bowery, at 2nd ☏212/228-8200, ⓦwww.amato.org. This Bowery venue presents an ambitious and varied repertory of classics performed by up-and-coming young singers and conductors. Performances at weekends only. Closed in the summer.

Juilliard School Map 7, D4. 60 Lincoln Center Plaza, at 65th and Broadway ☏212/799-5000, ⓦwww .juilliard.edu. Right next door to the Met (see below), Juilliard students often perform under the direction of a famous conductor, usually for low ticket prices.

Metropolitan Opera House Map 7, D4. At Lincoln Center, 64th and Columbus ☏212/362-6000, ⓦwww .metopera.org. New York's premier opera venue is home to the Metropolitan Opera Company from Sept to late April. The sets are typically unbelievably lavish (several classic productions are by Zeffirelli) and performances of the first order. Tickets are expensive and can be quite difficult to obtain, though 175 standing-room tickets for $12–16 go on sale every Sat morning at 10am (the line has been known to form at dawn).

The New York State Theater Map 7, D4. At Lincoln Center, 64th and Columbus ☎212/870-5570, ⓦwww .lincolncenter.org. Playing David to the Met's Goliath, the City Opera's wide and adventurous program varies wildly in quality – sometimes startlingly innovative, occasionally mediocre, but seats go for less than half the Met's prices.

Concert halls

The Alice Tully Hall Map 7, D4. At Lincoln Center, 64th and Columbus ☎212/721-6500, ⓦwww.lincolncenter.org. A smallish venue for chamber orchestras, string quartets, and instrumentalists. Prices similar to those at Avery Fisher, below.

The Avery Fisher Hall Map 7, D4. At Lincoln Center, 64th and Columbus ☎212/875-5030, ⓦwww .lincolncenter.org. Home of the New York Philharmonic, as well as visiting orchestras and soloists. Ticket prices for the Philharmonic are in the range of $12–50. An often fascinating bargain are the NYP open rehearsals at 9.45am on concert days, which cost just $14. Avery Fisher also hosts the very popular annual Mostly Mozart Festival (☎212/875-5103) in Aug.

Bargemusic Map 4, J5. Fulton Ferry Landing, Brooklyn ☎718/624-4061, ⓦwww.bargemusic.org. Chamber music in a wonderful river setting below the Brooklyn Bridge on Thurs and Fri at 7.30pm, and Sun at 4pm. Tickets are $30, or $25 for senior citizens and $15 for students.

Brooklyn Academy of Music 30 Lafayette St, between Ashland and St Felix, Brooklyn ☎718/636-4100, ⓦwww.bam.org. The BAM Opera House is the perennial home of Philip Glass operatic premieres and also hosts a number of contemporary imports from European and Chinese companies, often with a large modern dance component.

Carnegie Hall Map 7, F6. 154 W 57th St, at 7th ☎212/247-7800, ⓦwww .carnegiehall.org. The greatest names from all schools of music performed here in the past, from Tchaikovsky and Toscanini to Gershwin and Billie Holiday. Labeled "one of the finest orchestral showplaces on the planet" by Alex Ross in *The New Yorker*.

Merkin Concert Hall Map 7, D3. 129 W 67th St, between Broadway and Amsterdam ☎212/501-3330, ⓦwww.merkinconcerthall.org.

In the Elaine Kaufman Cultural Center, this intimate and adventurous venue is a great place to hear music of any kind. Plays host to the New York Guitar Festival in September.

Free summer concerts

In the light of high concert ticket prices, it's welcoming that so many events in the city, especially during summer, are **free**. **The SummerStage Festival** (☎212/360-2777, ⓦwww.summerstage.org) in **Central Park** puts on an impressive range of free concerts of all kinds of music throughout the summer (see box, p.120). On occasional Wednesday nights the **New York Grand Opera** performs Verdi operas at SummerStage. Central Park is also one of the many open-air venues for the **New York Philharmonic's Concerts in the Park** series (☎212/875-5709, ⓦwww.nyphilharmonic.org), which are held all over the city and the outer boroughs in July, and the similar **Met in the Parks** series (☎212/362-6000, ⓦwww.metopera.org) in June and July. All summer, **Lincoln Center Out-of-Doors** (☎212/875-5766, ⓦwww.lincolncenter.org) puts on a varied slate of free music and dance performances on the plaza.

Cabaret and comedy

Comedy clubs are rife in New York, though the **cabaret** scene – after a brief uptick in the late 1990s – is less than omnipresent at the moment; the list below represents the best-known venues in town, but as ever, check *Time Out New York* and the *Village Voice* for the fullest and most up-to-date listings.

Café Carlyle Map 7, I1. 35 E 76th St, at Madison ☎212/570-7189, ⓦwww.thecarlyle.com. Legendary crooner Bobby Short may be

gone, but the *Carlyle* still has a full line-up of name performers like Elaine Stritch and the Woody Allen–fronted New Orleans Jazz

Band on Monday nights from Sept to Dec. Cover $40, with a two-drink minimum. Jackets required for men.

Caroline's Map 7, F8. 1626 Broadway, at 49th ⏂212/757-4100, ⓦwww.carolines.com. Having moved to Times Square from the Seaport, *Caroline's* still books some of the best stand-up acts in town. Cover $15–30 Sun–Thurs, $25–40 Fri and Sat. Two-drink minimum. Also has a restaurant, *Comedy Nation*, upstairs.

Chicago City Limits Theater Map 7, K5. 1105 1st Ave, at 61st ⏂212/888-5233, ⓦwww.chicagocitylimits.com. New York's oldest improv theater, playing one show nightly, two on weekends. Closed Tues. Admission is $15 with a two-drink minimum.

Collective Unconscious Map 4, E2. 279 Church St, at White ⏂212/254-5277, ⓦwww.weird.org. The Sunday-night open-mics here are

some of the most raucous and amusing in town. Cover $15.

Joe's Pub Map 5, H3. 425 Lafayette St, between Astor and 4th ⏂212/239-6200, ⓦwww.publictheater.org. The hipper, late-night arm of the Public Theater (see p.261), this is one of the nicest and most popular music venues in town, with a wide range of cabaret acts nightly, from Broadway crooner Donna McKechnie to Norwegian folk icon and Hardanger fiddle virtuoso Annbjørg Lien, and everything in between.

Stand Up New York Map 7, C1. 236 W 78th St, at Broadway ⏂212/595-0850, ⓦwww.standupny.com. Upper West Side all-ages forum for established comics, many of whom have appeared on Leno, Letterman, and the like. Nightly shows, three on weekends. Weekdays $10 cover, Fri and Sat $16. Two-drink minimum.

Film

New York is a **movie-lover's dream**, sporting a slew of mainstream Hollywood megaplexes with all the charm of airport terminals but great seating and sound systems, plus a good number of downtown art venues featuring a range of foreign and local independent flicks. Simply put, there's something here for everyone. For **listings** your best bets are the weekly *Village Voice* or the *New York Press* (both free), *Time Out New York*, or the daily papers on Fridays, when reviews come out. Beware that listings in papers are not *always* entirely accurate, but you can phone ☎212/777-FILM or visit Ⓦwww.moviefone.com for accurate showtimes; you can also purchase tickets in advance. Ticket prices have risen to as high as $10.75, and there are no reduced matinee prices in Manhattan, nor cheap evenings.

The city also supports a number of major **film festivals** (see also Chapter 30), the biggest being the New York Film Festival, which runs for two weeks from the end of September, at Alice Tully Hall (Ⓦwww.filmlinc.com; see p.266 under "Concert halls"). Lastly, if you don't mind the heat and would rather watch your movies outside, Bryant Park, at Sixth Avenue and 42nd Street (☎212/512-5700, Ⓦwww.bryantpark.org), hosts free, outdoor screenings of old Hollywood favorites on Monday nights at sunset throughout the summer – be sure to get there early, as space on the grass fills up almost immediately.

Arthouse and revivals

The American Museum of the Moving Image 35th Ave, at 36th St, Astoria, Queens ☎718/784-0077, Ⓦwww.ammi.org. Showing films only on weekends during the day, the AMMI (see p.172) is well worth a trip out to Queens either for the films – serious director retrospectives, silent films, and a good emphasis on cinematographers – or for the cinema museum itself.

Anthology Film Archives Map 5, I5. 32 2nd Ave, at 2nd ☎212/505-5181, Ⓦwww.anthologyfilmarchives.org. Bastion of experimental filmmaking where programs of mind-bending abstraction, East Village indie flicks, auteur retrospectives, and the year-round Essential Cinema series rub shoulders.

Cinema Classics Map 5, J2. 332 E 11th St, between 1st and 2nd ☎212/677-6309, Ⓦwww.cinemaclassics.com. Though a grungy, sit-on-folding-chairs affair, the film selections here are excellent, the café's sofas and cakes divine, and all tickets are just $6. There's an esoteric collection of cult videos for sale.

Film Forum Map 5, C6. 209 W Houston St, between 6th and 7th ☎212/727-8112, Ⓦwww.filmforum.org. The cozy three-screen Film Forum has an eccentric but famously popular program of new independent movies, documentaries, and foreign films, plus the occasional revival.

IFC Center Map 5, D4. 323 6th Ave, at 3rd ☎212/924-7771, ⓦwww.ifccenter.com. Multiple revivals daily and a good number of very small indie films from the newest entrant into the arthouse scene, affiliated with the US's popular cable TV Independent Film Channel. Features a much larger screen and a better sound system than you'll find at its competitors.

Ocularis 70 N 6th St, between Wythe and Kent, Williamsburg, Brooklyn ☎718/388-8713, ⓦwww.billburg.com/ocularis. This small space housed inside the arty *Galapagos* bar is transformed into an independent cinema on Sunday nights, screening rarely-seen cult classics, foreign gems, and pioneering work by new directors.

Walter Reade Theater Map 7, D4. 165 W 65th St, between Broadway and Amsterdam ☎212/496-3809, ⓦwww.filmlinc.com. Simply the best place in town to see great films. Opened in 1991, this beautiful modern theater, with perfect sightlines, a huge screen, and impeccable sound, elevates the art of cinema to the position it deserves within Lincoln Center. The emphasis is on foreign cinema and the great auteurs.

26

Gay and lesbian New York

T here are few places in America – indeed in the world – where **gay culture** thrives as it does in New York. A glance at the pages of the *Village Voice*, where gay theater, gossip, and politics share space with more mainstream goings-on, gives a quick inkling of what's on offer.

Socially, lesbians and gay men are fairly visible in the city, and while it's not recommended that you and your partner

---

Gay media

The following are a selection of outlets with up-to-date listings and insider information on the gay and lesbian scene.

The Advocate Ⓦ www.advocate.com. National gay and lesbian newsmagazine.

HX Magazine Ⓦ www.hx.com. Vital homosexual listings mag.

Metrosource Magazine Ⓦ www.metrosource.com. National gay and lesbian lifestyle magazine with a local directory of gay-friendly professionals and businesses.

Out Magazine Ⓦ www.out.com. A lifestyle magazine covering everything from politics to health.

hold hands in public before checking out the territory, there are several New York neighborhoods where you'll find yourself in the comfortable majority. A strong presence lingers in the vicinity of **Christopher Street** in the West Village, but it's in **Chelsea** that gay socializing is most out and open. The other havens are Brooklyn's **Park Slope** and **Williamsburg** 'hoods, for women and men, respectively.

Accommodation

The following places are friendly to gay men and lesbians and convenient for the scene.

Chelsea Mews Guest House Map 6, D9. 344 W 15th St, between 8th and 9th ⊕212/255-9174. A large Victorian home converted into an all-male guesthouse with eight rooms available, two with private bath. No kitchens, but there are hot plates in the rooms, which are very well-appointed. The best feature, though, is the large backyard garden. Local calls are included in the price. Rooms from $100–150.

Chelsea Pines Inn Map 6, D9. 317 W 14th St, between 8th and 9th ⊕212/929-1023, ⓦwww .chelseapinesinn.com. Well-priced hotel, whose guests are mostly gay, housed in an old brownstone on the Greenwich Village/Chelsea border that offers clean, comfortable, attractively furnished rooms. Best to book in advance; three-night minimum stay at weekends. Rooms from $140.

Chelsea Savoy Hotel Map 6, F6. 204 W 23rd St, at 7th ⊕212/929-9353, ⓦwww.chelseasavoynyc.com. This relative newcomer, housed in a new building, makes up for a lack of charm with clean and modern amenities in every room. Rooms from $145.

Colonial House Inn Map 6, D7. 318 W 22nd St, btw 8th and 9th ⊕212/243-9669, ⓦwww .colonialhouseinn.com. Economical twenty-room bed-and-breakfast in the heart of Chelsea. Also welcomes straight guests. Boasts a clothing-optional roof deck. Rooms $104–130.

Incentra Village House Map 5, A1. 32 8th Ave, between 12th and Jane ⊕212/206-0007. Twelve-room townhouse, some rooms with kitchenette. Three-night minimum stay at weekends. Also welcomes straight guests. Rooms from $169.

Bars

Gay men's **bars** cover the spectrum: from relaxed, mainstream cafés to some hard-hitting clubs full of glamour and attitude. Most of the more established places are in Greenwich Village and Chelsea, and along Avenue A in the East Village. For **women**, Park Slope in Brooklyn edges out the East Village and Hudson Street in the West as the center of happenings. Things tend to get raunchier further west as you reach the bars and cruisers of the wild West Side Highway and the Meatpacking District, both of which are pretty hardcore.

Mainly for men

Barracuda Map 6, F7. 275 W 22nd St, between 7th and 8th ☎212/645-8613. A favorite spot in New York's gay scene, and as laid-back as you'll find in Chelsea. Two-for-one happy hour from 4–9pm during the week, crazy drag shows and pick-up lines, and a hideaway lounge out back.

Brandy's Piano Bar Map 8, K8. 235 E 84th St, between 2nd and 3rd ☎212/744-4949. Handsome uptown cabaret/piano bar with a crazy, mixed, and generally greying clientele. Definitely worth a visit.

The Dugout Map 5, A5. 185 Christopher St, at Weehawken ☎212/242-9113. Right by the river, this friendly West Village hangout with TV, pool table, and video games might be the closest you'll find to a gay sports-bar.

Dusk Lounge Map 6, G6. 147 W 24th St, between 6th and 7th ☎212/924-4490. A great place to chill out and unwind, this Chelsea stalwart is perfect for a weekday afternoon.

g Map 6, E8. 223 W 19th St, between 7th and 8th ☎212/929-1085. Nearly as stylish as its "guppie" clientele, this large and deservedly popular lounge also features a DJ nightly.

Marie's Crisis Map 5, C4. 59 Grove St, between 7th and Bleecker ☎212/243-9323. Often packed and always fun, this well-known cabaret/piano bar is popular with tourists and locals alike. Features old-time singing sessions nightly.

The Monster Map 5, C3. 80 Grove St, at Waverly ☎212/924-3558. Large, campy bar with drag cabaret, piano, and downstairs dance floor. Very popular, especially with tourists, yet still has a strong neighborhood feel.

Phoenix Map 5, J1. 447 E 13th St, between 1st and A ☎212/477-9979.

This relaxed East Village favorite is much loved by the so-not-scene-they're-scene boys and guys who really just want a drink.

Rawhide Map 6, E7. 212 8th Ave, at 21st ☏ 212/242-9332. Hell-bent for leather, Chelsea's Rough Rider Room opens at 8am for those who have beer for breakfast (and closes late, too).

The Slide Bar Map 5, H4. 356 Bowery, at 4th ☏ 212/420-8885. An original underground nineteenth-century gay bar with the feel of a Roaring Twenties speakeasy. Unique atmosphere, great shows, and high-speed, factory-line-like cruising. The crowd is college-age on weekends.

Stonewall Map 5, C3. 53 Christopher St, between Waverly and 7th ☏ 212/463-0950. Yes, that *Stonewall*, site of the seminal 1969 riot, mostly refurbished and flying the pride flag like they own it = which, one supposes, they do.

Mainly for women

An Beal Bocht 445 W 238th St, between Greystone and Waldo, The Bronx ☏ 718/884-7127. Equal parts students, lesbians, and Irish expats, this Riverdale favorite pulls in women from across the city and serves up Guinness, oatmeal, and frequent live music until all hours.

Clubshelter Map 6, H2. 20 W 39th St, between 5th and 6th ☏ 212/252-3397, ⊕ www.lovergirlnyc.com. The Saturday-night *Lovergirl* dance parties at this underground bar are extremely popular.

Cubbyhole Map 5, A2. 282 W 12th St, between Greenwich and 4th ☏ 212/243-9041. Welcoming, kitschy West Village dyke bar. Small but generally crowded and something of a required stopover as it's been here forever.

Ginger's 363 5th Ave, Park Slope, Brooklyn ☏ 718/788-0924. Best bar in this lesbian-heavy Brooklyn neighborhood, ethnically diverse and mellower than Manhattan clubs, with the likes of Bob Marley and John Coltrane on the jukebox. It's a great hangout, with a super-comfortable space and friendly people.

Henrietta Hudson Map 5, B5. 438 Hudson St, at Morton ☏ 212/924-3347, ⊕ www.henriettahudson.com. Laid-back bar by day, dance club by night, and a great local lesbian spot to chill.

Rubyfruit Bar & Grill Map 5, A4. 531 Hudson St, at 10th ☏ 212/929-3343. A cozy, friendly place for grown-up dykes, *Rubyfruit* is all about couches, cheap drinks, and good company.

Starlight Bar & Lounge Map 5, K2. 167 Ave A, at 11th ☏ 212/475-2172. This gay bar, which is commandeered by lesbians every Sunday night, is the best meeting-place for women, as it's perpetually packed and has a large, loyal local following. Top-line house DJs, slick decor, and a happening dance floor.

Clubs

Gay and lesbian **clubs** in New York can be some of the most outrageous in the world, while many of the city's non-denominational nightspots have a very open-door policy (as regards sexuality) and often host weekly gay parties. Again, check out the *Village Voice* (Ⓦ www.villagevoice.com) and *HX* (Ⓦ www.hx.com) for the latest in homosexual hip.

2i's Map 5, B1. 248 W 14th St, between 7th and 8th ☎212/807-1775, Ⓦwww.2isnightclub.com. Thursday is dyke night at this chic, low-key African-American joint. Dancers, an open-mic, and other diversions (see website for schedule) get the girls going.

Don Hill's Map 5, B7. 511 Greenwich St, at Spring ☎212/334-1390, Ⓦwww.donhills.com. An open-to-all, up-for-anything place where you'll find Britpop drag queens, mod-rock dominatrixes, and the occasional submissive metal fan. Pole dancers and porn complete the vibe.

The Eagle Map 6, B5. 554 W 28th St, between 10th and 11th ☎646/473-1866, Ⓦwww.eagle-ny.com. Bi-level leather club with regular and special fetish events, by far the most storied and popular in New York. Dress code some nights; check the website.

Heaven Map 6, G8. 479 6th Ave, at 16th ☎212/539-3982, Ⓦwww.juliesnewyork.com. Women-owned and -operated club with Wednesday *Noche Latina* dyke night and multiracial *Kaleidoscope* Fridays.

Henrietta Hudson Map 5, B5. 438 Hudson St, between Morton and Barrow ☎212/924-3347, Ⓦwww.henriettahudsons.com. Relaxed in the afternoon but brimming by night, especially on weekends. Weekly theme nights include Latin and "baby dyke." Lounging, pool, and dancing areas are all separate.

La Nueva Escuelita Map 6, E2. 301 W 39th St, at 8th ☎212/631-0588. Exclusive and elusive, this is also one of the city's very best gay clubs. It's all about kitsch, dress-up, salsa, drag, and (wo)men. Expect to wait in line for a while.

27

Shopping

New York's **shops** cater to every possible taste, in any combination, and in many cases at any time of the day or night. As such, they're a great reason for visiting the city, even if the invasion of chains, like Barnes & Noble, Filene's Basement, and even the world's largest K-Mart have caused some worry. Nevertheless, many of the oddest and oldest stores remain, and nothing beats discovering a quirky, independent shop that may specialize only in vintage cufflinks or rubber stamps.

Remember that an 8.25 percent **sales tax** will be added to your bill; this is bypassed sometimes when paying cash in a market or discount store. Finally, wherever you're shopping, be careful: Manhattan's crowded, frenzied stores are ripe territory for pickpockets and bag-snatchers.

Antiques

New York is the premier **antique** source in the country, great for browsing, with museum-quality pieces available (typically costing a fortune) as well as lots of interesting, fairly priced stuff at the junkier end of the market. Prime locations are the East and West Villages, SoHo, Chelsea, Lower Broadway, and the Upper East Side.

Chameleon Map 5, G7. 231 Lafayette St, between Spring and Prince
☎212/343-9197. Interesting
collection of antique lighting fixtures dating from the nineteenth
century to the 1960s, many from
NYC residences.

The Showplace Map 6, H6. 40 W
25th St, between 6th and Broadway
☎212/741-8520. Indoor market
of more than 100 dealers of
antiques and collectibles plus an
espresso bar. Mon–Fri 9am–6pm,
Sat & Sun 8.30am–5.30pm.

Las Venus Map 5, K6. 163 Ludlow
St, at Stanton ☎212/982-0608.
Best mid-century furniture in
town at bargain prices in this
fun basement shop packed with
Eames chairs, Verner Panton
lamps, and more. Open from
noon daily.

Books

Book lovers bemoan the steady disappearance of New York's
independent bookstores, and attribute their loss to the phenomenon of Barnes & Noble superstores, but there's still no
shortage of places to find **books**, no matter how esoteric
your tastes may be.

Superstores

Barnes & Noble Map 5, G3. 4 Astor
Place, at Broadway ☎212/420-
1322; Map 6, I3. 385 5th Ave, at
36th ☎212/779-7677; Map 6, G7.
675 6th Ave, at 22nd ☎212/727-
1227; Map 7, H8. 600 5th Ave, at
48th ☎212/765-0592; Map 7, J8.
750 3rd Ave, at 47th ☎212/697-
2251; Map 8, B8. 2289 Broadway, at
82nd ☎212/362-8835; Map 8, K7.
240 E 86th St, at 2nd ☎212/794-
1962; Map 8, J7. 1280 Lexington
Ave, at 86th ☎212/423-9900; Map
7, D4. 1972 Broadway, across from
Lincoln Center ☎212/595-6859; and
Map 6, J8. 33 E 17th St, at Union
Square ☎212/253-0810. Major US
bookseller, many of its stores
with attendant *Starbucks* cafés.
Author readings take place about
five evenings a week.

McNally Robinson Map 5, H6. 50
Prince St, at Mulberry ☎212/274-
1160. This Canadian superstore
chain has gained a foothold in
the heart of Manhattan with a
prime SoHo outpost. Great service = the staff here are friendly
and actually knowledgeable
about books (imagine that). The
small tea-room offers nightly
readings.

Independent bookstores

St Mark's Bookshop Map 5, H3. 31 3rd Ave, at 9th ℡212/260-7853. One of the best independent bookstores in the city, with a good array of titles on politics, feminism, the environment, and literary criticism, as well as more obscure subjects. Also the best place to buy radical and art magazines.

Shakespeare & Co. Map 7, J3. 939 Lexington Ave, at 69th ℡212/570-0201; Map 5, G4. 716 Broadway, at Washington ℡212/529-1330; Map 6, K7. 137 E 23rd St, at Lexington ℡212/570-0201; and Map 4, E8. 1 Whitehall St, at Stone ℡212/742-7025. New and used books, paper and hardcover, with some great fiction and psychology selections. There's also a branch in Brooklyn, at the Brooklyn Academy of Music (see p.163).

Three Lives & Co. Map 5, C3. 154 W 10th St, at Waverly ℡212/741-2069. Excellent literary bookstore that has an especially good array of books by and for women, as well as general titles. There's an excellent reading series in the fall.

Secondhand books

Argosy Bookstore Map 7, I5. 16 E 59th St, between Lexington and Park ℡212/753-4455. Unbeatable for rare books, Argosy also sells clearance books and titles of all kinds, though the shop's reputation means you may find mainstream works cheaper elsewhere.

The Strand Map 5, G2. 828 Broadway, at 12th ℡212/473-1452. With about eight miles of books and a stock of 2.5 million+, this is the largest book operation in the city – and one of the few survivors in an area once rife with secondhand bookstores.

Travel and other specialty bookstores

The Complete Traveler Map 6, I3. 199 Madison Ave, at 35th ℡212/685-9007. The city's premier travel bookshop, excellently stocked with new and secondhand titles, including a huge collection of *Baedeker*s.

Oscar Wilde Memorial Bookshop Map 5, C3. 15 Christopher St, between Gay and Greenwich ℡212/255-8097. Aptly situated gay and lesbian bookstore – probably the first in the city – with a rare book collection, signed and first editions, and signed, framed letters from famous authors.

Clothes, fashion, and accessories

If you are prepared to search the city with sufficient dedication you can find just about anything, though it's designer clothes (and haughty fashionista attitude) that predominate. **Secondhand clothes**, of the "vintage" or "antique" variety, have caught on and are also very popular. If you're looking for things to complete your look, plenty of **shoe** stores are available, especially around West 8th St; and there's no shortage of **make-up** emporia either.

Chain stores

Benetton Map 7, H8, 597 5th Ave, at 48th ☎212/317-2502. Italian chain offering youthful, contemporary, casual, bright-colored clothing for women, men, and children.
Brooks Brothers Map 7, I9, 346 Madison Ave, at 44th ☎212/682-9136. Something of an institution in New York, this flagship store, founded in 1915, offers classic conservative style, selling tweeds and quietly striped shirts and ties.
Burberry Map 7, H6, 1350 6th Ave, at 55th ☎212/246-1147. Classic plaids and tweeds, with a distinctly British feel to the conservative design.
Diesel Map 7, J5, 770 Lexington Ave, at 60th ☎212/308-0055. One of five US stores that sell this Italian-designed label. Funky, vintage-inspired clubwear and lots of denim.
Eileen Fisher Map 6, I8, 166 5th Ave, between 21st and 22nd ☎212/924-4777. This is the largest of their five NY shops, full of loose and elegantly casual clothes for women.

Designer stores

Anna Sui Map 5, F6, 113 Greene St, between Prince and Spring ☎212/941-8406.
Bagutta Map 7, H6, 49 West 57th St, between 5th and 6th ☎212/750-5606. A confluence of top designers including Helmut Lang, Prada, Gaultier, Plein Sud, and Dolce & Gabbana.
DKNY Map 7, I5, 655 Madison Ave, at 60th ☎212/223-3569.
Dolce & Gabbana Map 7, I3, 816 Madison Ave, between 68th and 69th ☎212/249-4100.
Gianni Versace Map 7, H7, 647 5th Ave, between 51st and 52nd ☎212/317-0224; Map 7, I4, 815 Madison Ave, at 68th ☎212/744-6868.
Giorgio Armani Map 7, I4, 760 Madison Ave, at 65th ☎212/988-9191.
Gucci Map 7, H7, 685 5th Ave, at 54th ☎212/826-2600.

Helmut Lang Map 5, F7. 80 Greene St, at Spring ⓣ212/925-4519.

Hermes Map 7, H6. 55 E 59th St, between Park and Madison ⓣ212/759-7585.

Marc Jacobs Map 5, F6. 163 Mercer St, between Houston and Prince ⓣ212/343-1490.

Marni Map 5, F6. 159 Mercer St, between Houston and Prince ⓣ212/343-3912.

Zero (Maria Cornejo) Map 5, H6. 225 Mott St, between Houston and Prince ⓣ212/925-3849.

Funky, trendy, hip

Canal Jean Co Map 5, F7. 718 Broadway, at 7th ⓣ212/226-3663. Enormous warehousey store sporting a prodigious array of jeans, jackets, T-shirts, dresses, hats, and more, new and secondhand. Young, fun, and reasonably cheap.

Old Japan Map 5, A3. 382 Bleecker St, at Perry ⓣ212/633-0922. Gorgeous, authentic Japanese clothes and trinkets, with a fantastic selection of antique kimonos.

X-Large Map 5, G6. 267 Lafayette, between Prince and Spring ⓣ212/334-4480. Check out the Mini line for women, X-Large for men. Cutting-edge streetwear for B-boys and gals. Sonic Youth's Kim Gordon and the Beastie Boys' Mike D are part owners.

Vintage and secondhand

Allan & Suzi Map 8, C9. 416 Amsterdam Ave, at 80th ⓣ212/724-7445. Beautiful, way-over-the-top fashion from the 60s and 70s. Claims to have single-handedly restarted the platform-shoe craze back in the late 90s, and continues to offer a wide range of outlandish vintage threads.

Edith & Daha Map 5, K6. 104 Rivington, at Ludlow ⓣ212/979-9992. Extremely popular with the trendy vintage set, this used-clothing emporium has some amazing finds (particularly shoes) for those willing to sift through the massive stock.

INA Map 5, H6. 21 Prince St, at Elizabeth ⓣ212/334-9048. Designer resale shop usually crammed with end-of-season, barely worn pieces by the hot designers *du jour* at fair prices. The men's store is at 262 Mott St, between Houston and Prince (ⓣ212/334-2210).

Love Saves the Day Map 5, I3. 119 2nd Ave, at 7th ⓣ212/228-3802. Cheap vintage as well as classic lunchboxes and other kitschy nostalgia items, including valuable Kiss and *Star Wars* dolls.

Resurrection Map 5, H7. 27 Mott St, between Prince and Spring ⓣ212/929-3349. An amazing selection of vintage clothes, many rented out for period films, with a good supply of classic Pucci dresses.

Screaming Mimi's Map 5, G4, 382 Lafayette St, between 4th and Great Jones ☎212/677-6464. One of the most established vintage stores in Manhattan, with vintage threads (including lingerie), bags, shoes, and housewares at reasonable prices.

Tokio 7 Map 5, J3, 64 E 7th St, between 1st and 2nd ☎212/353-8443. Attractive secondhand and vintage designer consignment items = a little pricier than most, but a good selection.

Thrift and discount

Dave's Army & Navy Map 6, G8, 581 6th Ave, between 16th and 17th ☎212/989-6444. The best place to buy jeans in Manhattan. Helpful assistants, no blaring music, and brands other than just Levi's.

Housing Works Map 6, G8, 143 W 17th St, between 6th and 7th ☎212/366-0820. Upscale thrift shop where you can find secondhand designer wear in very good condition. All proceeds benefit Housing Works, an AIDS social-service organization.

Loehmann's Map 6, F8, 101 7th Ave, between 16th and 17th ☎212/352-0856. New York's best-known department store for designer clothes at knockdown prices. No refunds and no exchanges, however.

Sample sales

At the beginning of each season, designers' and manufacturers' showrooms are full of **leftover merchandise** that is removed via informal **sample sales**. You'll always save at least fifty percent off the retail price, though you may not be able to try on the clothes and you can never return them. The best times for sample sales are spring and fall. Short of waiting for advertisement fliers to be stuffed into your hands while walking through the Garment District, the following sources are helpful. *Time Out New York*, available at any newsstand, also lists sales happening that week.

Daily Candy ⓦ www.dailycandy.com. *The* website to find out about coveted designs at bargain rates before the city's fashionistas commence their stampede.

Nice Price Map 8, D8, 493 Columbus Ave, at 84th ☎212/362-1020. Pick up a printed card at the store or call their sample sale hotline on ☎212/947-8748.

Shoes and other accessories

Kate Spade Map 5, F7. 454 Broome St, at Mercer ⊤212/274-1991. The boxy fabric handbags with the little logo-label from this once cutting-edge, now mainstream, accessory boutique are still quite popular, though perhaps not as ubiquitous as they were a few years ago.

Kenneth Cole Map 7, H8. 610 5th Ave, at 49th ⊤212/373-5800. Classic and contemporary shoes, beautiful bags, excellent full-grain leather. Call for more locations.

Manolo Blahnik Map 7, H7. 31 W 54th St, at 5th ⊤212/582-3007. World-famous strappy stilettos, good for height (of fashion), hell for feet. More popular than ever thanks to Carrie Bradshaw & Co in *Sex and the City*.

Otto Tootsi Plohound Map 6, I7. 413 W Broadway, between Prince and Spring ⊤212/925-8931; and **Map 7, I6. 38 E 57th St, near Park** ⊤212/231-3199. If you want to run with a trendy crowd, these shoes will help. Very current designs.

Robert Marc Map 7, I6. 575 Madison Ave, between 56th and 57th ⊤212/319-2000. Exclusive New York distributor of designer glasses frames like Lunor and Kirei Titan; also sells Retrospecs, restored antique eyewear from the 1890s to the 1940s. Very expensive and very hot. Call for four other locations.

Sephora Map 7, H7. 636 5th Ave, at 51st ⊤212/245-1633. Breathtaking "warehouse" of perfumes, make-up, and body-care products. You have to see (or smell) it to believe it. Call for more locations.

Sigerson Morrison Map 5, H6. 28 Prince St, at Mott ⊤212/219-3893. Kari Sigerson and Miranda Morrison make timeless, simple, and elegant shoes for women, and have just expanded into a large new shop. A required pilgrimage for shoe-worshippers.

Department stores

Barney's Map 7, I5. 600 Madison Ave, at 61st ⊤212/826-8900. Though a proper department store, Barney's concentrates heavily on clothes, with the emphasis on high-flying, up-to-the-minute designer garments and women's wear. Long the top-tier department store in town, though the service here is not as good as it used to be. They have a department-store exclusive with designer Balenciaga.

Bergdorf Goodman Map 7, H6. 754 5th Ave, at 57th ☎212/753-7300. Come if only to ogle the windows, which approach high art with their rhinestone-encrusted diaphanous dress displays. Everything about Bergdorf's speaks of its attempt to be New York City's most elegant and wealth-oriented department store. The men's store is across 5th Ave. They have a department-store exclusive with designer Chloé.

Bloomingdale's Map 7, J5. 1000 3rd Ave, at 59th ☎212/705-2000. "Bloomy's," as it's referred to affectionately by regulars, has the atmosphere of a large, bustling bazaar, packed with concessionaires offering perfumes and designer clothes – though it's now more of a tourist trap. Still popular, but it's seen hipper days.

Henri Bendel Map 7, H6. 712 5th Ave, between 55th and 56th ☎212/247-1100. This store, more gentle in its approach than the biggies – its refinement thanks in part to its classy reuse of the Coty perfume building, with windows by René Lalique – has a name for exclusivity and top modern designers.

Jeffrey Map 6, C9. 449 W 14th St, at 10th ☎212/206-3928. Generally regarded as the most cutting-edge (and snooty) department store in the city, this all-white outpost in the far west of Downtown is the place to come for that logo'd thong or boilersuit. Recommended for the adventurous and the shameless.

The Diamond District

The strip of 47th Street between Fifth and Sixth avenues is known as the **Diamond District**. Crammed into this one block are more than 100 shops: combined they sell more jewelry than any other block in the world. The industry has traditionally been run by Hasidic Jews, and you'll run into plenty of black-garbed men with *payess* (sidelocks) here.

Some good starting points are Andrew Cohen, Inc, for **diamonds** (579 5th Ave, 15th floor); Myron Toback, a trusted dealer of **silver** findings (25 W 47th St); and Bracie Company, Inc, a friendly business specializing in antique and estate **jewelry** (608 5th Ave, suite 806). Once you buy, there's AA Pearls & Gems, the industry's choice for pearl- and gem-stringing (10 W 47th St), and, if you want to get your gems graded, the Gemological Institute of America (580 5th Ave, 2nd floor).

Macy's Map 6, G3. 151 W 34th St, on Broadway at Herald Square ☏212/695-4400 or 1-800/289-6229. Quite simply, the largest department store in the world, with two buildings, two million square feet of floor space, and ten floors (four for women's garments alone). Unfortunately, most merchandise is of mediocre quality, although real fashion is returning slowly.

Saks 5th Avenue Map 7, H8. 611 5th Ave, at 50th ☏212/753-4000. The name is virtually synonymous with style, and, although Saks has retained its name for quality, it has also updated itself to carry the merchandise of all the big designers. The first floor is lovely when decorated with sparkling white branches at Christmastime.

Takashimaya Map 7, H6. 693 5th Ave, btw 54th and 55th ☏212/350-0100. This beautiful Japanese department store offers a scaled-down assortment of expensive merchandise simply displayed, and exquisitely wrapped purchases. The café, *The Tea Box*, on the lower level, has an assortment of teapots and loose teas.

Food and drink

Food – the buying as much as the consuming of it – is a New York obsession. Though you can find a deli on pretty much any corner, it's in the gourmet markets and specialty shops – cheese, bread, smoked fish, what have you – that the city really shines.

Agata & Valentina Map 8, L9. 1505 1st Ave, at 79th ☏212/452-0690. Considered by many to be the top gourmet grocer in town, with fresh pastas made on the premises, an enviable gourmet deli and cheese counter, a variety of pricey delicacies, and the best butcher in town.

Astor Wines and Spirits Map 5, G3. 12 Astor Place, at Lafayette ☏212/674-7500. Manhattan's best selection, at some of the city's most competitive prices. Good kosher and organic wine section, too.

Barney Greengrass Map 8, C7. 541 Amsterdam Ave, btw 86th and 87th ☏212/724-4707. "The Sturgeon King" – an Upper West Side smoked-fish brunch institution since 1908 that also sells brunch-makings to go.

Chelsea Market Map 6, D9. 75 9th Ave, btw 15th and 16th ☏212/243-6005. A complex of eighteen former industrial buildings, among them the late nineteenth-century Nabisco Cookie Factory. Houses a number of small grocers, including a fishmonger, a butcher, two bakers, and a cheese shop – all of which are of high quality.

Dean & Deluca Map 5, G6. 560 Broadway, btw Prince and Spring ☏212/226-6800. One of the original big neighborhood food emporia. Very chic, very SoHo, and not at all cheap.

Murray's Cheese Shop Map 5, C4. 257 Bleecker St, btw 6th and 7th ☏212/243-3289. A variety of more than 300 fresh cheeses and excellent fresh panini sandwiches, all served by knowledgeable staff. Free tastings on Sat afternoons.

Russ & Daughters Map 5, J5. 179 E Houston St, btw Allen and Orchard ☏212/475-4880. Technically, this store is known as an "appetizing" – the original Manhattan gourmet shop, set up around 1900 to sate the appetites of homesick immigrant Jews, selling smoked fish, caviar, pickled vegetables, cheese, and bagels.

Zabar's Map 8, B9. 2245 Broadway, btw 80th and 81st ☏212/787-2000. The apotheosis of New York food-fever, Zabar's is still the city's pre-eminent foodstore. Choose from an astonishing variety of cheeses, cooked meats, salads, fresh-baked bread and croissants, excellent bagels, and cooked dishes to go. Not to be missed.

Greenmarkets

Several days each week, long before sunrise, hundreds of farmers from Long Island, the Hudson Valley, and parts of Pennsylvania and New Jersey set out in trucks transporting their fresh-picked bounty to New York City, where they are joined by bakers, cheesemakers, and others at **greenmarkets**. Usually you'll find apple cider, jams and preserves, flowers and plants, maple syrup, fresh meat and fish, pretzels, cakes and breads, herbs, honey – just about anything and everything produced in the rural regions around the city – not to mention occasional live-worm composts and baby dairy goats.

Call ☏212/788-7476 for the greenmarket nearest you; the largest and most popular is held in **Union Square** at East 17th St and Broadway, year-round on Mon, Wed, Fri & Sat from 8am to 6pm.

Music

While the top **music** megastores in New York are Tower Records and Virgin, specialty rock and pop shops are clustered in the East and West villages.

Chains

J&R Music World Map 4, E5. 23 Park Row, between Beekman and Anne ☎212/238-9000. A large downtown store with a decent selection and good prices.

Tower Records Map 5, G4. 629 Broadway, at 4th ☎212/505-1500; and Map 7, D4. 1961 Broadway, at 66th ☎212/799-2500. The coolest of the megastores, and with an encyclopedic selection.

Virgin Megastore Map 7, F9. 1540 Broadway, at 45th ☎212/921-1020; and Map 6, J9. 52 E 14th St, at Union Square ☎212/598-4666. A bit more expensive than the other megastores, but with a genuinely colossal selection of every imaginable genre.

Special interest and secondhand

Fat Beats Map 5, D3. 406 6th Ave, between 8th and 9th, 2nd floor ☎212/673-3883. The name says it all. It's *the* source for hip-hop on vinyl in New York City.

Footlight Records Map 5, G2. 113 E 12th St, between 3rd and 4th ☎212/533-1572. The place for show music, film soundtracks, and jazz. Everything from Broadway to Big Band, Sinatra to Merman. A must for record collectors.

Vinyl Mania Map 5, C5. 60 Carmine St, between Bleecker and 7th ☎212/924-7223. This is where DJs come for the newest, rarest releases, especially of dance music. Hard-to-find imports too, as well as homemade dance tapes.

28

Commercial galleries

There are roughly five hundred **art galleries** in New York, and even if you have no intention of buying, many of these galleries are well worth seeing. Most are found in six main areas: in the 60s and 70s on the Upper East Side, for antiques and the occasional (minor) Old Master; 57th Street between Sixth and Park avenues for big, established modern and contemporary names; SoHo for a few remaining well-established artists; Chelsea for established but hip ones; TriBeCa for more experimental displays; and DUMBO in Brooklyn for up-and-coming types.

Gallery **opening hours** are roughly Tuesday to Saturday 10am–6pm, though many galleries have truncated summer hours and are closed in August. The best time to gallery-hop is on weekday afternoons; the absolute worst is Saturday. Pick up a copy of the *Gallery Guide* – available upon request in the larger galleries – for listings of current shows and each gallery's specialty. The weekly *Time Out New York* magazine also offers broad **listings** of the major commercial galleries.

SoHo and TriBeCa

123 Watts Map 4, B1. 123 Watts St, between Greenwich and Hudson ☏ 212/219-1482, ⓦ www.123watts .com. Trendy gallery known for its photography, along with other forms of contemporary art; has shown work by Robert Mapplethorpe, Arturo Cuenca, and Bruno Ulmer.

Louis Meisel Map 5, E6. 141 Prince St, at West Broadway ☏ 212/677-1340, ⓦ www.meiselgallery.com. Specializes in Photorealism – past shows have included Richard Estes and Chuck Close – as well as Abstract Illusionism.

Chelsea

Annina Nosei Map 6, B7. 530 W 22nd, between 10th and 11th, 2nd floor ☏ 212/741-8695. Global works, especially contemporary pieces by emerging Latin American and Middle Eastern artists. Mon–Fri 11am–6pm.

Cheim & Read Map 6, B6. 547 W 25th, between 10th and 11th ☏ 212/242-7227, ⓦ www.cheim read.com. Established gallery featuring works by highly regarded American and European artists such as Andy Warhol, Robert Mapplethorpe, and Louise Bourgeois, as well as younger types.

Gagosian Gallery Map 6, B6. 555 W 24th St, between 10th and 11th ☏ 212/741-1111. This stalwart of the New York scene, owned by an ex–LA poster salesman, features modern and contemporary art by the likes of De Kooning, Lichtenstein, and Schnabel.

Gladstone Gallery Map 6, B6. 515 W 24th St, between 10th and 11th ☏ 212/206-9300, ⓦ www.gladston egallery.com. Paintings, sculpture, and photography by hot contemporary artists such as Matthew Barney, Sarah Lucas, and Rosemarie Trockel.

Lehmann Maupin Map 6, B6. 540 W 26th St, between 10th and 11th ☏ 212/255-2923, ⓦ www.lehman nmaupin.com. Shows a range of established international and American contemporary artists working in a wide range of media.

Matthew Marks Gallery Map 6, B7. 523 W 24th St, between 10th and 11th ☏ 212/243-0200, ⓦ www .matthewmarks.com. The centerpiece of Chelsea's art scene, this gallery shows the work of such well-known minimalist and abstract artists as Sam Taylor-Wood, Terry Winters, Nan Goldin, and Lucian Freud. See also the branches at 522 W 22nd St and 521 W 21st St.

Paula Cooper Map 6, B7. 534 and 521 W 21st St, between 10th and 11th, 2nd floor ☏ 212/255-1105. Another influential gallery that shows a wide range of contemporary painting, sculpture, drawings, prints, and photographs, particularly minimalist and abstract works by the likes of Sophie Calle and Sol LeWitt.

Robert Miller Map 6, B6. 524 W 26th St, between 10th and 11th ☎212/366-4774, ⓦwww .robertmillergallery.com. Exceptional shows of twentieth-century art, including sculpture, paintings by David Hockney and Lee Krasner, and photographs by artists such as Diane Arbus and Robert Mapplethorpe.

Sonnabend Map 6, B7. 536 W 22nd St, between 10th and 11th ☎212/627-1018. ⓦwww.artnet .com/sonnabend. A top gallery featuring painting, photography, and video from contemporary American and European artists, including Jeff Koons, Candia Höfer, and Gilbert and George.

Midtown and the Upper East Side

Knoedler & Co. Map 7, H3. 19 E 70th St, between 5th and Park ☎212/794-0550, ⓦwww.knoedler gallery.com. Highly renowned gallery specializing in abstract, Pop Art, postwar, and contemporary, with a focus on the New York School. Shows some of the best-known names in twentieth-century art, including Stella, Rauschenberg, and Fonseca.

Leo Castelli Map 7, H1. 18 E 77th St, between 5th and Madison ☎212/249-4470, ⓦwww.castel-ligallery.com. One of the original dealer-collectors, Castelli was instrumental in aiding the careers of Rauschenberg and Warhol, and offers big contemporary names at big prices.

Mary Boone Map 7, H6. 745 5th Ave, between 57th and 58th, 4th floor ☎212/752-2929, ⓦwww .maryboonegallery.com. This top gallery specializes in installations, paintings, and works by up-and-coming European and American artists. Check out the interesting Chelsea branch at 541 W 24th St, between 10th and 11th (☎212/752-2929).

PaceWildenstein Map 7, I6. 32 E 57th St, at Madison ☎212/421-3292, ⓦwww.pacewildenstein.com. Celebrated gallery that has carried works by most of the great modern American and European artists, from Picasso to Rothko. Its Chelsea satellite, located at 534 W 25th St (☎212/929-7000), specializes in edgier works and large installations.

DUMBO

5 + 5 Gallery Map 4, G7. 111 Front St, near Wall, suite 210 ☎718/488-8383, ⓦwww.5plus5gallery.com. An exciting print and printmaking gallery showcasing emerging

COMMERCIAL GALLERIES

artists as well as established ones like Chuck Close. In the same building as Howard Schickler (see below).

Howard Schickler Fine Art Map 4, G7. 111 Front St, near Wall, suite 208 ☏718/408-1220, ⊛www .schicklerart.com. Gallery and bookstore specializing in vintage photography from such movements as Russian Constructivism and European avant-garde.

Alternative spaces

The galleries below provide a forum for the kind of **risky** and non-commercially viable art that many other galleries – reliant on trying to get art into the hands of buyers – may not be able to afford to show.

Artists Space Map 4, E1. 38 Greene St, between Canal and Grand, 3rd floor ☏212/226-3970, ⊛www.artistsspace.org. One of the most respected alternative spaces, with frequently changing theme-based exhibits, film screenings, and the like.

DIA Center for the Arts Map 6, B7. 548 W 22nd St, between 10th and 11th ☏212/989-5566, ⊛www.diacenter.org. The pre-eminent Alternative Art Foundation's largest gallery space shows year-long exhibitions of work by artists such as Joseph Beuys, Dan Graham, Robert Ryman, and Kids of Survival. At time of writing the gallery was closed for renovation, though it plans to reopen in 2006.

Smack Mellon Studios Map 4, K5. 56 Water St, at Hanover, Brooklyn ☏718/834-8761, ⊛www.smackmellon.org. A DUMBO gallery for mid-career and women artists. Part of a nonprofit organization that provides studios, metalwork shops, and computers for under-recognized creative types.

29

Sports and outdoor activities

N ew York is one of the most avid **sports** cities in
America. TV stations cover most regular-season
games and all postseason games in the big four
American team sports: **baseball**, **football**, **basketball**, and **ice hockey**. Some tickets can be hard to find,
some impossible, and most don't come that cheap. **Tickets** for most events can be booked through Ticketmaster
(☎212/307-7171, ⓦwww.ticketmaster.com), though it's
cheaper (and of course riskier for popular events) to try to
pick up tickets on the day of the event. You can also get
advance tickets direct from the stadium box office. Bars
– specifically **sports bars** – are a good alternative to actually being there.

Many **participatory activities** in the city are free or
affordable. You can **swim** either at the local pools or the
borough beaches, usually for a small fee; **jog**, still one of the
city's main obsessions; or have your fill of an ever-increasing
number of spaces to **bike** or **rollerblade**.

Baseball

From April to October, the **New York Yankees** and the **New York Mets** play 162 games (81 home games each; playoffs run through Oct), giving you plenty of excuses to head out for a sunny day at the ballpark, not to mention the fact that baseball games, of all spectator sports, are by far the least expensive.

The Yankees (lovingly called the Bronx Bombers) are the most successful baseball franchise in history, with the most World Series titles (26 through the year 2005). If you get to the game early, you can visit Monument Park, where all their greats are memorialized (see p.175 for more on Yankee Stadium). The Mets have been on a rollercoaster ride ever since the lovably inept team of 1962 matured into the 1969 World Series champions, and then took a nose dive from their second World Series win in 1986 to the "worst team money can buy" in the early 1990s, and back up to making the finals – only to be beaten by the Yankees – in 2000.

Shea Stadium 126th St, at Roosevelt Ave, Queens; box office Mon–Fri 9am–6pm, Sat, Sun & holidays 9am–5pm; tickets $5–60; ☎718/507-TIXX, ⓦwww.mets.com. #7 to Willets Point/Shea Stadium.

Yankee Stadium 161st St, at River Ave, The Bronx; box office Mon–Sat 9am–5pm, Sun 10am–4pm; tickets $12–65; ☎718/293-6000, ⓦwww.yankees.com. #D or #4 to 161st Street/Yankee Stadium.

Basketball

The National Basketball Association's (NBA) regular season begins in November and runs through the end of April. The two professional teams in the New York area are the **New York Knicks** (ⓦwww.nba.com/knicks), who play at Madison Square Garden, and the **New Jersey Nets** (ⓦwww.nba.com/nets), whose venue is the Continental Airlines Arena at the Meadowlands Sports Complex in New Jersey. The **New**

York Liberty, of the Women's NBA, also play their games at Madison Square Garden during the summer.

The Knicks have a loyal following that counts such celebrities as Spike Lee, Woody Allen, Sarah Jessica Parker, and more. It can be difficult to get tickets to see them play, though less so than in the past. Long playing in the long shadow of the Knicks, the Nets have emerged as one of the more exciting teams in the NBA, and tickets can now also prove difficult to obtain.

Madison Square Garden **Map 6, E4.** 7th Ave, betweeen 31st and 33rd; tickets $10–330; box office Mon–Fri 9am–6pm, Sat 10am–6pm, closed Sun; ☏212/465-JUMP, ⓦthegarden.com. #A, #B, #C, #D, #E, #F, #N, #Q, #R, #V, #W, #1, #2, or #3 to Penn Station.

Continental Airlines Arena Meadowlands Sports Complex, off routes 3, 17, and Turnpike exit 16W, East Rutherford, New Jersey; box office 9am–6pm, Sat 10am–6pm, Sun noon–5pm; tickets $10–215; ☏1-800/7NJ-NETS, ⓦwww.meadowlands.com.

Football

The **National Football League** (NFL) season stretches from September until the Super Bowl, typically played on the fourth Sunday in January. Although tickets for both local teams, the **Giants** (ⓦwww.giants.com) and **Jets** (ⓦwww.newyorkjets.com), sell out well in advance, if you're willing to pay the price you can buy tickets outside the stadium before the game (from scalpers). Both teams play at Giants Stadium in East Rutherford, New Jersey.

With a twenty-year waiting list for season tickets, the Giants, who have won two Super Bowls (in 1987 and 1991), have a devoted following. Since 1984, the Jets have been subtenants at Giants Stadium. While the Jets have not had the historical success of the Giants, they are generally as competitive.

Giants Stadium Meadowlands Sports Complex, off routes 3, 17, and Turnpike exit 16W, East Ruther-

ford, New Jersey; box office Mon–Fri 9am–6pm, Sat 10am–6pm, Sun noon–5pm; tickets $45 and $50;

Ice hockey

After a players' strike that scrapped the entire 2004–2005 season, the two New York National Hockey League (NHL) teams, the **Rangers** and the **Islanders**, are back up and skating. The Rangers (ⓦ www.newyorkrangers.com) play at Madison Square Garden (see listing overleaf, under "Basketball"), while the Islanders (ⓦ www.newyorkislanders.com) take the ice at Nassau Coliseum on Long Island. The New Jersey Devils (ⓦ www.newjerseydevils.com), who will soon set up shop in a new stadium in Newark, are not too far from the city, either. The regular season lasts throughout the winter and into early spring, when the playoffs take place. Prices for games range $15–100 and, post-strike, are a good bit easier to get than before.

As for team quality, the Rangers ended a 54-year drought in 1994, when they won the Stanley Cup, hockey's biggest prize. Since then they've not had as much success, though they remain perennial contenders. The Islanders, New York's "other" hockey team, have recently undergone something of a resurgence after years of mediocrity.

Bicycling

There are over one hundred miles of **cycle paths** in New York; those in Central Park, Riverside Park, and the East River Promenade are among the nicest. Transportation Alternatives, at 127 W 26th St (☎ 212/629-8080, ⓦ www.transalt.org), concentrates on the environmental aspects and physical benefits of bicycling while lobbying for funding for bike-related projects, like ramps for bridge access, free bike racks, and additional car-free hours in Central Park. They also sponsor the Century Bike Tour in September (a 35-, 50-, 75-, or 100-mile ride through the boroughs), and have some good maps and links to other routes in areas close to the city.

Bicycle Habitat Map 5, G3. 244 Lafayette St, btw Prince and Spring ☏212/431-3315, ⓦwww.bicycle habitat.com Known for its excellent repair service, this punk-rock bike shop offers tune-ups and free estimates. The very knowledgeable staff helps cyclists of all levels of expertise, and they have a great gear selection too.

Five Borough Bike Club ☏212/932-2300 ext 115, ⓦwww.5bbc.org. This club organizes rides throughout the year, including the Montauk Century, a hundred-mile ride from New York to Montauk on Long Island.

New York Cycling Club ☏212/828-5711, ⓦwww.nycc.org. Very friendly cycling club offering day rides, evening whizzes around Central Park, weekends away, and lots of social activities in between.

Chelsea Piers

The **Chelsea Piers** complex, entered at West 23rd St at the Hudson River (☏212/336-6666, ⓦwww.chelseapiers.com), covers six blocks and is comprised of four completely renovated piers, on which all manner of activity takes place.

At Pier 60, the **Sports Center** (☏212/336-6000) features a quarter-mile running track, the largest rock-climbing wall in the Northeast, three basketball courts, a boxing ring, a 24-yard swimming pool, whirlpool, indoor sand-volleyball courts, exercise studios offering more than one hundred classes weekly, a cardiovascular weight-training room, a sundeck right on the Hudson River, and spa services. Day-passes are available for $50. Open Mon–Fri 6am–11pm, Sat & Sun 8am–9pm.

The outdoor **Roller Rink** (☏212/336-6200), on Pier 62, is open year-round, weather permitting. Skating sessions begin daily at noon and cost $6.50, or $5.50 for children under 12; skate and pad ($19) and helmet ($7.50) rentals are also available. The **Sky Rink** (☏212/336-6100), meanwhile, is on Pier 61, and offers year-round ice-skating on an indoor rink. Sessions also start at noon and cost $11, or $7.50 for children under 12 and seniors. Ice-skate rentals cost $5.

SPORTS AND OUTDOOR ACTIVITIES

Bowling

Bowlmor Lanes **Map 5, F2.** 110 University Pl, between 12th and 13th ☎212/255-8188, ⓦwww.bowlmor.com. Fun bowling alley with a bar that boasts Monday-night glow-in-the-dark bowling, to the sounds of a live DJ. Open daily from 11am to 1am or later. Before 5pm $7.45 ($8.45 Fri & Sun, $8.95 Sat & holidays) per game per person, after 5pm $8.45 ($8.95 Fri, Sat & holidays),

shoe rental $5.
Leisure Time Bowling **Map 6, E1.** Port Authority Bus Terminal, 8th Ave near 40th St, 2nd floor ☎212/268-6909, ⓦwww.leisuretimebowl.com. The best place to bowl in the city. Open Mon–Wed 10am–midnight, Thurs & Fri 10am–2am, Sat 11am–2am, Sun 11am–midnight. $6 per game per person ($8 after 5pm), plus $5 shoe rental.

Pools and baths

John Jay Pool **Map 7, M1.** 77th St, at Cherokee Place ☎212/794-6566. Above the FDR Drive, this six-lane, fifty-yard pool is surrounded by playgrounds and park benches. Although it opened in 1940, it is in remarkably great condition and is free to all.
Russian & Turkish Baths **Map 5, I2.** 268 E 10th Street. ☎212/473-8806 or 674-9250. An ancient place, something of a neighborhood landmark

and still going, with steam baths, sauna, and an ice-cold pool, as well as massage facilities and a restaurant. Towels, robe, and slippers included with $25 admission (extra for massages, treatments, etc). Open Mon, Tues, Thurs & Fri 11am–10pm, Wed 9am–10pm, Sat & Sun 7.30am–10pm. Coed except for men-only Sun 7.30am–2pm and women-only Wed 9am–2pm.

Horse racing

Aqueduct Racetrack, in Howard Beach, Queens, has thoroughbred racing from October to May. To get there by subway, take the #A train to the Aqueduct station. **Belmont Park**, meanwhile, in Elmont, Long Island, is home to the

Belmont Stakes in June, one of the three races in which 3-year-olds compete for the Triple Crown, horse racing's highest honor. Belmont thoroughbred racing is open May to July and Septembr to Oct. Take the #F train to 169th Street and then the N6 bus to the track, or take the Long Island Railroad to the Belmont Race Track stop. For both Belmont and Aqueduct, call ☎718/641-4700, or visit ⓦwww.nyra .com/belmont or ⓦwww.nyra.com/aqueduct. **Admission** at both tracks ranges from nothing to $5 depending on when you go and where you sit. Wagering, on the other hand, runs from $2 on up into the stratosphere.

Ice-skating

The Pond at Bryant Park Map 6, H1. 5th Ave, between 40th and 42nd ☎212/768-4242, ⓦwww.bryant park.org/amenities/the pond.php. New York City's brand-new (as of winter 2005) place to skate is Bryant Park, where a medium-sized rink awaits those brave enough to face the winter cold. Skating is free and skate rental is $7.50. Open Nov through mid-Jan daily 8am–10.30pm.

Rockefeller Center Ice Rink Map 7, H8. 5th Ave, between 49th and 50th ☎212/332-7654. Without a doubt the slickest place to skate, though you may have to wait in line and it's pricier than anywhere else: $9–17, depending on the time. Skate rental is $7. Call for hours.

Sky Rink Map 6, A8. At Chelsea Piers, W 23rd St, at the Hudson River ☎212/336-6100. See the box on p.295.

Wollman Rink Map 7, G5. In Central Park at 62nd St ☎212/396-1010. The city's most wonderful skating experience, where you can skate to the marvelous, inspiring backdrop of the lower Central Park skyline – incredibly impressive at night. Adults $8.50, $11 at weekends; children $4.25, $7.50 at weekends; skate rental $4.75. Bring a lock or rent one onsite for $3.75. Open Mon & Tues 10am–2.30pm, Wed & Thurs 10am–10pm, Fri & Sat 10am–11pm, Sun 10am–9pm.

Central Park

Central Park is an obvious focus for recreation, from croquet and chess to soccer and swimming. Joggers, in-line skaters, walkers, and cyclists have the roads to themselves on weekdays 10am–3pm & 7–10pm and all day on weekends. In addition, boaters can head to the **Loeb Boathouse** (☎212/517-2233; $10/hr), which hires out rowboats in warm-weather months. To find out what is going on where and when, try the Arsenal, 830 5th Ave at 64th St, and pick up the **Green Pages**, which tell you about every activity, from archery to wild-food walks. For much more on Central Park, see Chapter 14.

In-line skating

You'll see commuters to freestylists on **in-line skates** – also known as **rollerblades** – in New York. For the best place, go to the skate circle near Naumberg Bandshell in Central Park at 72nd Street. World-class bladers also maneuver between cones with all kinds of fancy footwork just inside Central Park's *Tavern on the Green* entrance, near West 68th Street. Other than Central Park, the best place to skate is Battery Park or along the greenways by the Hudson and East rivers.

Blades Map 6, G4. 901 6th Ave, at 33rd, in the Manhattan Mall, level C2 ☎212/563-2448; Map 7, D2. 120 W 72nd St, between Columbus and Broadway ☎212/787-3911; Map 5, G5. 6559 Broadway, between Bond and Bleecker ☎212/447-7350; Map 6, A8. 12th Ave, at Chelsea Piers ☎212/336-6299; Map 4, D4. 128 Chambers St, at West Broadway ☎212/964-1944. Rents out skates for $20 for 24 hours.

Jogging

Jogging is still very much the number-one fitness pursuit in the city. A favorite circuit in the park is 1.57 miles around the reservoir; just make sure you jog in a counterclockwise direction. For company, contact the New York Road Runners

Club, 9 E 89th St (☎212/860-2280, Ⓦwww.nyrrc.org), to get their schedule for Central Park and elsewhere. The East River Promenade, Riverside Park, and almost any other stretch of open space large enough to get up speed are also well-used New York jogger haunts.

Soccer

The **New York/New Jersey Metrostars** (Ⓦmetrostars .mlsnet.com/MLS/met/), who play at Giants Stadium (see p.293), are the area's Major League Soccer representatives; tickets are often available and range $16–35. The season runs from April to mid-November.

Tennis

The **US Open Championships**, held each September at the National Tennis Center in Flushing Meadows Corona Park in Queens (see p.173), is the top US **tennis** event of the year. Tickets go on sale the first week or two of June at the Tennis Center's box office (☎718/760-6200), which is open Monday to Friday 9am–5pm and Saturday 10am–4pm. To book by phone, call Ticketmaster on ☎866/673-6849. Promenade-level seats at the stadium cost $22–96 (better seats can cost several hundred dollars), and become more expensive at night and closer to the finals – for which they are incredibly hard to obtain.

If you'd like to **play**, there are courts both public and private all round the city, but getting on can be difficult; the former are all controlled through the City Parks department, and require a $50 permit (☎212/360-8133). The nicest such courts are probably at Central Park, but they are also the most crowded; try Riverside Park (see p.150) instead. Otherwise, rates at places like Sutton East Tennis Club, at York

Avenue and 59th Street (☎212/751-3452), and Midtown Tennis Club, at 341 Eighth Ave (☎212/989-8572), can run anywhere from $30 to $100 per hour, depending on the season and the time of day.

30

Parades and festivals

Major cultural holidays in New York are celebrated with **parades and festivals**, which – especially the parades – are taken very seriously. Almost every large ethnic group in the city holds an annual get-together, often using Fifth Avenue as the main drag. The events are often political or religious in origin, though now are just as much an excuse for music, food, and dance as anything else.

No matter when you visit, chances are your stay will coincide with at least one such celebration. For more details and exact dates, phone ☏1-800/NYC-VISIT or go to ⓦwww .nycvisit.com. Also, look at listings in *New York* magazine's "CUE" section, the *New Yorker*'s "Goings On About Town," the *Village Voice*'s "Cheap Thrills," or the weekly "Obsessive guide to impulsive entertainment," in *Time Out New York*.

January

Chinese New Year and Parade First full moon between Jan 21 and Feb 19; ☏212/431-9740. A noisy, colorful occasion celebrated from noon to sunset around Mott Street. Though dragons still dance in the street, firecrackers no longer chase away evil spirits because former Mayor Giuliani banned them for most events. The chances of getting a meal anywhere in Chinatown at this time are slim.

Winter Antiques Show Mid-Jan; ☎ 212/777-5218. Held at the Seventh Regiment Armory, at Park Ave and 67th St (see p.139), this is the foremost American antiques show in the country.

February

Empire State Building Run-Up Mid-Feb; ☎ 212/860-4445, ⊕ www.nyrrc.org. Sponsored by the New York Road Runners Club, contenders race up the 1575 steps of this New York City landmark.

Westminster Kennel Club Dog Show Mid-Feb; ☎ 212/323-2340, ⊕ www.westminsterkennelclub.org. Second only to the Kentucky Derby as the oldest continuous sporting event in the country, this show (often held at Madison Square Garden) welcomes 2500 dogs competing for best in breed, not to mention legions of fanatic dog-lovers.

March

St Patrick's Day Parade March 17; ☎ 212/484-1222. Celebrating an impromptu march through the streets by Irish militiamen on St Patrick's Day in 1762, this has become a draw for every Irish band and organization in the US and Ireland. Usually starting just before noon, it heads up 5th Ave between 44th and 86th streets.

Greek Independence Day Parade Late March; ☎ 718/204-6500. Not as long or as boozy as St Pat's, this more-patriotic nod to the old country consists of floats of pseudo-classically dressed Hellenes. When the Greek Independence Day falls in the Orthodox Lent, the parade is shifted to April or May. It usually kicks off from 62nd St and runs up 5th to 79th.

The Circus Animal Walk Late March to early April; call ☎ 212/465-6741 for tickets, visit ⊕ www.ny1.com for the exact date. At midnight the animals from Ringling Brothers' Barnum & Bailey Circus march from their point of arrival to Madison Square Garden prior to opening of the circus; a unique, special city sight.

April

Easter Parade Easter Sun. From Central Park down to Rockefeller Center on 50th St, New Yorkers march from 10am–5pm in outrageous Easter bonnets. There's also an "Eggstravaganza," a children's festival including an egg-rolling contest on the Great Lawn in Central Park.

New Directors, New Films Early April; ☎212/875-5638, Ⓦwww .filmlinc.com. Lincoln Center and MoMA have presented this popular two-week film festival for more than a quarter-century, showcasing films of overlooked or emerging auteurs.

May

Sakura Matsuri: Cherry Blossom Festival Early May; free with $5 garden admission; ☎718/623-7200, Ⓦwww.bbg.org/exp/cherrywatch. Music, art, dance, traditional fashion, sword-fighting, and karate celebrate Japanese culture and the brief sublime blossoming of the Brooklyn Botanic Garden's (see p.166) two hundred cherry trees.

The Great Five Boro Bike Tour Early May; ☎212/932-2453, Ⓦwww .bikenewyork.org. A 42-mile ride (without NYC traffic) through all five boroughs.

Ukrainian Festival Mid-May; ☎212/674-1615. This extravaganza fills a weekend on East 7th St between 2nd and 3rd aves with marvelous Ukrainian costumes, folk music and dance, plus authentic foods. At the Ukrainian Museum (12th St and 2nd Ave) there's a special exhibition of *pysanky* – traditional hand-painted eggs.

Fleet Week End May; Ⓦwww .fleetweek.navy.mil. The annual welcome of sailors from the US, Canada, Mexico, and the UK, among others, is held at the Intrepid Sea, Air & Space Museum (see p.110). Visit the website for activities and events.

June

Museum Mile Festival First Tues evening; ☎212/606-2296, Ⓦwww .museummile.org. Museums along the Mile (see p.131), including the Museum of the City of New York, the Jewish Museum, the Guggenheim, the Met, and others are open free from 6 to 9pm.

Puerto Rican Day Parade Second Sun; ☎718/401-0404, Ⓦwww .nationalpuertoricanparade.org. This raucous, wild parade, the largest of several Puerto Rican celebrations in the city, sees seven hours of bands and baton-twirling from 44th to 86th streets on 5th Ave, then east to 3rd.

Mermaid Parade First Sat after June 21; ☎718/372-5159, Ⓦwww .coneyislandusa.com. At this hilarious event, participants dress like mermaids and King Neptune, and saunter down the Coney Island boardwalk, after which everyone throws fruit into the sea. Not to be missed.

Lesbian and Gay Pride Week Late June; ☎212/807-7433, Ⓦwww .nycpride.org. The world's biggest

Pride event kicks off with a rally and ends with a parade, street fair, and dance.

JVC Jazz Festival Late June; ☎212/501-1390, ⓦwww.festival-productions.net. The jazz world's top names appear at Carnegie Hall, *Birdland*, the Apollo, the *Village Vanguard*, and other city music venues.

July

Independence Day July 4, at around 9pm ☎212/484-1222 or 560-4060. The fireworks from Macy's, South Street Seaport, and the display over the East River are visible all over Manhattan, but the best place to view them is either from the Seaport, Battery Park, the Esplanade at Brooklyn Heights or from atop almost any building.

New York City Tap Festival Mid-July; ☎646/230-9564, ⓦwww.nyctapfestival.com. A week-long festival featuring hundreds of tap dancers who perform and give workshops.

August

Harlem Week Third week in Aug; ☎212/862-8477, ⓦwww.harlemdiscover.com. Celebration of African-, Caribbean-, and Latin culture includes a children's festival, dance show, fashion parade, talent contest, and other events.

New York International Fringe Festival Mid-Aug; ☎212-279-4488, ⓦwww.fringenyc.org. Cutting-edge performance art, theater, dance, puppetry, and more at many different venues on the Lower East Side.

September

West Indian-American Day Parade and Carnival Labor Day (first Mon in Sept); ☎718/625-1515, ⓦwww.wiadca.com. Brooklyn's largest parade, modeled after the carnivals of Trinidad and Tobago, features West Indian music, food, and dance.

Broadway on Broadway Sun after Labor Day; ☎212/768-1560, ⓦwww.broadwayonbroadway.com. Held in Times Square, free performances of songs by casts of almost every Broadway musical, culminating in a shower of confetti.

Festival of the Feast of San Gennaro Ten days in mid-Sept; ☎212/226-6427, ⓦwww.sangenanaro.org. Boisterous event in honor of the patron saint of Naples, held along Mulberry Street in Little Italy (see p.57). On the final Sunday, the saint's statue is carried through the streets with donations of dollar bills pinned to his cloak; the rest of the time it's basically a bridge-and-tunnel boozefest.

African-American Day Parade Late Sept; ☎212/862-7200. Runs from 111th St and Adam Clayton Powell Blvd to 142nd St, then east toward 5th Ave in Harlem. Features loudspeakered hip-hop floats, drum-and-bugle corps, and plenty of local politicians.

New York Film Festival Late Sept to mid-Oct; ☎212/875-5600, Ⓦwww.filmlinc.com/nyff/nyff.htm. One of the world's leading film festivals unreels for two full weeks at the Upper West Side's Lincoln Center (see p.145).

October

Columbus Day Parade Second Mon in Oct; ☎212/249-9923, Ⓦwww.columbuscitizensfd.org. One of the city's largest binges pays tribute to New York's Italian heritage and commemorates the day Columbus "disovered" America; runs along 5th Ave from 44th to 79th.

DUMBO Art Under the Bridge Festival Mid-Oct; ☎718/624-0831, Ⓦwww.dumboartscenter.org/festival. More than 700 emerging and professional artists show their work in 250 open galleries. The Parade of Concept (robots, remote-control vehicles, and floats) kicks off the show in the neighborhood of DUMBO (Down Under the Manhattan Bridge Overpass), in Brooklyn between the Manhattan and Brooklyn bridges.

Village Halloween Parade Oct 31; Ⓦwww.halloween-nyc.com. In the 7pm procession on 6th Ave from Spring to 23rd streets you'll see spectacular costumes, floats, and more. The music is great and the spirit is wild and gay. Get there early for a good viewing spot; the parade is very popular.

November

New York City Marathon First Sun in Nov; ☎212/423-2249, Ⓦwww.ingnycmarathon.org. Some 30,000 runners from all over the world – including local and national celebrities such as the mayor and (in 2003) P. Diddy – assemble for this 26-mile run on city pavement through the five boroughs. One of the best places to watch is Central Park South, almost at the finish line.

Veteran's Day Parade Nov 11; ☎212/693-1476. The United War Veterans sponsor this annual event on 5th Ave from 39th to 23rd streets, in which uniformed US veterans from World War II onward march by military unit along flag-lined boulevards, the confetti descending like snow from above.

Macy's Thanksgiving Day Parade Thanksgiving Day (last Thurs in Nov); ☎212/494-4495, Ⓦwww.macysparade.com. New York's most televised parade, with floats, dozens of marching bands from around the country, Radio City's Rockettes, and Santa Claus's first appearance of the season. More than two million spectators watch it (9am–noon) from 77th St down Central Park West to Columbus Circle, then down Broadway to Herald Square.

December

Holiday Windows Beginning Dec 1. The famous Christmas windows on 5th Ave, especially those of Lord & Taylor and Saks Fifth Avenue, are well worth waiting on their long lines for (which often stretch around the block). Ornate Christmas displays vary from year to year and are a big New York holiday tradition.

Rockefeller Center Christmas Tree Lighting Late Nov; ☎212/632- 3975. The lighting of a massive, three-story-tall tree by the city mayor begins the official New York Christmas festivities. Check Ⓦ www.nyctourist.com/xmas_ rockcenter1.htm for the exact date and time.

Hanukkah Celebrations Usually in mid-Dec; ☎718/778-6000. During the eight nights of this Jewish holiday, usually in mid-Dec, a menorah-lighting ceremony takes place at Brooklyn's Grand Army Plaza.

New Year's Eve in Times Square Dec 31; ☎212/768-1560, Ⓦ www .timessquarebid.org. Some 200,000-plus revelers party in the cold streets. There are also fireworks at the South Street Seaport, Central Park, and Brooklyn's Prospect Park. More family-oriented, alcohol-free First Nights with dancing, music, and food take place throughout the city.

Kids' New York

New York can be a wonderful city to visit with **children**. Obvious attractions include museums, skyscrapers, and ferry rides, as well as the simple pleasures of just walking the streets, seeing the street performers, and taking in the shopping scene. Free events, especially common in the summer, range from puppet shows and nature programs in the city's parks to storytelling hours at local libraries and bookstores. In addition, many museums and theaters have specific children's programs.

For further **listings** of what is available when you're in town, see Friday's *Daily News* or *New York Times*, and "Activities for Children" in the weekly *New York* magazine, as well as *Time Out* and the *Village Voice*. An excellent automated directory of family-oriented current events all around the city is available through the New York CVB, 810 Seventh Ave, between 52nd and 53rd streets (Mon–Fri 8.30am–6pm, Sat & Sun 8.30am–5pm; ℡212/484-1222, ⓦwww.nycvisit.com).

Museums

One could spend an entire holiday just checking out the city's many **museums**, which almost always contain something of interest for the kids; the following is a brief overview of the ones that should evoke more than just the usual enthusiasm. See the appropriate chapters for more details on these and other museums.

American Museum of Natural History and the Rose Center for Earth and Space Map 8, E9. Central Park West, at 79th. Daily 10am–5.45pm; Fri & Sat until 8.45pm; $13, students $10, children $7.50; IMAX films, the Hayden Planetarium, and certain special exhibits cost extra; ☎212/769-5100, ⓦwww.amnh.org. The planetarium is sure to sate most kids' intergalactic desires, and the dinosaurs are also a sure-fire attraction.

Children's Museum of the Arts Map 5, G8. 182 Lafayette St, between Broome and Grand. Wed, Fri, Sat & Sun noon–5pm, Thurs noon–6pm; $8, pay as you wish Thurs 4–6pm; ☎212/941-9198, ⓦwww.cmany.org. Art gallery of works by or for children. Kids are encouraged to look at different types of art and then create their own, with paints, clay, plaster of Paris, and many other simple media.

Children's Museum of Manhattan Map 8, C8. 212 W 83rd St, between Broadway and Amsterdam. June to early Sept Tues–Sun 10am–5pm, Sept to mid-June Wed–Sun 10am–5pm; $5; ☎212/721-1234, ⓦwww.cmom.org. A terrific participatory museum, with exhibit space over five floors; not to be missed is "Seuss!" – a whimsical area with decor inspired by the Dr. Seuss

books, where kids can (literally) cook up some green eggs and ham. For ages 1–12, and highly recommended.

Fire Museum Map 5, C7. 278 Spring St, between Hudson and Varick. Tues–Sat 10am–5pm, Sun 10am–4pm; $5, seniors/students $2, under-12s $1; ☎212/691-1303, ⓦwww.nycfiremuseum.org. More popular than ever now, this unspectacular but pleasing homage to New York City's firefighters, and indeed firepeople everywhere, has fire engines from yesteryear, helmets, dog-eared photos, and a motley crew of other objects.

Intrepid Sea, Air & Space Museum Map 7, A8. West 46th St and 12th Ave, at Pier 86. April–Sept Mon–Fri 10am–5pm, Sat–Sun 10am–6pm; Oct–March Tues–Sun 10am–5pm, last admission 1 hour prior to closing; $16.50, students/seniors $12.50, children ages 12–17 $11.50, children 6–11 $6, children 2–5 $4.50, under-2s free; ☎212/245-0072 or 1-877/957-SHIP, ⓦwww.intrepidmuseum.org. The world's fastest spy plane, a guided missile submarine, and other modern and vintage air- and sea-craft are all here; not recommended for kids under 5.

Museum of the City of New York Map 8, H3. 1220 5th Ave, at 103rd.

Tues–Sun 10am–5pm (Tues 10am–2pm for pre-registered tour groups only); suggested donation $7, students $4, families $12; ⊤ 212/534-1672, ⓦ www.mcny.org. The New York Toy Stories is a super way to bring young ones back to simpler times before video games, when wooden toys, rubber balls, and board games were just about the only options in the late 1800s. For girls (and grownups) there is a worthwhile and surprising group of dollhouses.

National Museum of the American Indian (Smithsonian Institution) Map 4, E8. 1 Bowling Green, at Battery Park. Daily 10am–5pm, Thurs until 8pm; free; ⊤ 212/514-3700, ⓦ www.si.edu/nmai. Kids will enjoy looking at the ancient dolls and feathered headdresses and the replicas of a reservation home and schoolroom. Programs often include theater troupes, performance artists, dancers, and films.

Central Park

Year-round, **Central Park** provides sure-fire entertainment for children. In the summer it becomes one giant playground, with activities ranging from storytelling to rollerblading to rowboating. The following are merely a few of the highlights – for much more detailed information on these and other sights, see Chapter 14.

The Carousel Mid-park at 64th St. For just $1, children can take a spin on the country's largest hand-carved horses.

Central Park Wildlife Conservation Center 5th Ave, at 64th. A small but enjoyable zoo, with sea lions, polar bears, monkeys, and the Tisch Children's Zoo.

Hans Christian Andersen statue 72nd St, on the East Side next to the Boat Pond. A forty-or-so-year tradition of storytelling sessions; June–Sept Wed & Sat 11am–noon.

Loeb Boathouse Mid-park at 72nd St. Rent a rowboat on the Central Park lake and enjoy the views or take a gondola ride in the evening. Bike rentals available too.

Wollman Rink Mid-park at 62nd St. ⊤ 212/396-1010. Roller/in-line skating during the summer and ice-skating during the winter. Skate rental and instruction available.

Sights and entertainment

The Bronx Zoo Bronx River Parkway, at Fordham Rd. End March to end Oct, Mon–Fri 10am–5pm, Sat, Sun & holidays 10am–5.30pm; winter daily 10am–4.30pm; summer $12, seniors and children $9, winter $8/$6, suggested donation year-round on Wed, rides and some exhibits additional; ⊤718/367-1010, ⓌÞwww.bronxzoo .com. #2 or #5 to Pelham Parkway. The largest urban zoo in America has more than 4000 species of animals, reptiles, and birds on display, many in huge simulated natural habitats. A children's section allows kids to climb around on large exhibits, including a giant spider web, and to pet some of the tamer animals.

New York Aquarium West 8th St and Surf Ave, Coney Island, Brooklyn. April–Oct Mon–Fri 10am–5pm, Sat & Sun 10am–6pm; Nov–April daily 10am–4.30pm; $11, seniors and kids ages 2–12 $7; ⊤718/265-FISH, Ⓦwww.nyaquarium.com. Walruses, sea otters, California sea lions, penguins, and seals as well as an extensive collection of seahorses abound, and open-air whale and dolphin shows are held several times daily, as are the shark, sea otter, and walrus feedings. Call for current show info.

Shopping: toys, books, and clothes

Books of Wonder Map 6, H8. 16 W 18th St, between 5th and 6th ⊤212/989-3270. Excellent kids' bookstore, with a great story hour on Sun at 11.45am, and author appearances in the spring and fall on Sat.

F.A.O. Schwarz Map 7, H6. 767 5th Ave, at 58th ⊤212/644-9400. Showpiece of a nationwide chain sporting three huge floors of everything a child could want. Fans of Barbie will want to check out the Barbie store, in the back of F.A.O. Schwarz, with its own Madison Ave entrance.

Penny Whistle Toys Map 8, I6. 1283 Madison Ave, at 91st ⊤212/369-3868; also 448 Columbus Ave, at 81st ⊤212/873-9090. Wonderful shop selling a fun, imaginative range of toys that deliberately eschews guns and war accessories, including replicas of rare old-fashioned toys. Highly recommended.

The Red Caboose Map 7, H9. 23 W 45th St, between 5th and 6th, on the lower level – follow the flashing railroad sign in back of lobby

⊤212/575-0155. A unique shop specializing in models, particularly trains and train sets. **Tannen's Magic, Inc. Map 6, G3. 45 W 34th St, between Broadway and 6th** ⊤212/929-4500. Kids will never forget a visit to the largest magic shop in the world, with nearly 8000 props and magic sets. The staff consists of magicians who perform free shows throughout the day.

Theater, puppet shows, circuses, and more

The following is a highly selective roundup of miscellaneous **activities**, particularly cultural ones that might be of interest to young children.

Barnum & Bailey Circus Map 6, E4. At Madison Square Garden ⊤212/465-6741, Ⓦwww.ringling.com. This large touring circus is usually in New York between the end of March and the beginning of May. **Big Apple Circus Map 7, D4. At Lincoln Center** ⊤212/721-6500, Ⓦwww.bigapplecircus.org. Small circus that performs in a tent in Damrosch Park next to the Met, from late Oct to early Jan. Tickets $10–50. **New Victory Theater Map 6, F1. 209 W 42nd St, at 7th** ⊤646/223-3020. There is always a rich mix of affordable theater, music, dance, storytelling, film, and puppetry here, in addition to pre-performance workshops and post-performance participation. Everything about this theater is child-oriented, including the duration of performances (60–90 minutes). Closed during the summer.

Thirteenth Street Repertory Company Map 5, D1. 50 W 13th St, between 5th and 6th aves. Sat & Sun 1 & 3pm; $7; ⊤212/675-6677, Ⓦwww.13thstreetrep.org. Forty-five-minute original musicals – such as *Rumplewho?* – specifically created for "little humans." Reservations needed, as these are very popular shows.

31

KIDS' NEW YORK

Directory

Consulates Australia, 150 E 42nd St, between Lexington and 3rd (☎212/351-6500); Canada, 1251 6th Ave, at 50th (☎212/596-1628); Ireland, 345 Park Ave, at 51st St, 17th floor (☎212/319-2555); New Zealand, 780 3rd Ave, between 48th and 49th (☎212/832-4038); UK, 845 3rd Ave, between 51st and 52nd (☎212/745-0200).

Electric current 110V AC with two-pronged plugs. Unless they're dual voltage, all British appliances will need a voltage converter as well as a plug adapter. Note that some converters may not be able to handle certain high-wattage items, especially those with heated elements. Most laptops these days come with alternate-voltage AC adapters, and therefore only need a plug adapter.

Emergencies For police, fire, or ambulance dial ☎911.

Identification Carry some at all times, as there are any number of occasions on which you may be asked to show it. Two pieces of ID are preferable and one should have a photo – passport and credit card or driving license are the best bets.

Laundry Hotels do it but charge a lot. You're much better off going to an ordinary laundromat or a dry cleaner, both of which you'll find plenty of in the *Yellow Pages* phone book.

Left luggage Since 9/11, left-luggage storage has been suspended in New York train and bus stations. Your best bet is to ask your hotel to keep your luggage for you until you are ready to leave – most are happy to do this, although there may be a fee.

Lost property For items lost on buses or on the subway, check with the NYC Transit Authority, at the 34th Street/8th Avenue subway station at the north end on the lower level mezzanine (Mon–Wed & Fri 8am–noon, Thurs 11am–6.45pm; ☎212/712-4500). For things lost in a cab, visit the Taxi & Limousine Commission (TLC) at 167 E 51st St, between Lexington and 3rd (☎212/826-3246).

Public holidays You'll find all banks, most offices, some stores, and certain museums closed on the following days: Jan 1, Martin Luther King's Birthday (third Mon in Jan), Presidents' Day (third Mon in Feb), Memorial Day (last Mon in May), Independence Day (July 4 or, if it falls on a weekend, the following Mon), Labor Day (first Mon in Sept), Columbus Day (second Mon in Oct), Veterans' Day (Nov 11), Thanksgiving (the fourth Thurs in Nov), and Christmas Day (Dec 25). Also, New York's numerous parades mean that on certain days – St Patrick's Day, Gay Pride Day, Easter Sunday, and Columbus Day, to name a few – much of 5th Ave will be closed to traffic altogether.

Tax Within New York City you'll pay an 8.25 percent sales tax on top of marked prices on just about everything but the essentials.

Time New York City is three hours ahead of West Coast North America, five hours behind Britain and Ireland, fourteen to sixteen hours behind East Coast Australia (variations for Daylight Savings Time), and sixteen to eighteen hours behind New Zealand (variations for Daylight Savings Time).

Tipping Expected everywhere a service is performed and preferred in cash; in restaurants, it's easiest just to double the tax (equaling around sixteen percent), but if the service was really quality, consider upping that amount to at least twenty percent. A dollar per bag for the bellhop is standard, as is fifteen percent or so for taxi drivers on top of the fare. In bars, standard New York practice is a dollar a drink.

32

Contexts

Contexts

A brief history of New York City

To Europe she was America, to America she was the gateway of the earth. But to tell the story of New York would be to write a social history of the world.

H.G. Wells

Early days and colonial rule

Before the arrival of European explorers, Native Americans populated the area now encompassing New York City. In 1524, 32 years after Christopher Columbus had sailed to the New World, **Giovanni da Verrazano**, an Italian in the service of the French king Francis I, arrived in New York Harbor. Less than a century later, in 1609, **Henry Hudson**, an Englishman employed by the Dutch East India Company, landed at Manhattan and sailed his ship upriver as far as Albany. The Dutch established a trading post at the most northerly point Hudson had reached, Fort Nassau. Meanwhile, just a few years after the Pilgrim Fathers had sailed to Massachusetts, thirty families left Holland in 1624 to become New York's first **European settlers**.

Most sailed up to Fort Nassau, but a handful – eight families in all – stayed behind on what is now Governors Island, which they called Nut Island because of the many walnut trees there. Slowly the community grew as more settlers arrived, and the little island became crowded; the decision was made to move to the limitless spaces across the water, and the settlement of **Manhattan**, taken from the Algonquin Indian word *Manna-Hata*, meaning "Island of the Hills," began.

The Dutch gave their new outpost the name **Nieuw Amsterdam**, though following British conquest of the island in 1664 the settlement took its new name from its owner, the Duke of York – **New York**.

Revolution

By the 1750s the city had reached a population of 16,000, spread roughly as far north as today's Chambers Street. As the new community grew more confident, it realized that it could exist independently of the government in Britain. In a way, New York's role during the **War of Independence** was not critical, for all the battles fought in and around the city were generally won by the British, who ultimately lost the war. **George Washington**, who had held the American army together by sheer willpower, celebrated in New York riding in triumphal procession down Canal Street and saying farewell to his officers at **Fraunces Tavern**, a building that still stands at the end of Pearl Street. On April 30, 1789, Washington took the oath of president at the site of the **Federal Hall National Memorial** on Wall Street. The federal government was transferred to the District of Columbia one year later.

Immigration and the Civil War

The opening of the **Erie Canal** in 1825 allowed New York to expand massively as a port. The Great Lakes were suddenly opened to New York, and with them the rest of the country; goods manufactured in the city could be sent easily and cheaply to the American heartland. It was because of this transportation network, and the mass of **cheap labor** that flooded in throughout the nineteenth and early twentieth centuries, that New York – and to an extent the nation – became wealthy. The first waves of **immigrants**, mainly **German** and **Irish**, began to arrive in the mid-nineteenth century, the latter forced out of their respective countries by the potato famine of 1846, the former by the failed revolutions of 1848–49. The city could not handle people arriving in such great numbers and epidemics of yellow fever and cholera were common, exacerbated by poor water supplies, unsanitary conditions, and the poverty of most of the newcomers. Despite this, in the 1880s large-scale **Italian** immigration began, while at the same time refugees from **Eastern Europe** started to arrive – many of them Jewish. The two communities shared a home on the **Lower East Side**, which became one of the worst slum areas of its day. On the eve of the Civil War (1861–65) the majority of New York's 750,000 population were immigrants; in 1890 one in four of the city's inhabitants was Irish.

When the **Civil War** broke out, caused by growing differences between the Northern and Southern states, notably on the issues of slavery and trade, New York sided with the Union (North) against the Confederates (South). However, none of the actual hand-to-hand fighting that ravaged the rest of the country took place near the city itself – though New York did form a focus for much of the radical thinking behind the war, particularly with **Abraham Lincoln**'s influential "Might makes Right" speech from the **Cooper Union Building** in 1860. In 1863 a **conscription law** was passed that allowed the rich to buy themselves out of military service. Not surprisingly this was very unpopular, and New Yorkers rioted, burning buildings and looting shops. More than a thousand people were killed in these **Draft Riots**, mostly African Americans whose increase (if abolition succeeded) was perceived as a threat.

The late nineteenth century

The end of the Civil War saw much of the country devastated but New York intact, and it was fairly predictable that the city would soon become the wealthiest and most influential in the nation. New York was also the greatest business, commercial, and manufacturing center in the country. **Cornelius**

Vanderbilt controlled a vast shipping and railroad empire, and **J.P. Morgan**, the banking and investment wizard, was instrumental in organizing financial mergers that led to the formation of the prototypical corporate business.

The latter part of the nineteenth century was in many ways the city's golden age: **elevated railways** sprung up to transport people quickly and cheaply around the city; **Thomas Edison** lit the streets with his new electric light bulb, powered by the first electricity plant on Pearl Street; and in 1883, to the wonderment of New Yorkers, the **Brooklyn Bridge** was completed, linking Brooklyn and Manhattan – at the time it was opened, and for twenty years after, it was the largest and longest bridge in the world. Brooklyn, Staten Island, Queens, and the part of Westchester known as the Bronx, along with Manhattan, were officially **incorporated** into New York City in 1898. All this commercial expansion stimulated the city's cultural growth; **Walt Whitman** memorialized the city in his poetry, while **Henry James** recorded its manners and mores in such novels as *Washington Square*.

The turn of the century

At the same time, the emigration of Europe's impoverished peoples continued unabated, and in 1884 new immigrants from Asia settled in what became known as **Chinatown**. Jewish and other European immigrants continued to arrive as well, and in 1898 the population of New York amounted to more than three million, making it the largest city in the world. Twelve years earlier the **Statue of Liberty** had been completed, holding a symbolic torch to guide the huddled masses to their new home. Now pressure grew to limit immigration, but still people flooded in. **Ellis Island**, the depot that processed arrivals, was handling two thousand people a day, leading to a total of ten million by 1929, when laws were passed to curtail immigration. During the first two decades of the twentieth century one-third of all the Jews in Eastern Europe arrived in America, and upwards of 1.5 million of them settled in the city, primarily in the Lower East Side.

The war years and the Depression: 1914–1945

With America's entry into World War I in 1917, New York benefited from wartime trade and commerce. Perhaps surprisingly, there was little conflict between the various European communities crammed into the city. Although Germans comprised roughly one-fifth of the city's population, there were few of the attacks on their lives or property that occurred elsewhere in the country.

The postwar years saw one law and one character dominating the New York scene: the law was **Prohibition**, passed in 1920 (and not repealed until 1933) in an attempt to sober up the nation; the character was **Jimmy Walker**, elected mayor in 1925. Walker led a far from sober lifestyle: "No civilized man," he said, "goes to bed the same day he wakes up," and it was during his flamboyant career that the **Jazz Age** came to the city. In speakeasies all over town the bootleg liquor flowed and writers as diverse as Damon Runyon, F. Scott Fitzgerald, and Ernest Hemingway portrayed the excitement of the times, while musicians such as George Gershwin and Benny Goodman packed nightclubs with their new sound.

With the **Wall Street** crash of 1929 the party came to an abrupt end. Yet during the **Depression** three of New York's most opulent – and most beautiful – skyscrapers were built: the **Chrysler** in 1930, the **Empire State** in 1931, and in 1932 **Rockefeller Center**. All were (and remain) very impressive, but were of little immediate help to those in the other, more depressed parts of the city.

The country's entry into World War II in 1941 had little direct impact on New York City, though lights were blacked out at night in case of bomb attacks, two hundred Japanese were interned on Ellis Island, and guards were placed at the entrances to bridges and tunnels. New York's major contribution to the war, rather, was the **Manhattan Project**, which took place behind the scenes at Columbia University and succeeded in splitting the uranium atom, thereby creating the first atomic weapon.

The postwar years

Following racial tensions in the 1950s there was a general exodus of the white middle classes out of New York (and indeed out of many major American cities) and into the suburbs – the **Great White Flight** as the media labeled it. Between 1950 and 1970 more than a million families left the city. Things went from bad to worse during the 1960s with **race riots** uptown in Harlem and in Brooklyn's Bedford-Stuyvesant neighborhood. The **World's Fair** of 1964 was a white elephant to boost the city's international profile, but on the streets the call for civil liberties for blacks and protest against US involvement in Vietnam (1964–75) were as strong as any in the rest of the country. On a side note, the **Twin Towers** of the World Trade Center, which would later meet their end on 9/11, were opened in 1973.

Manhattan reached a **crisis point** in 1975, when the city was spending more than it received in taxes – billions of dollars more. Essential services, long shaky due to underfunding, were ready to collapse. Tourism, spurred by cheap transatlantic airfares, and a new go-get-'em mayor, **Edward I. Koch**, helped save the city. Despite the fact that New York was no longer facing bankruptcy, it was still suffering from the massive nationwide recession, and the city turned to its nightlife for relief. Starting in the mid-1970s, singles bars sprang up all over the city, gay bars proliferated in the Village, and Disco was King. **Studio 54** was an internationally known hotspot, and drugs and illicit sex were the main events off the dance floor.

In the 1980s the real estate and stock markets boomed and another era of Big Money was ushered in; fortunes were made and lost overnight and big Wall Street names, most notably **Michael Milken**, were thrown in jail for insider trading. A spate of building gave the city yet more fabulous architecture, notably **Battery Park City** downtown, and master builder **Donald Trump** provided glitzy housing for the super-wealthy.

In typical boom-and-bust pattern, the stock market crash of 1987 presaged another downturn. This led in part to Koch losing the Democratic nomination for mayor (rare for an incumbent) to the more even-tempered **David Dinkins**, who, after besting the brash young district attorney **Rudolph Giuliani** in the general election, would go on to become the first African-American mayor of New York. However, by the time Dinkins took office the city had already slipped hard and fast into a **massive recession**: in 1989 New York's budget deficit ran at $500 million, and one in four residents was officially classed as poor – a proportion unequaled since the Depression. In the 1993 mayoral elections, Dinkins narrowly lost to his erstwhile adversary Giuliani: New York, traditionally a firmly Democratic city, wanted a change and with Rudy – the city's first Republican mayor in 28 years – it got it.

The Giuliani years

Though it may have been coincidental, **Giuliani's first term** helped usher in a dramatic upswing in New York's prosperity. A *New York Times* article described 1995 as "the best year in recent memory for New York City." Even the pope came to town and called New York "the capital of the world." The city's reputation flourished, with remarkable decreases in crime statistics and a revitalized economy. Such successes helped the mayor withstand a bitter fight over rent control as well as continued concern over serious overcrowding in the public school system and cutbacks in health and welfare programs. Giuliani won re-election in 1997 in a landslide.

The early years of his **second term** were characterized by the continued growth of the city's economy and more civic improvements, such as the cleaning up of previously crime-ridden neighborhoods like Times Square, the renovation of Grand Central Station, and the building of new hotels and office buildings. All these developments greatly boosted tourism (and thus the city's coffers), but they also raised protests that the mayor would do anything to attract national chains to the city, often at the expense of local business and local workers.

Several high-profile incidents involving shocking allegations of police brutality, such as the **Abner Louima** torture case, led to charges of disregard for minority rights as well. With reports on racial profiling reinforcing the claim, Giuliani's popularity, once amazingly high in this heavily Democratic city, dwindled significantly – though it was soon to be resuscitated in a big, albeit tragic, way.

9/11 and beyond

Nothing could have prepared New York – or indeed the world – for the morning of **September 11, 2001**, when terrorists hijacked four airplanes, crashing two of them into the Twin Towers of the World Trade Center and a third into the Pentagon in Washington, DC; the fourth was brought down by a passenger revolt in a field south of Pittsburgh, Pennsylvania. New York was hit hardest by far: within hours, each tower had collapsed, and the fallout and debris resulted in the destruction of a number of nearby buildings. In all, 2986 people were killed in the attack, with smoking rubble piled several stories high. New York's signature skyline was changed forever.

Beyond the staggering number of lives lost, the billions in assets wiped out, the wreckage of subway lines and so on, there were other holes to deal with: entire firefighting crews, and quite a few at or near the top of the ranks in the fire and police departments, died in the collapse. New Yorkers – and many from around the world – rallied to the rescue effort under the compassionate yet firm leadership of Giuliani. Suddenly, few wanted to see him go, though he was precluded by law for running for a third term in the elections (whose primaries, ironically, had been scheduled for September 11th).

Although recovery seemed unthinkable at the time, New York rebounded as always. **Michael Bloomberg**, a billionaire businessman, Republican in name but actually more socially liberal than his predecessor, replaced Giuliani as mayor soon after the attacks. Most of Bloomberg's successes have been fiscal, as he's used his corporate know-how to shore up the city's shaky finances, though he has also smoothed race relations in the city – often a sore point during Giuliani's tenure. The mayor's most controversial act to date has been to follow California's lead and **ban smoking** in bars, clubs, and all restaurants; there's been both fierce approval and pounding criticism of his decision, though, as one might expect from fiercely independent New Yorkers, the law is occasionally flaunted.

Meanwhile, things are moving onward and upward in most of the city, with the construction of the **Time Warner Center** at Columbus Circle, the reopening of the **Museum of Modern Art**, and still another hideously ugly and expensive Trump development on the west side of Midtown. The economy is finally gaining steam after the dot-com downturn of the early 2000s and 9/11, and the city may even serve as launching pad for a future president, current New York Senator **Hillary Clinton**, should she decide to run, as many speculate, for the White House in 2008.

Books

S ince the number of **books** about or set in New York
is so vast, what follows is necessarily selective – use
it as a launchpad for further sleuthing. Publishers
are given in the order British/American if they are
different for each country; where a book is published only
in one country, it is designated UK or US; o/p indicates a
book is out of print; and UP indicates university press.

Essays, poetry, and impressions

Joyce Johnson *Minor
Characters: A Beat Memoir*
(Penguin, US). Women were
never a prominent feature
of the Beat generation; its
literature examined a male
world through strictly male
eyes. This book, written by
the woman who lived for a
short time with Jack Ker-
ouac, redresses the balance
superbly; there's no better
novel on the Beats in New
York.

Phillip Lopate (ed) *Writing New York* (Pocket Books,
US). A massive literary
anthology taking in both
fiction and nonfiction writ-
ings on the city, and with
selections from everyone
from Washington Irving to
Tom Wolfe.

Federico García Lorca
Poet in New York (Penguin/
Farrar, Strauss & Giroux).
The Andalusian poet and
dramatist spent nine months
in the city around the time
of the Wall Street Crash.
This collection of over thirty
poems reveals his feelings on
the brutality, loneliness, greed,
corruption, racism, and mistreatment of the poor.

Joseph Mitchell *Up in the
Old Hotel* (Vintage, US).
Mitchell's collected essays
(he calls them stories), all
of which appeared in *The
New Yorker*, are works of a
sober if manipulative genius.
Mitchell depicts characters
and situations with a reporter's precision and near-
perfect style – he is the

C

CONTEXTS | Books

definitive chronicler of NYC street life.

Jan Morris *Manhattan '45* (Penguin/Johns Hopkins UP). Morris's best piece of writing on the city, recon- structing New York as it greeted soldiers returning from WWII in 1945. Effort- lessly written, fascinatingly anecdotal, and marvelously warm about the city.

History, politics, and society

Herbert Asbury *The Gangs of New York* (Arrow/ Thunder's Mouth Press). First published in 1928, this fascinating account of the seamier side of New York is essential reading; it was also the inspiration for the film of the same name. Full of historical detail, anecdotes, and character sketches of crooks, the book describes New York mischief in all its incarnations and locales.

Edwin G. Burrows and Mike Wallace *Gotham: A History of New York City to 1898* (Oxford UP). Enor- mous and encyclopedic in its detail, this is a serious history of the development of New York, with chapters on everything from its role in the American Revolu- tion to reform movements to its racial make-up in the 1820s.

Robert A. Caro *The Power Broker: Robert Moses and the Fall of New York* (Random House, US). Despite its imposing length, this brilliant and searing critique of New York City's most powerful twentieth-century figure is one of the most important books ever written about the city and its environs. Caro's book brings to light the megalomania and manipula- tion responsible for the creation of the nation's largest urban infrastructure.

Kenneth T. Jackson (ed) *The Enyclopedia of New York City* (Yale UP). Mas- sive, engrossing, and utterly comprehensive guide to just about everything in the city. Much dry detail, but packed with incidental wonders as well.

John B. Manbeck (ed) *The Neighborhoods of Brooklyn*

(Yale UP). Wonderfully thorough account of the diversity of Brooklyn's neighborhoods, filled with first-hand accounts, photographs, maps, and local lore celebrating the borough in all its complexity.
Luc Sante *Low Life: Lures and Snares of Old New York* (Farrar, Strauss & Giroux, US). This chronicle of New York's underbelly between 1840 and 1919 is a pioneering work. Full of outrageous details usually left out of conventional history, it reconstructs the day-to-day life of the urban poor, criminals, and prostitutes with a shocking clarity. Sante's prose is poetic and nuanced, and his evocations of the seedier neighborhoods, their dives and pleasure-palaces, quite vivid.

Russell Shorto *Island at the Center of the World: The Story of Dutch Manhattan and the Forgotten Colony that Shaped America* (Vintage/Knopf). An intriguing account of how important the Dutch really were to the founding of New York City, and how this colonial nation's sense of adventure kept Manhattan from falling to the English and becoming just another quaint port town. Vividly written and thoroughly researched, Shorto brings his reader back to a pre-skyscraper, pre-asphalt Big Apple.

Art, architecture, and photography

H. Klotz (ed) *New York Architecture 1970–1990* (Prestel/Rizzoli). Extremely well-illustrated account of the shift from modernism to postmodernism and beyond. (o/p)
Jacob Riis *How the Other Half Lives* (Dover/Hill & Wang). Republished photo journalism reporting on life in the Lower East Side at the end of the nineteenth century. Its original publication awakened many to the plight of New York's poor.
Stern, Gilmartin, Mellins/Stern, Gilmartin, Massengale/Stern, Mellins, Fishman *New York*

1900/1930/1960 (Monacelli, US). These three exhaustive tomes, subtitled *Metropolitan Architecture and Urbanism*, contain all you'd ever want or need to know about architecture and the organization of the city. The facts are both dazzling and mind-numbing, the photos nostalgia-inducing.

N. White and E. Willensky (eds) *AIA Guide to New York* (Macmillan/Crown). Perhaps even more than the above, the definitive contemporary guide to the city's architecture, far more interesting than it sounds, and useful as an on-site reference.

Gerard R. Wolfe *New York: A Guide to the Metropolis* (McGraw-Hill, US). Set up as a walking tour, this is a little more academic – and less opinionated – than others, but it does include some good stuff on the outer boroughs. Also informed historical background.

Fiction

Martin Amis *Money* (Vintage/Penguin). Following the wayward movements of degenerate film director John Self between London and New York, a weirdly scatological novel that's a striking evocation of 1980s excess.

James Baldwin *Another Country* (Vintage/Penguin). Baldwin's best-known novel, tracking the feverish search for meaningful relationships among a group of 1960s New York bohemians.

The so-called liberated era in the city has never been more vividly documented – nor its knee-jerk racism.

Truman Capote *Breakfast at Tiffany's* (Penguin/Random House). Far sadder and racier than the movie, this novel is a rhapsody to New York in the early 1940s, tracking the dissolute, youthful residents of an uptown apartment building and their movements about town.

Chester Himes *The Crazy Kill* (Canongate/Knopf). Himes wrote violent, fast-moving, and funny thrillers set in Harlem; this and *Cotton Comes to Harlem* are among the best.

Henry James *Washington Square* (Penguin/Modern Library). Skillful and engrossing examination of the mores and strict social expectations of New York genteel society in the late nineteenth century.

Jonathan Lethem *Motherless Brooklyn* and *Fortress of Solitude* (Faber & Faber/Knopf). Lethem's *Motherless Brooklyn* is a noir-ish modern classic set in the 1970s, starring "The Human Freakshow," a local private investigator with Tourette's. *Fortress of Solitude*, meanwhile, tells the tale of two Brooklyn boys, white Dylan and black Mingus. Spanning over thirty years in the lives of these best friends, it's an epic work, and comes highly recommended.

Jay McInerney *Bright Lights, Big City* (Flamingo/Knopf). A trendy, "voice of a generation" book when it came out in the 1980s, *Bright Lights* follows a struggling New York writer in his job as a fact-checker at a literary magazine, and from one cocaine-sozzled nightclub to another. Amusing now, as it vividly captures the times.

Henry Miller *Crazy Cock* (HarperCollins/Grove Atlantic). Semiautobiographical work of love, sex, and angst in Greenwich Village in the 1920s. The trilogy of *Sexus*, *Plexus*, and *Nexus* (HarperCollins/Grove) and the famous *Tropics* duo (*...of Cancer*, *...of Capricorn*) contain generous slices of 1920s Manhattan sandwiched between the bohemian life in 1930s Paris.

Dorothy Parker *Complete Stories* (Penguin). Parker's stories are, at times, surprisingly moving. She depicts New York in all its glories, excesses, and pretensions with perfect, searing wit. *The Lovely Leave* and *The Game*, which focus, as many of the stories do, on the lives of women, are especially worthwhile.

Damon Runyon *First to Last* and *On Broadway* (Penguin, US); also *Guys and Dolls* (River City, US). Collections of short stories drawn from the chatter of Lindy's Bar on Broadway and since made into the successful musical *Guys 'n' Dolls*.

J.D. Salinger *The Catcher in the Rye* (Penguin/Bantam). Salinger's classic, gripping novel of adolescence, following Holden Caulfield's sardonic journey of discovery through the streets of New York.

Hubert Selby Jr. *Last Exit to Brooklyn* (Bloomsbury/ Grove Atlantic). When first published in Britain in 1966 the author of this novel was tried on charges of obscen-

ity – and even now it's a disturbing read, evoking the sex, immorality, drugs, and violence of downtown Brooklyn in the 1960s with fearsome clarity. An important book, but to use the words of David Shepherd at the obscenity trial, you will not be unscathed.

Betty Smith *A Tree Grows in Brooklyn* (Arrow/HarperCollins). Something of a classic, and rightly so, in which a courageous Irish girl learns about family, life, and sex against a vivid prewar Brooklyn backdrop. Totally absorbing.

Edith Wharton *Old New York* (Pocket). A collection of short novels on the manners and mores of New York in the mid-nineteenth century, written with *Jamesian* clarity and precision.

New York in film

With its dashing skyline and rugged facades, its mean streets and swanky avenues, New York is probably the most filmed city on Earth – or at least the one most instantly recognizable from the **movies**. It would be fruitless to enumerate them all; we've just given a small sampling below of films that best capture the city's atmosphere, its pulse and style, and, if nothing else, give you a pretty good idea of what you're going to get before you get here.

Twelve great New York movies

Annie Hall (Woody Allen, 1977). Oscar-winning autobiographical comic romance, which flits from reminiscences of Alvy Singer's childhood living beneath the Coney Island rollercoaster to life and love in uptown Manhattan, is a valentine both to then-lover and co-star Diane Keaton if not to the city. Simultaneously clever, bourgeois, and very winning. All of Allen's movies are New York–centric; don't miss **Manhattan** (1979), which, with its Gershwin soundtrack and stunning black-and-white

photography, is probably the greatest memorial to the city ever made.

Breakfast at Tiffany's (Blake Edwards, 1961). This most charming and cherished of New York movie romances stars Audrey Hepburn as party girl Holly Golightly amid the glittering playground of the Upper East Side. Hepburn and George Peppard run up and down each other's fire escapes and skip down Fifth Avenue, taking in the New York Public Library and that certain famous jewelry store.

Do the Right Thing
(Spike Lee, 1989). Set over 24 hours on the hottest day of the year in Brooklyn's Bedford-Stuyvesant section – a day on which the melting pot is reaching boiling point – Spike Lee's colorful, stylish film moves from comedy to tragedy to compose an epic tale of New York.

The French Connection
(William Friedkin, 1971). Plenty of heady Brooklyn atmosphere in this sensational Oscar-winning cop thriller starring Gene Hackman, whose classic car-and-subway chase takes place under the Bensonhurst Elevated Railroad.

The Godfather Part II
(Francis Ford Coppola, 1974). Flashing back to the early life of Vito Corleone, Coppola's great sequel re-created the Italian immigrant experience at the turn of the century, portraying Corleone quarantined at Ellis Island and growing up tough on the meticulously re-created streets of Little Italy.

Midnight Cowboy (John Schlesinger, 1969). The odd love story between Jon Voight's bumpkin hustler and Dustin Hoffman's touching urban creep Ratso Rizzo plays out against both the seediest and swankiest of New York locations.

On the Town (Gene Kelly and Stanley Donen, 1949). Three sailors get 24 hours' shore leave in NYC and fight over whether to do the sights or chase the girls. This exhilarating, landmark musical with Gene Kelly, Frank Sinatra, and Ann Miller flashing her gams in the American Museum of Natural History was the first to take the musical out of the studios and onto the streets.

On the Waterfront (Elia Kazan, 1954). Few images of New York in this unforgettable story of long-suffering longshoremen and union racketeering are as indelible as Marlon Brando's rooftop pigeon coop at dawn and those misty views of New York Harbor (actually shot just over the river in Hoboken).

Rosemary's Baby
(Roman Polanski, 1968).
Mia Farrow and John Cassavettes move into their dream New York apartment in the Dakota Building (see p.147) and think their problems stop with nosy neighbors and thin walls until Farrow gets pregnant and hell, literally, breaks loose. Arguably the most terrifying film ever set in the city. Compare to **Panic Room**, a thrilling game of a film starring Jodie Foster (David Fincher, 2002) and also set in the Upper West Side.

The Sweet Smell of Success (Alexander Mackendrick, 1957). Broadway as a nest of vipers. Gossip columnist Burt Lancaster and sleazy press agent Tony Curtis eat each other's tails in this jazzy, cynical study of showbiz corruption. Shot on location, and mostly at night, in steely black and white, Times Square and the Great White Way never looked so alluring.

Taxi Driver (Martin Scorsese, 1976). A long night's journey into day by the great chronicler of the dark side of the city – and New York's greatest filmmaker. Scorsese's New York is hallucinatorily seductive and thoroughly repellent in this superbly unsettling study of obsessive outsider Travis Bickle (Robert De Niro).

West Side Story (Robert Wise and Jerome Robbins, 1961). Sex, singing, and Shakespeare in a hyper-cinematic Oscar-winning musical (via Broadway) about rival street gangs. Lincoln Center now stands where the Sharks and the Jets once rumbled and interracial romance ended in tragedy.

Small print &
Index

A Rough Guide to Rough Guides

Published in 1982, the first Rough Guide – to Greece – was a student scheme that became a publishing phenomenon. Mark Ellingham, a recent graduate in English from Bristol University, had been traveling in Greece the previous summer and couldn't find the right guidebook. With a small group of friends he wrote his own guide, combining a highly contemporary, journalistic style with a thoroughly practical approach to travelers' needs.

The immediate success of the book spawned a series that rapidly covered dozens of destinations. And, in addition to impecunious backpackers, Rough Guides soon acquired a much broader and older readership that relished the guides' wit and inquisitiveness as much as their enthusiastic, critical approach and value-for-money ethos.

These days, Rough Guides include recommendations from shoestring to luxury and cover more than 200 destinations around the globe, including almost every country in the Americas and Europe, more than half of Africa, and most of Asia and Australasia. Our ever-growing team of authors and photographers is spread all over the world, particularly in Europe, the USA, and Australia.

In the early 1990s, Rough Guides branched out of travel, with the publication of Rough Guides to World Music, Classical Music, and the Internet. All three have become benchmark titles in their fields, spearheading the publication of a wide range of books under the Rough Guide name.

Including the travel series, Rough Guides now number more than 350 titles, covering: phrasebooks, waterproof maps, music guides from Opera to Heavy Metal, reference works as diverse as Conspiracy Theories and Shakespeare, and popular culture books from iPods to Poker. Rough Guides also produce a series of more than 120 World Music CDs in partnership with World Music Network.

Visit ⑩www.roughguides.com to see our latest publications.

Rough Guide travel images are available for commercial licensing at ⑩www.roughguidespictures.com.

Publishing information

This 2nd edition published March 2006 by:
Rough Guides Ltd, 80 Strand, London WC2R 0RL.
345 Hudson St, 4th Floor, New York, NY 10014, USA.
Distributed by the Penguin Group
Penguin Books Ltd, 80 Strand, London WC2R 0RL
Penguin Group (USA), 375 Hudson Street, NY 10014, USA
14 Local Shopping Centre, Panchsheel Park, New Delhi 110017, India
Penguin Group (Australia), 250 Camberwell Road, Camberwell, Victoria 3124, Australia
Penguin Group (Canada), 10 Alcorn Avenue, Toronto, ON M4V 1E4, Canada
Penguin Group (New Zealand), Cnr Rosedale and Airborne Roads, Albany, Auckland, New Zealand
Typeset in Bembo and Helvetica

to an original design by Henry Iles.
Printed and bound in Italy by LegoPrint
© Martin Dunford and Rough Guides 2006
No part of this book may be reproduced in any form without permission from the publisher except for the quotation of brief passages in reviews.
348pp includes index
A catalog record for this book is available from the British Library
ISBN 1-84353-586-0
The publishers and authors have done their best to ensure the accuracy and currency of all the information in The Mini Rough Guide to New York City, however, they can accept no responsibility for any loss, injury, or inconvenience sustained by any traveler as a result of information or advice contained in the guide.
1 3 5 7 9 8 6 4 2

Help us update

We've gone to a lot of effort to ensure that the 2nd edition of **The Mini Rough Guide to New York City** is accurate and up to date. However, things change – places get "discovered," opening hours are notoriously fickle, restaurants and rooms raise prices or lower standards. If you feel we've got it wrong or left something out, we'd like to know, and if you can remember the address, the price, the time, the phone number, so much the better.

We'll credit all contributions, and send a copy of the next edition (or any other Rough Guide if you prefer) for the best letters. Everyone who writes to us and isn't already a subscriber will receive a copy of our full-color thrice-yearly newsletter. Please mark letters: **"Mini Rough Guide New York City Update"** and send to: Rough Guides, 80 Strand, London WC2R 0RL, or Rough Guides, 345 Hudson St, 4th Floor, New York, NY 10014. Or send an email to **mail@roughguides.com**

Have your questions answered and tell others about your trip at ⊛**www.roughguides.atinfopop.com**

Rough Guides credits

Text editor: Hunter Slaton
Layout: Link Hall
Cartography: Rajesh Mishra
Picture editor: Sarah Smithies

Production: Katherine Owers
Proofreader: Diane Margolis
Cover design: Chloë Roberts
Photographer: Nelson Hancock

Acknowledgments

Nicky Agate would like to thank Rich Nisa, Hunter Slaton, Richard Koss, and New York City.

The editor would like to thank Martin Dunford, Nicky Agate, and Sean Harvey for all their hard work.

Martin Dunford would like to thank Hunter Slaton, Richard Koss, and all the folk in the Rough Guides' New York office, who always make a trip to the city such a pleasure.

Readers' letters

Thanks to all the readers who have taken the time to write in with comments and suggestions (and apologies if we've inadvertently omitted or misspelt anyone's name):

Angela Dutton, Christopher Hallam, Andy Pusey, Gwyn Williams, Malachi, Jan Willem Reitsma, P. Rajaram, Tasmim Noor, Jeannette Binns, Geoff Sharpe, Adam McAuley, Karen Baldwin, Gerard & Mary Platt, Ken Scudder, Carl Annall, Matthew Blanchard, Susanne Francke, Sue Oldroyd, Christopher & Lorenza Matthews, Jim Rankine, Sal and Ed Bentley, Gary Stoppelman, Magdalena Smidova, Michael Lewis, Marc Tolud, Matt McCabe, Carol Hamilton, R.J. Kemp, Mark Ainsworth, Josie McClellan, Pamela Dunn, Jennifer Coleman, Steve Griffin.

ROUGH GUIDES

SMALL PRINT

SMALL PRINT

Index

Map entries are in color.

I

INDEX

N

O

P

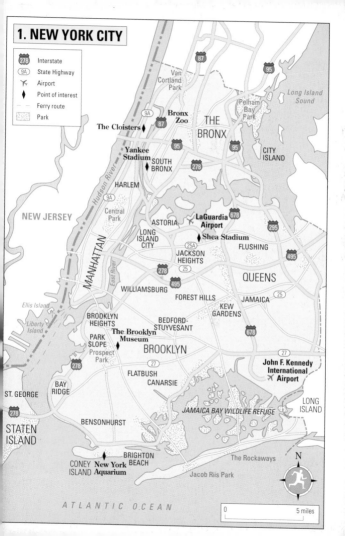

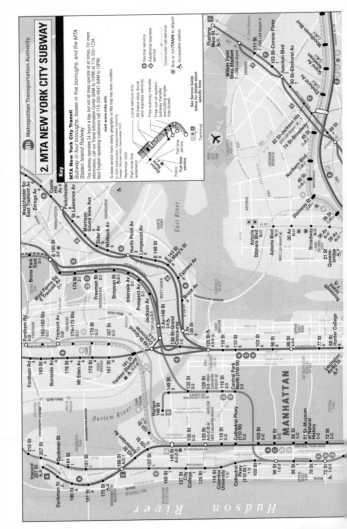

2. MTA NEW YORK CITY SUBWAY

Subway in four boroughs, buses in five boroughs, and the MTA Staten Island Railway

MTA New York City Transit

The subway operates 24 hours a day, but all lines operate at all times. For more information, call our Travel Information Center (6AM to 10PM) at 718-330-1234. Non-English-speaking customers call 718-330-4847 (6AM to 10PM).

visit www.mta.info

To show service more clearly, geography on this map has been modified.

© 2005 Metropolitan Transportation Authority
Design: Michael Hertz Associates, NYC
September 2005.

Key

Normal service
Additional express service
Commuter rail service
Bus is AIRTRAIN to airport
Accessible station

See Service Guide below for details about specific lines.

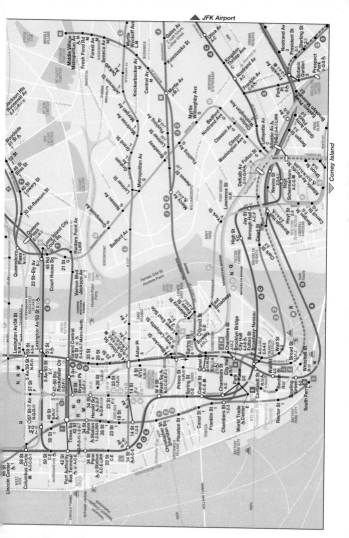

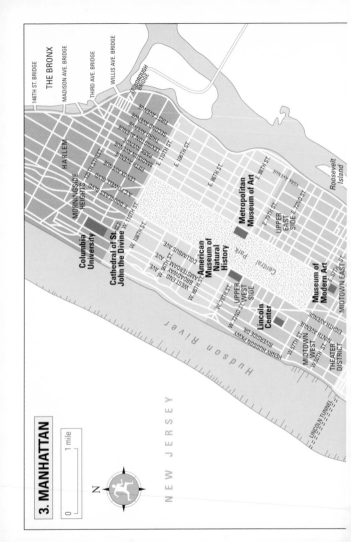

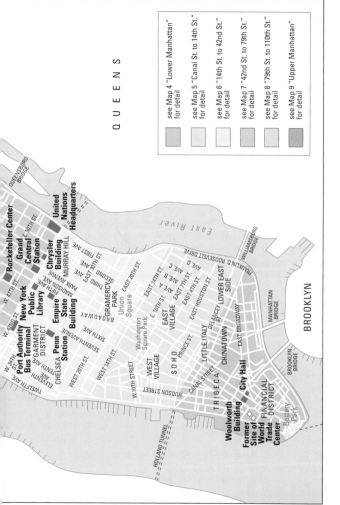

QUEENS

see Map 4 "Lower Manhattan" for detail

see Map 5 "Canal St to 14th St." for detail

see Map 6 "14th St. to 42nd St." for detail

see Map 7 "42nd St. to 79th St." for detail

see Map 8 "79th St. to 110th St." for detail

see Map 9 "Upper Manhattan" for detail

QUEENSBORO BRIDGE

Rockefeller Center

Grand Central Station

United Nations Headquarters

Chrysler Building

E.60TH ST.

E.40TH ST.

FIRST AVE

SECOND AVE

THIRD AVE

New York Public Library

Empire State Building

W. 47TH ST.

MADISON AVE

PARK AVENUE

Port Authority Bus Terminal

W. 42ND ST.

W. 34TH ST.

GARMENT DISTRICT

Penn Station

FIFTH AVE

LEXINGTON AVE

East River

MURRAY HILL

GRAMERCY PARK

EAST 20TH ST.

CHELSEA

WEST 20TH ST.

SIXTH AVE

SEVENTH AVE

BROADWAY

Union Square

E. 10TH ST.

EAST 14TH ST.

EAST 7TH ST.

AVE A

AVE B

AVE C

AVE D

ELEVENTH AVE

TWELFTH AVE

WEST 14TH ST.

W. 10TH STREET

WEST VILLAGE

EAST 4TH ST.

EAST VILLAGE

EAST HOUSTON ST.

FRANKLIN D. ROOSEVELT DRIVE

Washington Square Park

SOHO

PRINCE ST.

LITTLE ITALY

DELANCEY ST.

LOWER EAST SIDE

WILLIAMSBURG BRIDGE

HUDSON STREET

CANAL ST.

TRIBECA

CHINATOWN

EAST BROADWAY

HOLLAND TUNNEL

Woolworth Building

Former Site of World Trade Center

City Hall

FINANCIAL DISTRICT

Battery Park

MANHATTAN BRIDGE

BROOKLYN BRIDGE

BROOKLYN

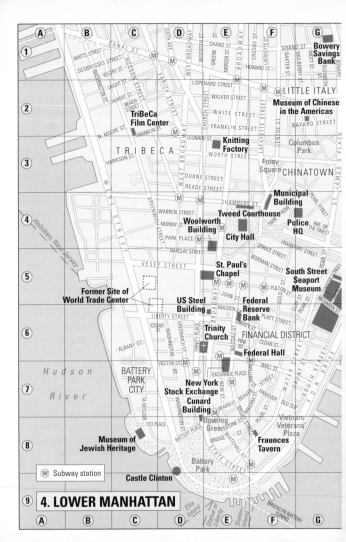

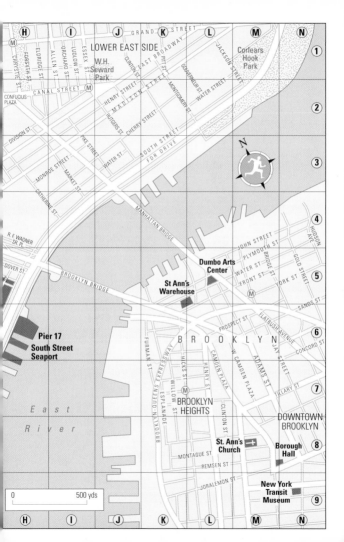

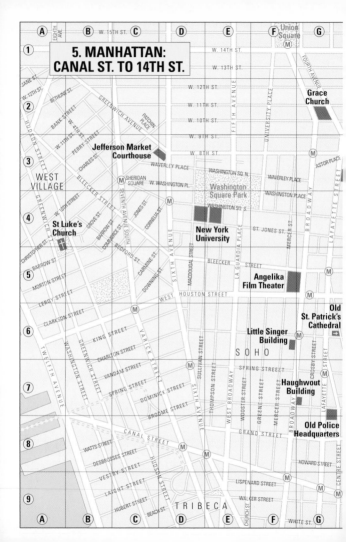

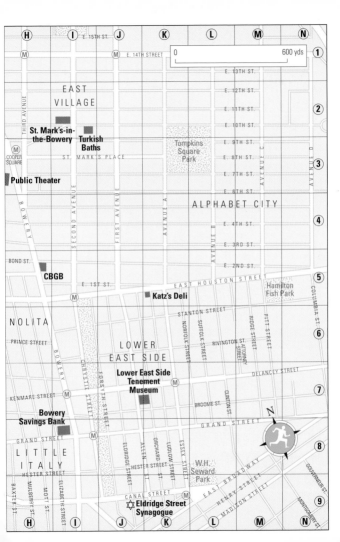

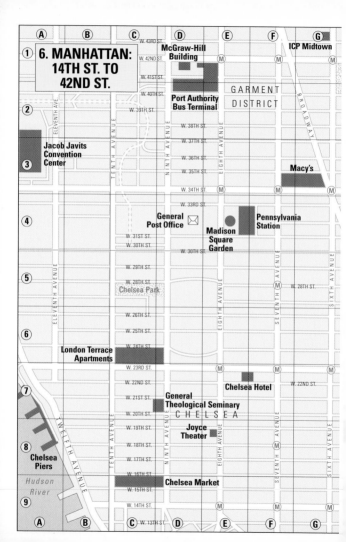

6. MANHATTAN: 14TH ST. TO 42ND ST.

McGraw-Hill Building

ICP Midtown

GARMENT DISTRICT

BROADWAY

Jacob Javits Convention Center

Port Authority Bus Terminal

ELEVENTH AVENUE

TENTH AVENUE

NINTH AVENUE

EIGHTH AVENUE

Macy's

General Post Office

Madison Square Garden

Pennsylvania Station

Chelsea Park

SEVENTH AVENUE

SIXTH AVENUE

London Terrace Apartments

Chelsea Hotel

General Theological Seminary

CHELSEA

Joyce Theater

TWELFTH AVENUE

TENTH AVENUE

NINTH AVENUE

EIGHTH AVENUE

Chelsea Piers

Chelsea Market

Hudson River

W. 43RD ST.
W. 42ND ST.
W. 41ST ST.
W. 40TH ST.
W. 39TH ST.
W. 38TH ST.
W. 37TH ST.
W. 36TH ST.
W. 35TH ST.
W. 34TH ST.
W. 33RD ST.
W. 31ST ST.
W. 30TH ST.
W. 29TH ST.
W. 28TH ST.
W. 26TH ST.
W. 25TH ST.
W. 24TH ST.
W. 23RD ST.
W. 22ND ST.
W. 21ST ST.
W. 20TH ST.
W. 19TH ST.
W. 18TH ST.
W. 17TH ST.
W. 16TH ST.
W. 15TH ST.
W. 14TH ST.
W. 13TH ST.

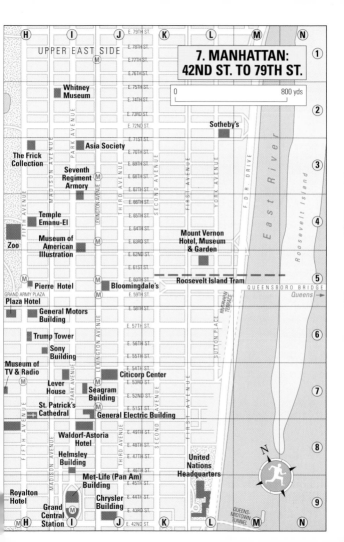

7. MANHATTAN: 42ND ST. TO 79TH ST.

0 — 800 yds

UPPER EAST SIDE

Whitney Museum

The Frick Collection

Asia Society

Seventh Regiment Armory

Temple Emanu-El

Zoo

Museum of American Illustration

Sotheby's

Mount Vernon Hotel, Museum & Garden

Roosevelt Island Tram

Pierre Hotel

Bloomingdale's

QUEENSBORO BRIDGE

Queens →

Plaza Hotel

GRAND ARMY PLAZA

General Motors Building

Trump Tower

Sony Building

Museum of TV & Radio

Citicorp Center

Lever House

Seagram Building

St. Patrick's Cathedral

General Electric Building

Waldorf-Astoria Hotel

Helmsley Building

United Nations Headquarters

Met-Life (Pan Am) Building

Royalton Hotel

Grand Central Station

Chrysler Building

QUEENS-MIDTOWN TUNNEL

East River

Roosevelt Island

FDR DRIVE

SUTTON PLACE

FIFTH AVENUE

MADISON AVENUE

PARK AVENUE

LEXINGTON AVENUE

THIRD AVENUE

SECOND AVENUE

FIRST AVENUE

YORK AVENUE

N

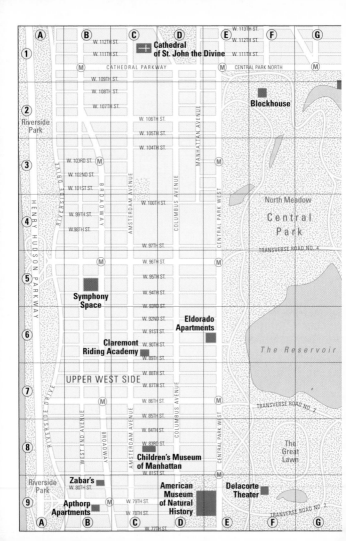

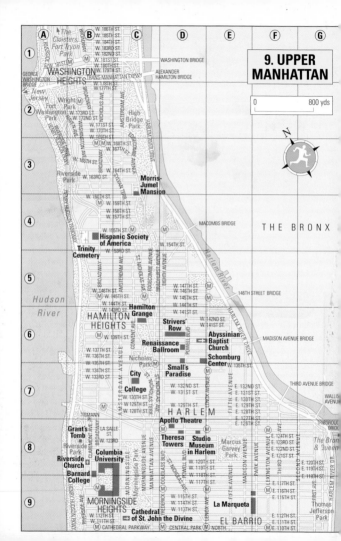